D1233278

ADAPTIVE GROWTH

ADAPTIVE GROWTH

RICHARD J. GOSS
Professor of Biology
Brown University

LOGOS PRESS
ACADEMIC PRESS

Published by
LOGOS PRESS LIMITED
in association with
ELEK BOOKS LIMITED
2 All Saints Street, London, N.1.

Distributed by
ACADEMIC PRESS INC.
111 Fifth Avenue, New York, N.Y. 10003
and
ACADEMIC PRESS INC. (London) LIMITED
Berkeley Square House, Berkeley Square, London, W.1

Library of Congress Catalog Card Number 64–7980

*Affectionately dedicated to my
mother, and to the memory
of her mother*

Printed in Great Britain by
Cox and Wyman Ltd., London, Reading, and Fakenham

Contents

Preface

FOR nearly a century now, a wealth of data has been gathered on the phenomenon of growth regulation. This has prompted many attempts to formulate a theoretical basis for explaining how size is determined in biological systems. Originally, it was assumed that growth was a direct response to functional overload, for use and disuse seemed to be universally correlated with hypertrophy and atrophy, respectively. More recently, it has become fashionable to disregard functional considerations in favour of mechanisms by which the regulation of tissue mass might be an end in itself. Consequently, much of today's research is predicated on the assumption that humoral agents are responsible for adjusting the sizes of organs to certain predetermined dimensions. For many investigators, the major problem is to establish whether these hypothetical growth-regulators operate by stimulating or inhibiting growth. Implicit in much of the current research and thinking on this subject is the hope that tissue-specific growth-regulating factors might ultimately be isolated; that such an achievement will clear the way for man's control of growth, if not his conquest of cancer.

The time has come to make a fundamental decision concerning the strategy to be followed in future research on the problem of growth regulation. Heretofore, many of the theories that have been proposed have been intended to apply only to a limited number of growing systems, such as the regenerating liver, or the healing of epidermal wounds. Yet if we are to discover a truly unifying hypothesis to guide our studies of these important problems, I believe it is imperative that it be derived from as wide a spectrum of developmental phenomena as possible. Therefore, in the present account an attempt has been made to seek interrelations between many of the classic examples of vertebrate growth, including cell turnover, normal post-embryonic enlargement, compensatory hypertrophy, localized wound healing, and regeneration. Only by such a comparative approach will it be possible to identify the most common denominator by which these seemingly diverse, but actually similar, developmental events are controlled.

It is now possible to examine critically the rather massive backlog

9

of data which has accumulated over the years, in order to determine the validity of existing hypotheses and to serve as a basis, if necessary, for the formulation of a new one. As might have been expected, most hypotheses contain elements of the truth, but none can be considered entirely correct. Fundamental to any such hypothesis, however, is the question of whether growth is governed by considerations of organ size *per se*, or by the requirements for physiological activity. The facts lead us overwhelmingly towards the latter alternative. This, in a sense, constitutes a return to the classic notion of growth regulation by functional demands, yet it is also an important advance. It can warn us away from futile attempts to seek oversimplified solutions to difficult problems, and can redirect our research in what will hopefully become more productive channels. If future investigators are thus persuaded to concentrate on the biochemical mechanisms by which physiological demands are translated concomitantly into functional activity and cellular proliferation, this monograph will have been well worth writing.

In this endeavour, it has been my good fortune to have benefited from the intellectual stimulation of my many colleagues in the Department of Biology at Brown University. To my students, past and present, I am grateful for the occasional provocative questions we could not answer, and for their devotion to their research projects even when we only proved ourselves wrong. If parts of this monograph are free from errors in fact or reasoning, it is due to the efforts of Miss Marilynn Goldsmith and Miss Elizabeth Ballantine, who have been unselfish in expressing their constructive criticisms of the manuscript.

It is my pleasant duty to acknowledge the co-operation of my research assistants, Miss Marsha Rankin, Mrs. Sally Hoedemaker, Mrs. Linda Dyke, Miss Carol Weber, and Mrs. Hermine Torian, without whose devotion to the many duties of the laboratory my research on growth regulation could not have been so successfully pursued. Thanks to a generous scholarship from the Rhode Island Heart Association, Mr. John Russo was able to contribute significantly to the solution of some important problems. For the illustrations I am indebted to the graphic talents of Miss Suzanne Becker. Equally indispensable has been the expert secretarial assistance of Mrs. Eleanor Smilas. Financial support for my research relevant to the subject of this book has been provided by a grant from the National Institutes of Health (HD-00192) and a fellowship from the

Department of Embryology of the Carnegie Institution of Washington, for which I am very grateful.

For less tangible, but more important reasons, I wish to thank my wife, Marcella, and my children, for their patience, understanding, and love.

Providence, Rhode Island   R. J. G.
December, 1963

I
Introduction

FEW attributes of living systems are more important than the homoeostatic mechanisms by which the physiological and morphological conditions in the body are held constant despite the normal vicissitudes of the environment (or the interventions of the experimental biologist). Nowhere is this more dramatically illustrated than in the reparative responses of tissues and organs to injuries or to reductions in mass. First and foremost, such reactions involve prompt functional responses to compensate for whatever physiological disturbances may have been suffered. This ensures the temporary survival of the organism under conditions of sublethal injury, and reflects the existence of functional reserve capacities which in some vital organs may represent a margin of safety several times as great as the normal physiological requirements. Usually an animal cannot indefinitely endure at the expense of such emergency measures, so the physiological debt must be reimbursed by the morphological restoration of the affected part. On logical grounds alone, therefore, there is reason to expect a causal relationship between function and development.

Ontogeny
Fundamental to the understanding of compensatory growth is an appreciation of the wide spectrum of developmental phenomena which it embraces. In its simplest form, it may merely involve cellular hypertrophy as exemplified in muscle fibres. Alternatively, it may be expressed as cell regeneration, such as occurs in transected neurons. At the histological level, tissues capable of mitotic proliferation may make good a deficit by hyperplasia. This is best illustrated by liver regeneration and compensatory renal hyperplasia. Comparable responses are also known to occur in such other organs as the pancreas, salivary glands, thyroid, adrenal cortex, and ovary.

Hyperplastic compensation is restricted to organs of a compound nature, i.e. those composed of many identical functional units (figure 1). Where such units are represented by individual cells, as in the adrenal cortex, compensatory growth can be accomplished by direct

13

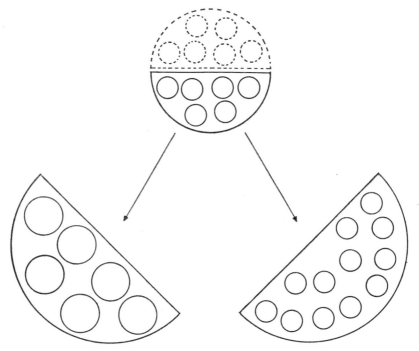

Figure 1. Schematic representation of alternative modes of compensatory organ enlargement following partial ablation. Constituent functional units (inner circles) may either enlarge (left) or multiply (right).

cellular proliferation. In other cases the physiological efficiency of an organ may depend upon the histological entities into which the cells may be organized. Represented by such structures as nephrons these functional units cannot ordinarily be multiplied beyond the normal adult complement. Restoration of these organs is perforce restricted to cellular hyperplasia and the consequent enlargement of the pre-existing functional units. Largely because of surface-volume relationships, there are limits beyond which such units cannot grow without reducing their functional capacities. Thus, the extent to which an adult organ of this kind can enlarge is theoretically subject to these limitations.

The instances of compensatory growth thus far cited all involve the proliferation or enlargement of cells already differentiated. In other cases, however, regeneration of a tissue may proceed by the proliferation of undifferentiated stem cells followed by their subsequent maturation into fully differentiated functional entities. Represented by those tissue systems which must constantly renew themselves, the replacement of lost parts is an exaggerated manifestation of their normal growth pattern. A case in point is the accelerated production of erythrocytes following loss of blood. Studies of erythropoiesis are especially rewarding, for they have revealed that compensatory production of red blood-cells, though usually induced by excessive loss or destruction of circulating erythrocytes, is not directly regulated by such a deficit. Rather, erythropoiesis is stimulated when the demand for oxygen by tissues exceeds the supply, a circumstance that can be induced either by loss of red blood-cells under conditions of constant oxygen tension or by hypoxia in the absence of alterations in the numbers of red blood-cells. The respiratory requirements of the body are communicated to the erythropoietic centres by erythropoietin, a compound believed to be manufactured in the kidneys and carried by the blood to the marrow where it stimulates erythropoiesis. In view of the relatively advanced state of our knowledge in this specific field, the erythropoietic regulatory system may well serve as a model upon which to base hypotheses concerning growth regulation in general.

It is well known that many tissues of the body do not exhibit compensatory hyperplasia in the usual sense. Thus, loss of part of the muscular, skeletal, or integumentary systems is not followed by growth of the residual homologous tissues throughout the body, presumably because such a response never represented a selective advantage phylogenetically. All tissues, however, are capable of repairing local injuries, a potential which has definite survival value. Most thoroughly investigated with reference to the healing of skin wounds and bone fractures, these are but special cases of a very general phenomenon that can occur to varying degrees in all parts of the body. The repair of localized injuries is restricted to those tissues which are directly affected and to others in the vicinity which may be secondarily influenced in ways not clearly understood. If an organ such as the liver or kidney is injured locally, the repair response will be local. If substantial portions of such organs are removed, there will be a generalized growth response throughout the remaining homologous tissues in addition to the local reaction. The difference between these two phenomena may be only a matter of degree, for the generalized compensatory hyperplasia may be in response to a diffuse, tissue-specific trauma induced by partial ablation and mediated by increased systemic demands for additional functional activity by the residual tissues. In a sense, local wound healing is a more complicated process than compensatory hyperplasia, for it involves not only mitosis and differentiation, but also cell migration and morphogenesis.

These same organizational activities of cells and tissues are likewise characteristic of morphological regeneration. By extension, therefore, regeneration of histologically complex structures may reasonably be regarded as another special case of the basic process of wound healing (or vice versa), the two differing from each other only in degree. It is significant and self-evident that in compensation for the loss of a limb in an amphibian, for example, neither the opposite limb nor the amputated stump doubles in size. This is the basic difference between limb regeneration and liver regeneration. Each limb represents a single functional unit, while the liver consists of many thousands of units. The former can restore its functional capacity only by qualitative replacement of lost portions, the latter solely by quantitative regeneration. In both cases, the mechanism that has been favoured by evolution has been the one that most efficiently restores the original physiological integrity of the injured part.

The foregoing examples have all related to developmental phenomena occurring in response to extrinsic stimuli. Remarkable as some of them may appear to be, none represents anything that cannot be reduced upon analysis to combinations of such fundamental processes as hypertrophy, mitosis, differentiation, and morphogenesis. Accordingly, it is pertinent to include in an account of regenerative processes those so-called natural instances of regeneration so clearly illustrated by the normal turnover of cell populations in certain of the "renewing" tissues of the body. To cite a few examples, epidermal wound healing, or the replacement of lost blood, may logically be regarded as extensions of the normal perpetual replenishment of these tissues. Moreover, compensatory enlargement of the ovary following unilateral castration finds its natural counterpart in the gonadotrophic events associated with puberty and the reproductive cycles. Even the regeneration of limbs recapitulates what happens in the embryo or during metamorphosis. Therefore, in seeking a common explanation of how such diverse examples of development are governed, it may be experimentally convenient to initiate growth by external stimuli, but it is not necessary.

Phylogeny

The mechanisms by which regenerative and compensatory growth processes occur in mammals are the end results of millions of years of natural selection. Their very persistence testifies to the survival value they have afforded the countless ancestors through which they have descended. Conversely, the lack of such growth processes in certain instances may also be significant, for what does not happen may sometimes be as revealing as what does.

Those who attempt to comprehend vertebrate appendage regeneration find it instructive to wonder why some parts of an organism can be replaced and others cannot, or why homologous appendages in members of different vertebrate classes exhibit varying degrees of regenerative abilities. Most would agree that the absence of limb regeneration in higher vertebrates, in contrast to its occurrence in amphibians, for example, reflects its incompatibility with other advantages which apparently had greater survival value. With the phylogenetic advent of the warm-blooded condition, perhaps those individuals capable of more precocious wound healing and scar formation were better able to resist infections by pathogens capable of rapid multiplication in a homothermic environment. This may well have outweighed any advantages of being able to regenerate appendages. If so, the dermal barrier produced at the wound site by the scar would have inhibited inductive interactions between the epidermis and the underlying mesodermal tissues of the amputated stump. Since such interactions are apparently essential to the production of a blastema, regeneration and scar formation would be expected to be mutually exclusive processes.

Even should a bird or mammal evolve a means of regenerating a lost limb, its survival value in a competitive world would be problematical. A serious disadvantage of the homothermic condition is the necessity of acquiring sufficient and frequent nourishment in order to maintain a high body temperature. Cold-blooded vertebrates can survive for months without eating, but warm-blooded animals will starve to death in days or weeks if crippled, long before a leg could be regenerated. Confronted with these mutually exclusive alternatives, the advantages of the warm-blooded state far surpassed those of being able to regenerate lost limbs, simply because limbs are usually vitally essential appendages and even animals capable of regenerating them would not survive long enough to perpetuate the capacity. Yet there is no reason why the ability to replace a non-essential appendage

B

might not have evolved in warm-blooded vertebrates should it be of some advantage. A case in point is the existence of antlers in deer which are annually shed and renewed. Moreover, they develop primarily from the dermis, the very tissue believed to be responsible for inhibiting regeneration elsewhere.

With reference to internal organs, the ultimate explanation of the occurrence or absence of compensatory growth cannot be categorically determined because of incomplete or conflicting evidence. However, in an inventory of various endocrine and exocrine organs, for example, it is evident that not all of them respond in identical fashion to their partial reductions in mass. The differences represented must have arisen through natural selection because of variations in their value to the evolving individuals. To cite an obvious example, the removal of a lens from one eye of a newt results in its replacement, and not in the enlargement of the lens in the opposite eye. Since the latter possibility would have added insult to injury by interfering with normal vision in the intact eye, it was a mode of growth response that could never have been expected to survive the discriminating course of amphibian evolution.

Mechanisms of Growth Regulation

Many other organs already mentioned compensate for their diminished mass by growth of the residual or contralateral portions. This of necessity involves a negative feedback mechanism capable of specifically communicating the effects of the loss to the remaining tissues, thus bringing about their compensatory enlargements. Clearly, the successful operation of such a mechanism depends upon the existence of appropriate and available means of communication, usually represented by humoral or nervous pathways. These reactions, of course, must take place within a closed system, commonly represented by the body as a whole, but occasionally by subdivisions thereof (figure 2). Thus, partial ablation of paired organs, such as the kidney or endocrine glands (figure 3A), or unpaired ones (e.g. liver, pancreas) (figure 3B), is followed by compensatory growth, indicating that some effect of their loss was systemically distributed and specifically detected by the reacting homologous tissues. If this message is represented by the physiological deficiencies resulting from a decrease in the amount of tissue, one might expect that organs servicing

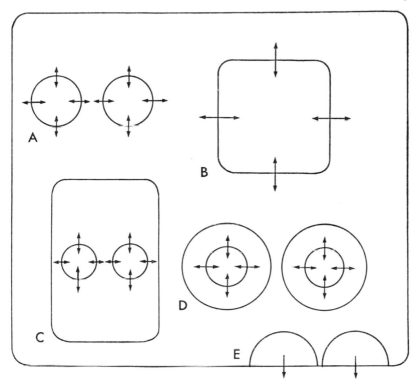

Figure 2. Classification of organs according to the systems with which they react. Paired (A) and unpaired (B) organs which exchange materials (arrows) with the entire body may be exemplified by the kidneys and liver, respectively. Those which react in a closed system within the body (C) are represented by salivary glands and the oral cavity. Organs that react in separate, but homologous, closed systems (D) may be illustrated by the lachrymal glands associated with the eyes. Glands which secrete into an open system (e.g. mammary glands and the outside environment) are designated by E.

separate closed systems would not react to each other's loss. Should growth responses be mediated by alterations in the humoral concentration of specific growth stimulators or inhibitors not directly related to tissue or organ function, then the capacity to exhibit compensatory growth following partial ablation would not necessarily be correlated with the physiological relationships of various representative organs. Thus, comparisons between such organs as the salivary glands and the lachrymal glands should be especially revealing. Inasmuch as the former are physiologically associated with a single closed system (figure 3C), namely, the oral cavity, compensatory growth would be a functionally meaningful response. Lachrymal glands, however, provide tears for separate eyes. Compensation by one gland for excision of the contralateral one would be physiologically useless (figure 3D).

Of special interest are those organs which react upon an open system (figure 3E). In this category one might classify many organs, the products of which are lost to the environment. Some of these, e.g. the kidneys or the nasal salt glands of marine birds, may react not to

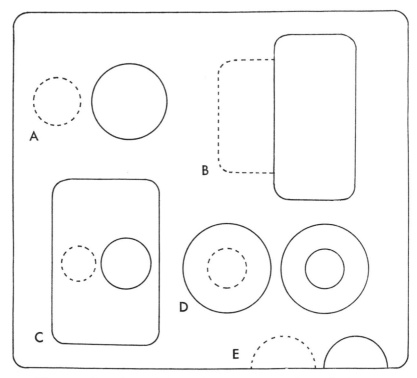

Figure 3. Reactions of the various organ types shown in figure 2 to partial ablation. Broken lines indicate parts of organs excised. Compensatory growth occurs in homologous organs physiologically associated with the same closed systems (A, B, C). When organs are in separate closed systems (D), or an open system (E), compensatory growth of residual homologous organs does not usually occur.

how much of a substance has been excreted but to the amount remaining within the organism. Others, however, may lack feedback communication with internal control mechanisms because their secretory products are not recovered or monitored. Thus, the growth and function of such organs are regulated by hormonal influences.

Investigations of the incidence of growth in response to the partial ablation of various organs with differing functions should yield compelling evidence upon which to base a decision as to the probable cause of compensatory hyperplasia. To this end, it is the purpose of the following chapters to explore the available data, and to decide which, if any, of the theoretical interpretations of growth-regulating mechanisms might most closely approximate the facts.

II

Allometry

In considering different kinds of explanations of biological phenomena, Mayr (1961) distinguishes between proximate and ultimate causes. The former are the immediate physiological antecedents of an event, while ultimate causes are represented by the many factors which have, through natural selection, affected the evolution of biological systems. Applied to the problem of size determination of organs and organisms, these principles indicate the importance of understanding not only the mechanisms of growth regulation during ontogeny, but also the phylogenetic history of such phenomena. Comparisons between ontogeny and phylogeny are not easily resisted and the problems of allometry are no exception. Despite the obvious limitations of such analogies, namely, that the mechanisms of development and evolution are not the same, the superficial resemblances between these two kinds of changes are compelling reasons for seeking causal factors which they might share in common.

Allometry refers to the size relationships between the whole and its parts. In comparing series of organisms, for example, the proportional dimensions of the parts seldom remain exactly the same throughout a wide range of sizes. In an evolutionary series, a succession of fossils representing a line of descent through geological time may exhibit modifications in body sizes accompanied by changes in the dimensions of component parts. The relative proportions of the parts to the whole usually vary linearly, though not necessarily at the same rate. Similarly, in a growing organism, relative organ size, if determined as a function of body size, undergoes alterations during the process of maturation which can be expressed quantitatively as a constant change. In view of such orderly patterns of ontogenetic growth and phylogenetic change, the promise of discovering the controlling factors has stimulated many studies of these phenomena.

Nowhere have these relationships been so eloquently and expertly analysed than in the writings of Thompson (1917). Providing a refreshing perspective in which to analyse evolutionary changes, his method of Cartesian transformations, for example, generated much of the impetus for subsequent mathematical investigations of morphology and growth. The implications of his studies were that the anatomical changes by which evolutionary progression is measured are brought about by alterations in growth rates and gradients thus causing shifts in the dimensions and proportions of organisms. In an attempt to reduce this differential growth to some comprehensive rule, Huxley (1932) proposed his heterogony (allometry) formula, $y = bx^k$, by which the size of an organ (y) is expressed as a function of body size (x) multiplied by a fractional coefficient (b = the fraction of the body size that the organ represents) and raised to the power, k. The growth coefficient, k, is the ratio of the relative growth rate of the organ to that of the body. When it is equal to unity, the growth rates of the organ and the body are the same, i.e. isometric. Allometric (heterogonic) growth may be positive or negative, depending on whether the rate of organ growth is greater $(k > 1)$ or less $(k < 1)$ than that of the body. There is a marked tendency in most systems for the growth rates of different parts to bear a constant relation to each other, an attribute that testifies to the operation of growth-regulating influences in the body. Factors that tend to disturb this equilibrium cause profound changes in the value of the growth coefficient, as in the cases of metamorphosis, puberty, or pathological conditions.

It was perhaps inevitable that the allometry equation should be applied to phylogenetic series as well as developmental ones, for in both instances the orderly relationship between the parts of changing systems was amenable to mathematical expression. Although it is not legitimate, *sensu strictu*, to attempt to equate comparisons between young *v.* mature animals with small *v.* large species, the close parallels between such systems may reflect the subordination of organ size and structure to considerations of physiological demands in both instances. The latter have unquestionably affected the course of evolution by providing the alternatives upon which natural selection operates. In a sense, therefore, evolution may be regarded as a kind of long range compensation for the physiological inadequacies engendered by changing environmental conditions and the necessity for organisms to adapt. Thus, organisms come equipped with genetic constitutions which tend to minimize, but never to abolish altogether, the necessity for the individual to undergo physiological adaptations to the demands of environmental changes. The extent to which ontogeny represents developmental responses to the requirements of physiological compensation, as distinguished from inherited patterns of growth, is an issue central to the problem of growth regulation.

Histological Consequences of Phylogenetic and Ontogenetic Enlargement
   The fact that a wide range of body sizes is often encountered among representatives of a given taxonomic group means that the constituent functional units must vary either in size or number as long as the body plan remains essentially unaltered. In general, units at lower levels or organization tend to vary in number rather than size, while those at higher levels or organization exhibit a wide range of sizes while remaining relatively constant in number. Thus, the dimensions of the smallest biologically functional units, the molecules, are immutable. Therefore, their numbers, not their sizes, vary in proportion to body volume. Similarly, the dimensions of various intracellular entities, such as endoplasmic reticulum, mitochondria, nucleus, chromosomes, etc., remain reasonably constant, or at least vary in proportion to factors other than size of organism. With respect to cells, there is likewise a remarkable uniformity of dimensions, within certain limits, from mite to monster. This is possible because most cells in the body retain the capacity to divide as the tissues and organs of which they are a part continue to grow. Even cells such as neurons and muscle fibres which lose the ability to proliferate in adult organisms tend to "anticipate" future needs by completing their multiplication during earlier stages of development.
   The implications of these relationships have been thoroughly explored by Rensch (1959). Recognizing the general validity of Cope's rule, that animals tend to enlarge during evolutionary descent, he has successfully demonstrated why this is of advantage in natural selection. Although unlimited increases in bulk are accompanied by disadvantages so serious as to have contributed significantly to the extinction of many animal groups, reasonable largeness confers obvious physiological benefits on an organism, not the least of which is the lowered respiratory and metabolic rates made possible by the decreased surface area in relation to body volume. Even more compelling advantages derive from the increase in body size coupled with the more or less constant dimensions of most of the constituent cells. This combination of circumstances produces some interesting and important results in the histology and physiology of organs and tissues. It is especially well illustrated in the eyes of arthropods in which limitations of cell size restrict the maximum dimensions to which

ommatidia can grow. Consequently, large compound eyes evolve primarily by virtue of the addition of more ommatidia, and only to a limited extent by enlargement of individual ones. Thus, visual acuity in arthropods may be improved by the phylogenetic enlargement of the eyes. Ontogenetically, however, the size of the compound eye keeps pace with progressive increments in body size by the enlargement of each ommatidium (Plate 2.1). This suggests that visual acuity is not much improved despite the increasing dimensions of the eyes at successive instars. In vertebrates, visual acuity is likewise a function of absolute eye size inasmuch as the rods and cones cannot increase in size in proportion to the eye as a whole. Large vertebrates, therefore, tend to have better vision than small ones because their eyes are larger and the image is projected on a greater retinal surface populated by more receptor cells.

For somewhat different reasons, the quality of the central nervous system of vertebrates improves directly with magnitude, despite the fact that the increase in numbers of neurons is not strictly proportional to size. Indeed, nerve-cells in big animals may be considerably enlarged in comparison to those in small ones, but this is compensated by more profuse dendritic branching which gives rise to a nervous system of greater complexity and capable of more elaborate mental processes.

Striated muscle fibres, like neurons, do not ordinarily proliferate in mature organisms. Correlated with this is the tendency of muscle fibres in large animals to exceed the dimensions of their homologues in smaller animals. Inasmuch as fibre size is not exactly proportional to body size, there are also conspicuous differences in the numbers of fibres in homologous muscles of large v. small animals. Rensch (1948) has illustrated this in the case of the thoracic musculature of some of the Diptera. Muscle fibres of very small flies are relatively large and compact, while those of large species are more numerous. Although the latter are larger in absolute size *vis-à-vis* the fibres of small insects, the proportional increase is not as great as the difference in body size. In larger insects the muscle fibres are also more diffusely arranged, thus providing more efficient spatial relationships with the tracheae in order to facilitate gas exchange.

Comparable studies have been pursued in the mammalian diaphragm musculature by Gauthier and Padykula (1963). The individual muscle fibres of very small mammals are smaller (and contain higher concentrations of mitochondria) than those of large mammals, thus reflecting morphological adaptations to metabolic differences (Plate 2.2). Clearly, muscle fibres have solved some of the problems attending phylogenetic increases in body size by undergoing hypertrophy. Yet because of surface-volume relationships, cells are subject to upper size limits beyond which they cannot grow without sacrificing physiological efficiency. To exceed this limit, muscle fibres must resort to population increases since the nature of their function is not compatible with changes in shape which might otherwise have brought about a more favourable surface-volume ratio. In contrast, enlarged nerve cells can alter their configurations by increased ramifications of their processes, a modification by which functional efficiency is enhanced.

While the advantages of largeness are readily evident with reference to the body as a whole and some of its parts, as discussed above, many organs in the body do not necessarily benefit by enlargement *per se*. Where the absolute size of the functional units remains essentially the same, increase in organ size is accomplished by multiplication of the constituent units. Endocrine glands of big animals, for example, are larger by virtue of the greater number of cells of which they are composed. In exocrine organs, largeness is achieved by the addition of more secretory acini, which in turn requires a longer and more extensive system of ducts. In these organs, mass can be increased without adversely affecting the function. In other cases, however, there are size limits beyond which the physiological efficiency must diminish.

The vertebrate kidney illustrates this point especially well, as the following data from Sperber (1944) attests. Phylogenetic enlargement of the kidney is accomplished by a general increase in the number of nephrons. There is also an enlargement of the individual nephrons, as expressed in their increase in volume and surface area (Table 1). Yet the nephrons are subject to definite size limitations beyond which their functional efficiency declines. Thus, it can be shown (figure 4) that in a series of mammalian species of different sizes, the diameters of Bowman's capsules increase from 48μ in shrew kidneys weighing 0.075 gm. to 135μ in squirrel kidneys weighing 1.7 gm. But beyond this the dimensions of the capsule, although rather variable, only double in size despite a thousandfold increase in kidney weight. Thus, the apparent upper size limits of the mammalian glomerulus lies between 200 and 350μ.

The dimensions of the proximal tubule show comparable modifi-

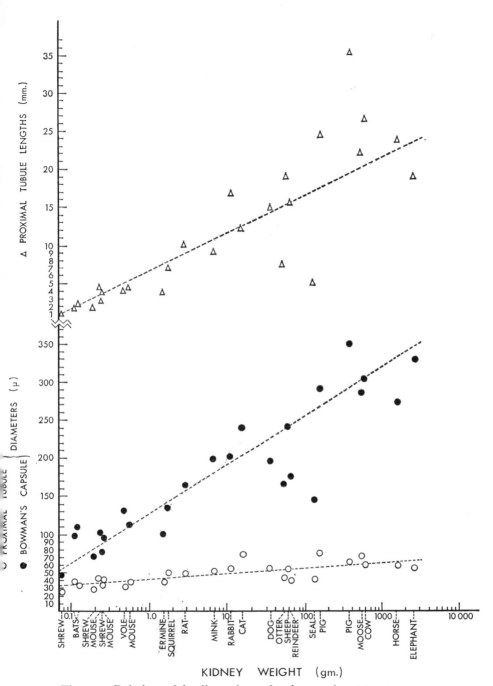

Figure 4. Relations of the dimensions of various nephron structures to phylogenetic increases in kidney weight. The latter, plotted logarithmically on the abscissa, ranges from the shrew with kidneys weighing 0·075 gm. to the elephant kidney which weighs 2575 gm. (Data compiled from Sperber, 1944.)

cations with increasing phylogenetic size of the kidney (figure 4). The width of these tubules shows some increase from small to large kidneys, but varies only slightly from the average diameter of 57μ. The maximum width of the proximal tubule (74μ in the cat) is only about three times the smallest measurement recorded (26μ in the shrew). In smaller kidneys, tubule diameter increases proportionately with tubule length. However, as figure 5 illustrates, over a wide range of larger kidneys the widths of the proximal tubules remain relatively constant despite considerable elongations.

	Total kidney weight (gm.)	Total number of nephrons	AVERAGE NEPHRON Surface area (mm²)	Volume (mm³)
Shrew	0·35	82,000	0·5015	0·004233
Mouse	0·42	72,000	0·7764	0·007096
Rabbit	22·0	315,000	4·327	0·06258
Dog	77·0	800,000	4·449	0·05305
Cow	1000·0	8,000,000	7·823	0·1112

TABLE 1. Relationship between animal size and renal structure. (Data from Sperber, 1944.)

The lengths of proximal tubules generally parallel glomerular size (figure 4). Among the smallest mammals there is the greatest proportionate increase in tubule-length commensurate with increments in renal weight. The shortest proximal tubule (one millimetre) occurs in the shrew, the longest (35 mm.) in the pig. In the blue whale, *Balaenoptera musculus*, the average proximal tubule measures only 13·26 mm. long. In kidneys weighing more than two grammes, the average length of the proximal tubule is about 17 mm., which probably represents the approximate maximum length which the proximal tubule can attain without sacrificing its functional competence. According to Sperber (1944), the proximal tubule length is also affected by diet, for in carnivores it represents about 40 per cent of the total nephron length, as compared with 53·4 per cent in herbivores.

Sperber (1944) concludes that the pressure needed to propel fluid through the tubules constitutes a major limiting factor accounting for the restrictions in nephron size outlined above. Inasmuch as tubule diameter must remain relatively small to maintain the optimal surface area for exchange, increased efficiency can only be achieved by elon-

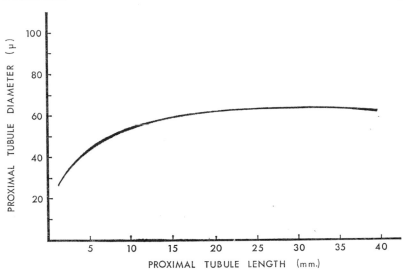

Figure 5. Graphic relationship between diameter and length of the proximal tubule. As the latter increases from small to large animals (abscissa), the width enlarges over a narrow range among smaller mammals, but in most larger species does not exceed a physiologically optimal size. (After Sperber, 1944.)

gation. This, however, necessitates increased pressure in Bowman's capsule to force urine along the tubule. Since such pressure cannot exceed the blood-pressure in the glomerular capillaries if filtration is to continue, there is a size limitation clearly imposed on the nephrons irrespective of the mass of kidney required by the animal. Obviously, the kidneys of a very large animal cannot be the same shape as those in a small animal if their nephrons are not to exceed these upper size limits. Hence, in small mammals the kidneys contain single renal papillae (figure 6A) as represented by the shrew, mouse, rat, rabbit, and cat, while in larger ones there may be many papillae per kidney (figure 6B), as in the human. With further increases in body size, in turn demanding still greater amounts of kidney tissue, there has occurred a subdivision of the organ into varying numbers of lobes, each of which represents a complete excretory organ (figure 6C). The surfaces of the kidneys of cattle, for example, are lined with grooves which delineate incompletely separated sub-units with fused cortices, but each of which contains a single papilla. In other species there are true renculi, each completely separate from the others. Such an adaptation, by which the total number of nephrons is allowed to increase without undue elongation, is encountered in such large animals as the bear, the elephant, and the whale (figure 6E). Certain other aquatic mammals which are not extra large (seal, otter), likewise have kidneys composed of numerous renculi, although the latter may exhibit partial fusion in the cortical regions (figure 6D). What physiological demands in these aquatic mammals are being compensated by

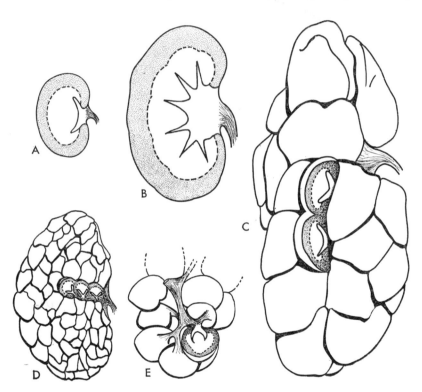

Figure 6. Representative types of mammalian kidneys all drawn to the same scale. Cortical portions stippled. A, rabbit kidney with a single renal papilla. B, human kidney, possessing many papillae. C, cow kidney, divided into cortically fused lobes, each with a single papilla. D, seal kidney, composed of numerous renculi with partially fused cortices and one papilla apiece. E, small part of a sperm whale kidney (from specimen in British Museum of Natural History) made up of completely separate renculi, each of which contains a single papilla and is connected with a branch of the ureter. $1/2\times$.

this anatomical adaptation remains to be explained. Since some of the herbivorous aquatic mammals (e.g. manitee) possess undivided kidneys, dietary considerations may be important in the evolution of renal anatomy.

Other systems, especially in which surface-volume relationships are important, have also undergone anatomical modifications on account of size changes. Thus, the intestines of large animals exhibit expansions of their inner surface areas to match the cubic increase in body volume, by elongation as well as by developing elaborate systems of infoldings and outfoldings of the mucosa. Similar adjustments could be predicted for the circulatory and respiratory systems. In general, it is evident that largeness is a mixed blessing in which the advantages outweigh the disadvantages mostly because so many tissues and organs have evolved such ingenious ways of maintaining their physiological efficiencies. In the opposite direction, reduction in body size is also accompanied by certain interesting anatomical adjustments designed to preserve optimal functions, as illustrated by the invertebrate examples cited by Rensch (1948).

Histological Effects of Polyploidy

While many factors contribute to the determination of body size, the ultimate explanation must lie in the genetic endowment which is the result of a long history of natural selection. The latter represents the mechanism by which the most efficient physiological systems have evolved, and this in turn is reflected in the morphological characteristics of organisms. As discussed above, the structure and size of all body parts are inevitably adjusted to the demands for maximal functional efficiency. Indeed, the tendency of organs to maintain the most physiologically optimum size and shape is so important that it transcends nearly all other alterations that may occur in the body.

This is dramatically illustrated by the analyses of polyploid amphibians reviewed by Fankhauser (1955). Inasmuch as nuclear and cell size corresponds to changes in the number of sets of chromosomes, these individuals afford a rare opportunity to determine the effects of alterations of cell volume on the size of tissues, organs, and total body in members of the same species. When individuals ranging from haploid to pentaploid are compared, it becomes evident that except for haploids which are usually smaller than normal, ploidy has little effect on body size. The inevitable result of increased cell size with progressively higher degrees of polyploidy combined with

relatively constant body size under the same circumstances is the production of individuals with fewer but larger cells in their bodies.
Moreover, histological examinations have revealed that the sizes and
proportions of constituent organs are not significantly altered. Tubular structures, for example, maintain the same dimensions in polyploid
salamander larvae although they are constructed of fewer and larger
cells than in normal larvae. Thus, pronephric tubules are approximately the same size and shape in haploid, diploid or pentaploid
animals (figure 7). The constituent cells in cases of polyploidy,
however, are larger and flatter. While a haploid pronephric tubule
may have an average of 11 cells in cross-section, corresponding diploid
and pentaploid tubules may average only six and three cells, respectively. Lens epithelium is similarly affected (figure 7).

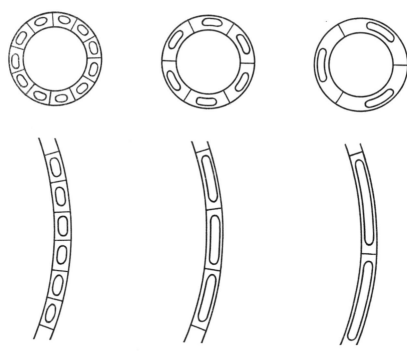

Figure 7. Transverse sections through pronephric tubules (above)
and lens epithelium (below) of haploid, diploid, and pentaploid
newts (left to right). Polyploid enlargement of cells, coupled with
constant histological dimensions, results in fewer cells per tissue.
(After Fankhauser, 1955.)

Such relationships between cell size and histological structure can lead to some interesting and potentially embarrassing consequences. The diameters of capillaries, for example, remain more or less constant despite increases in ploidy and cell size. Davison (1959) has compared diploid and triploid *Pleurodeles* larvae and has noted that the average capillary cross-sectional area is $184\mu^2$ in both cases. However, the red cell areas were $482\mu^2$ and $720\mu^2$ in 2n and 3n larvae, respectively. If the larger cells were to retain their original shapes they would be too big to pass through the capillaries. This conflict of dimensions is avoided by configurational adjustments such that the triploid red cells become disproportionately elongate (figure 8).

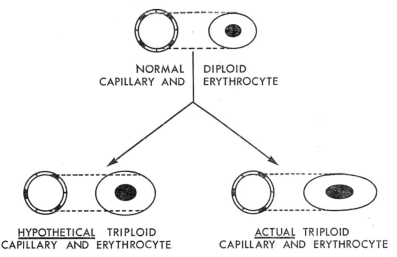

NORMAL | DIPLOID
CAPILLARY AND | ERYTHROCYTE

HYPOTHETICAL TRIPLOID
CAPILLARY AND ERYTHROCYTE

ACTUAL TRIPLOID
CAPILLARY AND ERYTHROCYTE

Figure 8. Alternative consequences of triploidy on capillary and erythrocyte dimensions in the newt. Since the capillary remains the same size, the triploid red blood-cell would be too wide to fit through the capillary lumen (left) unless the erythrocyte became longer and narrower, which it does (right).

Instead of a major to minor axis ratio of 1·36 as in diploid larvae, their average ratio is increased to 1·52. Hence, the shapes of red cells are determined by their sizes in relation to capillary diameters, such that larger cells are increasingly elongate, while the smallest ones may be nearly circular if their diameters do not exceed those of the capillaries through which they must flow.

c

Still another result of polyploid cell enlargement in the absence of bodily size increases is the occurrence of brains of normal proportions but composed of reduced numbers of neurons. Tests of learning capacities in triploid *v.* diploid salamanders have demonstrated the relatively inferior mental abilities of the former (Fankhauser, *et al.*, 1955). Thus, the quality of the central nervous system cannot be improved by increasing the sizes of neurons at the expense of their numbers. As stated earlier, however, mental competence can be improved phylogenetically by increasing both the size and number of nerve-cells.

A rather interesting situation obtains with reference to Mauthner's cells in polyploid newts. In normal diploid animals there is a single pair of these cells in the brain. Hence, it is impossible to reduce the number of such cells without depleting them altogether. Accordingly, in polyploid animals Mauthner's cells persist, but become progressively (and disproportionately) enlarged. In haploid newts, however, there may be *two* pairs of Mauthner's cells, each of which is reduced in size (Fankhauser, 1955).

Size Adjustments of Transplanted Organs

Clearly, the relative size of a histological structure is independent of the dimensions of its constituent cells. Nor is the magnitude of an organ automatically adjusted as a fixed proportion of body size, for although this may occasionally occur in cases of isometry, it is the exception. Extensive quantitative analyses of such relationships have indicated the allometric nature of organ growth as revealed in the changing, but predictable, proportions which characterize developing organisms (figure 9). Yet the very existence of orderly relationships in bodily dimensions testifies to the probable operation of size-controlling factors. Though much has been inferred from descriptive observations concerning the nature of such hypothetical factors, the contributions of certain experimental approaches as reviewed by Twitty (1940) have brought to light some previously unsuspected influences which organs exert on each other's rates of growth.

The rationale of such experiments has been to isolate a growing structure from its normal organic environment and to transplant it to another system with a different growth rate. Harrison (1924, 1929) achieved this by transplanting developing limbs and eyes between larvae of fast-growing *Amblystoma tigrinum* and slow-growing *A. punctatum*. In both instances, the grafts persisted in their normal

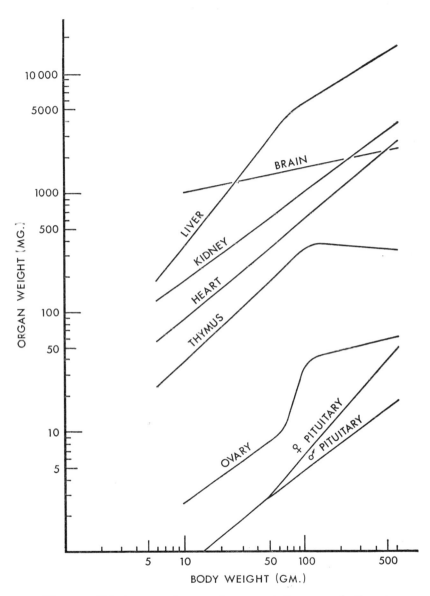

Figure 9. Relative growth rates of representative organs in the rat, plotted on logarithmic scale. (From data of Donaldson, 1924, and Bertalanffy and Pirozynski, 1952.)

growth rates irrespective of whether those of their hosts were faster
of slower. Consequently, there resulted small *A. punctatum* larvae
with disproportionately large limbs or eyes of *A. tigrinum* origin, and
vice versa (figure 10). On the basis of these results, it would seem that
organs are subject to intrinsic control of size which cannot be seriously affected by residence in other environments with different
growth rates. Subsequent investigations, however, showed that this
conclusion was valid only for certain kinds of structures, such as
limbs and eyes, when studied as interspecific grafts. When size
differences were a function of age instead of species, comparable
transplantations yielded somewhat different results. Heterochronic
grafts of eyes between young and old *Amblystoma* larvae of the same
species gave individuals which initially possessed eyes that were the
wrong size. However, continued growth of such larvae was attended
by retarded or accelerated growth of the grafted eyes until their
eventual sizes were adjusted harmoniously to the bodily proportions
of the hosts (Twitty, 1940). Nevertheless, in both of the above types
of experiments, whether involving interspecific or heterochronic
transplants, the grafted eyes always grew eventually to their same
normal dimensions.

Such is not always the case, however, when the responses of other
organs are investigated. Grafts of spinal cord segments from *A.
tigrinum* to *A. punctatum*, for example, eventually assumed proportions in accordance with the size of the host (Detwiler, 1932).
Similarly, Copenhaver (1930) has shown that cardiac rudiments transplanted between *A. tigrinum* and *A. punctatum* did not persist in
their normal specific growth rates, but underwent modifications
in their patterns of growth to reach ultimate dimensions appropriate to
their hosts' body sizes. These organs, therefore, react differently than
do eyes and limbs when grafted to other species that are larger or
smaller. Twitty (1940) reasoned that organs capable of adjusting to a
foreign systemic environment with a different growth rate are responding "to the functional demands imposed upon them by their
hosts, although, of course, the mechanism for such adjustment is not
clearly understood". "Eyes and limbs," he says, "play no crucial role
in the essential machinery of the organism, and are freer to express
their growth capacities independently of the scale or requirements of
the rest of the animal."

A rather similar principle applies to the growth of eyes resulting
from the interspecific exchange of lens and optic cup between *A.*

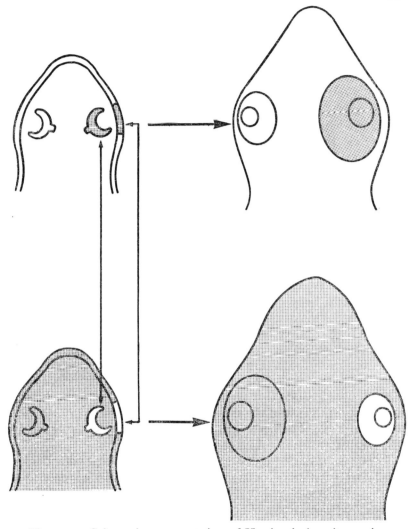

Figure 10. Schematic representation of Harrison's (1929) experiments in which the eyes of slow-growing *Amblystoma punctatum* (unshaded, above) and fast-growing *A. tigrinum* (shaded, below) were exchanged (left). Despite different systemic growth rates in the two species, the grafted eyes grew to their normal dimensions (right). The resultant *A. punctatum* host thus possessed a disproportionately large *A. tigrinum* eye (upper right) while the *A. tigrinum* larva had a small grafted eye of *A. punctatum* size (lower right).

tigrinum and *A. punctatum.* Harrison (1929) carried out experiments showing that when lens ectoderm from *A. tigrinum*, potentially capable of producing a large lens, is combined with the potentially smaller optic cup of *A. punctatum*, the mismatched components exert reciprocal influences on each other's growth rates. Thus, the production of a small eye with an extra-large lens is avoided by the accelerated growth of the former and the decelerated growth of the latter, yielding a harmoniously proportioned eye of intermediate dimensions (figure 11). Similar results were obtained in the reciprocal experiment (figure 12) involving the exchange of optic vesicles between the two species. Apparently the functional dependence between the lens and the rest of the eyeball, especially the retina, expresses itself by mutual growth regulation in the developing eye long before the visual function is realized.

Further light has been shed on this problem by investigations of the relative growth rates of various parts of the embryonic chick eye. Coulombre (1956) was able to retard the normal enlargement of the four-day embryonic chick eye by inserting a small capillary tube into the vitreous body, thereby relieving intraocular fluid pressure. Although the diameters of such intubated eyes were conspicuously smaller than controls during subsequent development, it was noted that the growth of the retina and lens was not seriously affected by this treatment (Coulombre and Coulombre, 1963). Seemingly inconsistent with the results of Harrison's (1929) experiments cited above, these results indicate that the development of the lens may be commensurate with that of the retina rather than with the growth of the eye as a whole. Further evidence along these lines is presented in Chapter VI.

It cannot be denied that organs possess an inherent potential for a particular growth rate leading to an ultimate size which is determined by the genetic constitution of the individual and the species. Whether or not this basic pattern of growth is modified by the surroundings in which the organ is developing apparently depends upon the degree to which the two systems are physiologically related. If the relationship is negligible, as in the case of the eye (or limb) *v.* the total body, then the influence of the latter on the former is minimal. This does not mean that the eye or limb is not subject to growth regulation, for as has been shown already, the growth of the eye is clearly influenced by the lens, with which it is functionally related. Presumably, the limb might be similarly affected by its component parts, e.g. skeleton

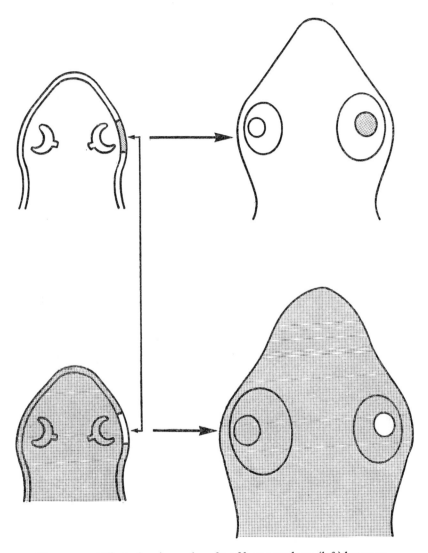

Figure 11. Effect of reciprocal grafts of lens ectoderm (left) between *Amblystoma punctatum* (unshaded, above) and *A. tigrinum* (shaded, below). As Harrison (1929) discovered, subsequent growth of these ocular chimerae resulted in mutual acceleration or retardation of lenses and eye cups to produce harmoniously proportioned eyes which were either too large (upper right) or too small (lower right) for the resulting host larvae.

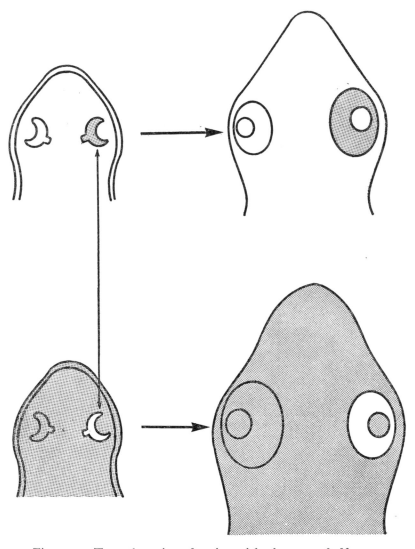

Figure 12. Transplantation of optic vesicles between *Amblystoma punctatum* (unshaded, above) and *A. tigrinum* (shaded, below) as performed by Harrison (1929). Combinations of fast-growing optic vesicle with slow-growing lens ectoderm, or vice versa, resulted in normally proportioned eyes intermediate in size between the smaller *A. punctatum* eye (upper right) and the larger *A. tigrinum* eye (lower right).

or muscle. It has also been shown that the spinal cord and heart undergo secondary developmental adjustments to accommodate to the physiological demands of the body. It might be predicted that various other organs (e.g. liver, kidney, endocrine glands) which perform functions of service to the entire organism might also express developmental modulations in accordance with systemic requirements. Thus, the anatomical harmony so characteristic of growing organisms may in large measure be attributed to numerous interrelationships, based upon present or anticipated functional needs, which maintain balanced growth rates among the various components of the body.

III

Theoretical

NEW facts contribute to intellectual progress only in so far as they can be assembled into an organized conceptual perspective. The discovery of common denominators among diverse systems of knowledge permits the conversion of miscellaneous data into well-integrated hypotheses which, to be useful, must be expressed in such specific terms that they can be proved right or wrong. When correct, however, their predictive value can be measured in the currency of scientific progress. Our understanding advances under the stimulus of, and at the expense of, many expendable hypotheses which never become laws. Yet the heuristic value of an evolving series of readily mutable hypotheses lies in the influence they exert on the direction of research. Ideally, the information which accrues is increasingly valid, pertinent, and consistent.

The theoretical approach to the general problem of growth regulation is especially important to bring some order to the rapidly expanding body of information in this field. Although existing hypotheses may be accused of being too specialized, too vague, not pertinent, or even inaccurate, hypotheses are made to be criticized, and each in its own way serves to sharpen our perspective. In the accumulation of knowledge about a subject there comes a time when the amount of data reaches a critical proportion of the theoretical total at which point it is possible by extrapolation to predict the rest. Since the theoretical total is seldom known beforehand, it is usually not possible to foretell when this breakthrough will occur. Whether as the result of a single revolutionary experiment or emerging from the accumulated backlog of data, most hypotheses are conceived in an atmosphere of guarded optimism in the hope that they will be more accurate than the pre-existing ones which they are intended to supersede.

There has been no dearth of hypotheses about the problem of growth regulation. The majority of them have been inspired by the phenomenon of compensatory hypertrophy which so often follows the loss of part of an organ or tissue. Yet most of these hypotheses have also recognized the relationship between compensatory growth and such other phenomena as regeneration, wound healing, and turnover of cell populations. Less often have attempts been made to compare compensatory growth phenomena to processes of normal ontogeny. And, although the latter have been related to phylogenetic changes (cf. Bertalanffy and Pirozynski, 1952), the successful integration of all these phenomena in a generalized theoretical scheme has not as yet been achieved.

Fundamental to all such theories is the concept of control mechanisms by which a critical mass of tissue is maintained in the face of disturbing influences. As Warburton (1955) has so incisively indicated, this implies the existence of a goal towards which processes may be directed by feedback mechanisms. A positive feedback, of limited value in biology, is one in which a departure from the norm results in the amplification of the original mistake thus leading a system from bad to worse. Negative feedbacks, however, tend to correct any deviation by setting in operation counteracting processes by which more accurate guidance towards the goal is achieved. The precision of such a system depends upon how much deviation occurs before it is detected, and how rapid and efficient the reacting mechanisms are. But the most important question raised by the problem of growth regulation is to determine the nature of the predetermined goal towards which growth is normally directed. The answer to this must be either morphological or physiological stability, but because the two are so inseparably linked the distinction has not always been obvious. In either case we have what Warburton (1955) calls a "linked feedback system", since the growth response to a reduction in organ mass, for example, is not an end in itself, but must be directed towards some other goal to which it is linked. Otherwise, growth would go on unchecked.

Notwithstanding the disagreement concerning the possible morphological or physiological nature of the goal, most authors concur on certain aspects of the most probable mechanism by which the negative linked feedback operates, namely, that there exist humoral agents capable of regulating the growth of homologous tissues. Normally operating to maintain the established size of a given organ within the body, such hypothetical agents are generally believed to be responsible for phenomena of compensatory hypertrophy as well. Whether they are represented as stimulating or inhibiting substances, however, remains a point of major contention. It is conceivable that if one of these dilemmas were solved, viz. the morphological as opposed to the physiological nature of the feedback goal, the choice between growth stimulation v. growth inhibition could be more intelligently and accurately made.

Growth Regulation by Tissue Mass

A feedback based upon a morphological goal, according to Weiss (1955) and Weiss and Kavanau (1957), is responsible for maintaining relative organ size in the body and for restoring its mass following reduction. The mechanism of this is believed to be a "direct chemical balance reaction (which) may turn out to be a ubiquitous and general principle to which functional and hormonal effects would be merely superimposed" (Weiss, 1955). In addition to its general consistency with most phenomena of compensatory hypertrophy following partial ablation of organs, the rationale for basing this hypothesis on considerations of tissue mass *per se* (rather than functional overload) lies in various reports in the literature describing compensatory growth after unilateral removal of certain invertebrate appendages, or of vertebrate testes and orbital glands. Inasmuch as each of these paired structures is considered to operate independently of its contralateral partner, its functional loss supposedly would not be felt by homologous tissues. Therefore, the growth reaction of the latter is taken to indicate a non-functional response, perhaps a direct effect of reduced tissue mass detectable by alterations in the concentrations of hypothetical inhibitors or stimulators. The invertebrate evidence clearly goes beyond the consideration of tissue mass alone since there is often a differentiation response, too. For example, when the left and right claws of certain crustaceans are of different types, removal of one sometimes causes a transformation of the other into a different kind of appendage during subsequent moults. To what extent it is valid to use such examples as testimony for or against mass v. functional hypotheses of compensatory growth must await more detailed experimental information from various invertebrate forms.

Among the vertebrate organs cited in evidence above, it seems altogether proper to expect the testes to undergo functional compensatory growth, at least in part. Being endocrine organs, the interstitial cells of the remaining testis should detect the effects of unilateral castration. And since spermatogenesis is hormonally controlled, the seminiferous tubules might be expected to respond just as do solitary remaining ovaries, that is, by enhanced gamete production. Unfortunately, the histology of compensatory testicular hypertrophy has not been studied in sufficient detail to yield unequivocal answers to these intriguing questions.

The orbital (lachrymal) glands of the rat provide perhaps the best opportunity to distinguish between the roles of mass $v.$ function in compensatory growth. As was indicated in Chapter I, these glands secrete tears into the left or right eye independently. Therefore, the enlargement of one after the extirpation of the other could not possibly alleviate the physiological distress of the operated eye. Though there is some evidence that *in situ* degeneration of one gland, or injection of tissue preparations, may stimulate proliferation in orbital glands, Teir and Sundell (1953) have shown that simple ablation of one gland in young rats is not reflected in altered mitotic activity of the opposite intact glands. Confirming this in adult rats, Goss (unpub.) has similarly detected no rise in mitotic rates in the right outer orbital glands 48 hours after excision of the left ones. Since certain other paired exocrine organs (e.g. salivary glands) do exhibit responses to unilateral ablation there is little reason to reject functional overload in favour of reduction in tissue mass as an explanation of compensatory hypertrophy in adult vertebrates.

A very compelling item of evidence against explaining compensatory growth as a reaction to increased physiological demands is provided by the experiments of Ferris (cited by Weiss, 1955) on the metanephros of 12 to 13-day-old chick embryos. At this stage of development the mesonephros performs the excretory functions of the embryo, and the metanephros was therefore assumed to be in a prefunctional state. Nevertheless, destruction of one metanephros by cauterization resulted in a 70 per cent increase in mitotic activity in the opposite unharmed organ within two days of operation. The possible alternative interpretations of these results all indicate the importance of establishing the validity of the assumption that the 12 to 13-day metanephros is non-functional. In the absence of proof either way, however, it would seem unwise to use this evidence as a major justification for denying functional considerations as a basis for compensatory hypertrophy.

Indeed, with reference to prenatal kidneys, Bagg (1925) has shown that in mice suffering from the congenital absence of one kidney, compensatory hypertrophy of the other does not commence until after birth. It is at this time that the mouse kidney becomes vitally essential (although it is capable of some prenatal function), for completely arenal mice develop normally as far as parturition and usually do not die until about 24 hours after birth. Moreover, Rollason (1961) and Goss (1963a) have found little or no evidence of hyperplasia in the foetal kidneys of pregnant rats subjected to nephrectomy. Thus, if the embryonic chick kidney exhibits compensatory hyperplasia, while mammalian foetal kidneys do not, the difference may be due to the fact that the chick embryo does not enjoy the benefits of a placenta which in the mammal is capable of excretory functions (Bremer, 1916). Under these circumstances, then, a functioning excretory system in the chick embryo would be obligatory and presumably more sensitive to physiological demands than its mammalian counterpart.

Despite these difficulties in resolving the relative roles of mass and function in regulating growth, the undeniable fact remains that during much of embryonic development growth does occur in an orderly manner. Since much of this takes place prior to the onset of functional competence, there is no choice but to assign embryonic growth to regulating factors other than physiological demands. Inasmuch as development itself is the most important, if not the only physiological process in prefunctional embryonic states, on logical grounds alone it might be predicted that embryonic organs should be refractory to the imposition of adult type functional demands. Thus, if the only function of an embryo is to develop, such factors as rates of differentiation and changes in tissue mass may well constitute the predetermined goals towards which embryonic feedback systems are directed. Whether the subsequent functional goals of mature animals are added to or substituted for these embryonic ones is going to be a challenging problem for future research.

Nevertheless, there is little reason to ascribe growth regulatory mechanisms in post-embryonic organisms primarily to non-functional attributes. Were compensatory hypertrophy largely the result of an automatic accommodation for the loss of homologous tissues, why is it manifested only by some organs and not by others? Any hypothesis intended to explain compensatory growth must take into account the uneven distribution of this ability among the various tissues and organs of the body. An explanation based solely on quantitative morphological features cannot account for the discriminating occurrence of compensatory hypertrophy among the homologous tissues of many of the visceral organs, and of its absence in skeletal muscle, bones, and integument, etc. Almost by default, therefore, we are forced to accept a more functional interpretation of growth regulation, a conclusion that is all the more inescapable in view of the positive correlation that exists between the distribution of physiological and developmental compensatory effects.

Growth Regulation by Functional Demand

There is widespread acceptance of the classical views that functional demands are responsible for governing the growth of body parts. At the turn of the century, Morgan (1901) expressed the prevailing notion that "the activity of the organ is the cause of its growth", although he was at a loss to understand "how the use of a part could make its growth increase, for by use the tissues break down; and we are not familiar with any other processes within the body that make for the building up of an organ in more than an inverse ratio to its breaking down". According to Boycott (1929) "hypertrophy and atrophy are generally the result of use and disuse, respectively". In the area of pathology, where physiological disturbances are so frequently diagnosed by their effects on morphology and growth, the causal relationship between function and growth has long been taken for granted. With reference to compensatory hypertrophy, Wright (1958) was of the opinion that "if, for some reason, the usual functional balance is disturbed, either because the demand upon the particular organ is increased, as upon the heart in hypertension, or because the amount of specialized protoplasm subserving the function is suddenly decreased, as that of the liver in subacute necrosis, a 'need-stimulus' is given to the specialized cells affected". Later he writes, "specialized cells only persist in the body in the numbers that are needed for the specialized work that they carry out". Along these same lines, Swann (1958) suggests that "control mechanisms probably vary a good deal, and . . . that, beyond the fact of their involving feedback mechanisms and blood-borne factors, the only common feature we can recognize at present is their appropriateness to the function of the particular organ in question . . . and we arrive at some sort of a justification for the classical idea of control by functional load".

These views are reinforced by phylogenetic considerations, for control mechanisms have had to evolve along with other physiological attributes of the organs whose functions and growth they govern. Since function is the *raison d'être* of morphology, it would appear logical to expect physiological factors to have been favoured by evolution as the primary objectives of feedback mechanisms responsible for regulating growth in post-embryonic organisms. "As natural selection is concerned only with the efficiency with which functions are performed", writes Warburton (1955), "a morphological property of a structure is important only if it affects its function". If this were not so, there would be no way of avoiding the accumulation, for example, of masses of non-functioning cells. Since structures without functions persist during evolution only at the risk of reducing an organism's general efficiency, there is little chance that mechanisms of growth regulation which are independent of functional considerations would have had sufficient selective advantage to survive.

As was indicated earlier, some structures are capable of compensatory hypertrophy following partial ablation while others are not. It is widely recognized that the liver and kidney, for example, enlarge in response to reductions in mass, and that such endocrine glands as the adrenals, ovaries, thyroid (and probably others) do likewise. Certain exocrine glands also exhibit compensatory hypertrophy as illustrated by hyperplasia in the residual mass of the exocrine pancreas, or that in the salivary glands following excision of the contralateral organ. Haemopoietic tissues are especially responsive to reductions in the numbers of circulating blood-cells, as is attested by the accelerated production of new cells to make good the loss. In contrast to these examples, there are many other tissues and organs that fail to undergo proliferation and growth following reduction in the total mass of homologous tissue. In this category can be listed such structures as skeletal muscle, bone, cartilage, skin, orbital glands, teeth, limbs, sense organs, and with certain reservations, the adult nervous system. There are some organs in the above lists which may, under special circumstances, be exceptions to the rule, and there are many others which have not been sufficiently investigated to permit accurate classification. Yet the pattern is already clear, despite the incomplete state of our knowledge on these matters.

The capacity to exhibit compensatory hypertrophy is not possessed by all organs sharing a common circulatory system, but appears to be restricted to those which are in physiological communication with one another. Thus, in order for a paired organ to respond to unilateral ablation, or an unpaired one to react to partial extirpation, the loss must be detected as alterations in functional demands and not just in terms of a reduction of homologous tissue mass *per se*. Clearly, the

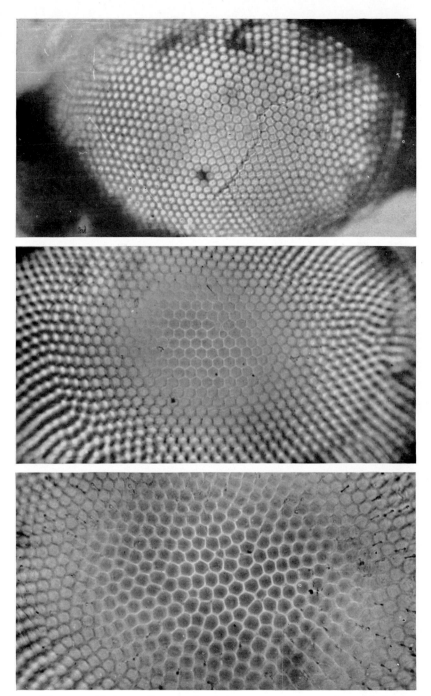

Plate 2.1. Ontogenetic growth of the compound eye of a cricket, *Gryllus assimilis*, as photographed in surface view at constant magnification (95 ×) in three different instars. Note that the individual ommatidia enlarge (top to bottom) as the eye as a whole increases in size.

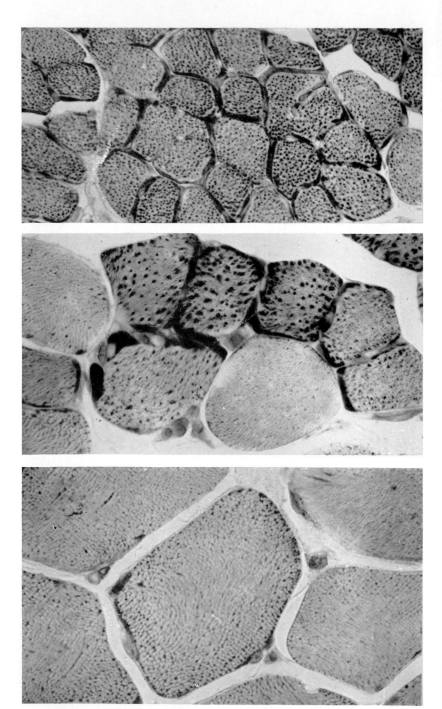

Plate 2.2. Transverse sections of skeletal muscle fibres from the diaphragm of the short-tailed shrew, albino rat, and cow (top to bottom). With increasing body size there is an enlargement in fibre dimensions. 625 ×. (Courtesy of Dr. Geraldine Gauthier.)

capacity of organs to accommodate for homologous tissue reduction by growth reactions is correlated with their abilities to undergo physiological compensation for functional deficiencies, whether the latter are caused by material loss or tissue incapacitation. Such reactions obviously depend on the existence of a communication system by which the effects of the loss can be conveyed to the homologous tissues. Although usually mediated via the blood circulation or other body fluids, such messages may also be sent by way of the nervous system.

It follows from this that any intervention resulting in a functional deficiency should bring about compensatory responses, both physiological and developmental, in residual homologous tissues. Actual tissue loss is but one way to achieve this result. The pathological and physiological literature is replete with comparable compensatory phenomena caused by functional disturbances not associated with the material reduction of tissues and organs. The functional hypertrophy of target organs under hormonal stimulation, of the heart in hypertension, of the kidneys following high protein diets, or of erythropoiesis under conditions of hypoxia, are all examples of growth responses which simulate compensatory hypertrophy in every detail except the initial loss of tissue. In point of fact, there are few tissues that will not enlarge (either by hypertorphy or hyperplasia) under conditions of heightened functional demands.

The specificity of compensatory growth responses has had significant theoretical implications, for upon its validity depends our conception of how the loss of part of a given kind of tissue is transmitted to the reacting systems. In general, it is recognized that removal of part of an organ results in a differential growth reaction restricted to the tissues of the affected organ or others of its kind. This is entirely consistent with the notion that compensatory growth may be a response solely to tissue loss, but hardly conforms to what is known of complex physiological interactions in the body. If compensatory hypertrophy is a direct reaction to the functional consequences of partial ablation it would be expected that growth should occur not just in the homologous tissues of the body but in any other organs which perform sufficiently similar functions to be affected by the loss. This is in fact the case, as can be illustrated by a few examples. When one submandibular gland of the rat is removed, mitotic activity is increased not only in the contralateral submandibular gland, but also in the major sublingual and parotid glands (though

D

not in other exocrine glands such as the outer orbitals) (Alho, 1961). Similarly, hypertension causes cardiac as well as renal hypertrophy since both of these organs affect, and are affected by, blood-pressure. By the same token, it might be expected that respiratory disturbances would be reflected in growth responses among all organs concerned with this function. Thus, reduction in the amount of lungs (or gills) might be predicted to result in accelerated erythropoiesis as well as in growth of the residual respiratory organs.

Further evidence that the specificity of compensatory growth is related to the functional activities of cells is provided by information concerning the particular parts of compensating organs that respond to partial ablation. Usually not all components of an organ react equally. Thus, when one kidney is removed growth occurs predominantly in the contralateral glomeruli and convoluted tubules. Even when extreme renal enlargement occurs owing to a five-sixths reduction in the original mass (Morrison, 1962), the papillae of the hypertrophic kidneys remain about the normal size. In the spleen, compensatory growth is largely restricted to the lymphoid components, while cardiac hypertrophy resulting from hypertension is usually limited to the left ventricle, this being the part which must react most vigorously to increased functional demands. Finally, in most exocrine glands undergoing compensatory hyperplasia, the extra mitotic activity is usually confined to the acini.

Hence, it appears that the most physiologically active part of an organ is selectively affected by partial ablation, which is to be expected if compensatory hypertrophy is the result of functional overload. This probably explains why many organs fail to regenerate to 100 per cent of the original mass following reduction. The liver, for example, usually exhibits complete regeneration of lost mass presumably because it is an organ very largely composed of functional parenchyma. Other organs such as the kidneys and exocrine glands generally stop growing before the total weights of the original organs are restored, perhaps because the original weight includes much more than just the components of primary physiological importance. Structures of secondary importance, such as ducts, may respond minimally, if at all, and only as a result of the indirect effects of the hypertrophied parts they serve.

The foregoing body of information emphasizes the importance of distinguishing between the roles of tissue mass and tissue function in regulating growth. It is generally impossible to reduce the mass of an organ without also decreasing its total function, at least temporarily, until the residual portions respond with increased physiological activity. However, it is possible to induce functional changes without affecting tissue mass. Under such circumstances, hypertrophy or atrophy generally accompany increased or decreased work loads, respectively. Coupled with the evidence that only those parts of the body that are functionally affected by partial ablation will undergo compensatory hypertrophy, the conclusion is inescapable that growth is governed by physiological demands. It remains to be determined if this is the only mechanism involved in the maintenance of cells and tissues.

The Nature of Growth Regulating Factors

Regardless of what the primary stimulus to compensatory hypertrophy may be, the existence of a communication system between cells of the same kind or function must be admitted. The general assumption that this involves specific molecules transmitted via the body fluids is probably correct, although the possibility that physical effects might occasionally exert significant influences cannot be ruled out, except in so far as they may be presumed to be translated back into chemical terms in the reacting system. Nevertheless, it is generally held that there must be blood-borne growth regulating substances, and considerable research and speculation has been brought to bear on this problem. Its theoretical aspects have been reviewed and amplified in recent years by Weiss (1955), Weiss and Kavanau (1957), Abercrombie (1957), Rose (1957), and Bullough (1962).

The problem reduces to a relatively simple set of alternatives, namely, whether growth is regulated by means of stimulation, inhibition, or a balance of both. Most theoretical contributions to this field in various ways favour the last possibility, that tissues and organs achieve a condition of dynamic equilibrium by reacting to both stimulatory and inhibitory factors. To account for the tissue-specificity of growth regulation, the general consensus of opinion favours the concept that tissues are autoregulatory, that is, that each one is responsible for its own growth controlling influences. It is further held that such influences are usually present in the blood, thus accounting for the necessary communication between homologous tissues in different parts of the body. Finally, there is general agreement that such humoral growth-regulating influences represent the

effects of chemical substances. Apropos of this, however, Abercrombie (1957) has pointed out the importance of determining whether
compensatory hyperplasia depends "on a specific 'regulatory substance' that the organ normally adds to the blood, or on one that it
normally subtracts from the blood". In the former instance, the
regulatory substance would be a growth inhibitor, in the latter a
growth stimulator.

With reference to the sources of these hypothetical compounds, it
is obvious that a growth inhibitor would be produced by the cells to
be specifically suppressed. This is consistent with the fact that compensatory growth occurs following reduction in homologous tissue
mass, because the systemic concentration of inhibitory materials
would be diminished. However, if growth regulation depends upon
the normal removal or inactivation of circulating stimulants by the
tissues for which they are specific, then it follows that they must be
derived from tissues other than the reacting ones. Otherwise, partial
ablation of an organ would reduce the concentration of stimulating
substances and cause "compensatory atrophy", a hypothetical condition which would contradict both theoretical expectations as well
as observed facts. The classic example of growth initiation under the
influence of stimulators from heterologous sources is, of course, the
hormone-target organ relationship. If this should represent a sim-
plified version of a more general, if not universal, mechanism, then
the growth of perhaps all tissues would be controlled by influences
emanating from other organs or even from the body as a whole.
Moreover, it is plausible that such influences may represent the
demands created by physiological needs normally fulfilled by the
reacting organs. Hence, the problem of growth regulation appears to
involve auto-inhibition and/or hetero-stimulation. The two alternatives are not necessarily mutually exclusive, although most theories
emphasize the former.

In an attempt to explain differentiation as well as size regulation,
Rose (1952) has proposed that multipotent embryonic cells undergo
sequential differentiation starting in the area of highest metabolic
activity. In this region the cells tend to differentiate preferentially in
one of various possible pathways, the choice being determined by
"an inherent rate advantage" presumably attributable to selective
gene activation. Differentiation of this primary tissue is accompanied
by the production of specific products which are assumed to diffuse
throughout neighbouring undifferentiated cells and inhibit their

potential differentiation into cells of the first type. By elimination, the cells in the next highest metabolic state, therefore, differentiate into the next tissue in the hierarchy, and so on. Thus, in a spatial and temporal sequence of events, each group of cells differentiates until a critical mass is attained which is sufficient to secrete an effective concentration of inhibitor, whereupon the adjacent group is enabled to differentiate in the next uninhibited direction. Though Rose (1952) specifically applies this hypothesis to tissues in the vertebrate embryo (notochord, somites, pronephros, mesothelium, and blood), it is similar to Brønsted's (1954) "time-graded regeneration field" as proposed to explain differentiation by sequential gene action in regenerating planarians. In this case, differentiation commences medially with the formation of the brain. Subsequently, neoblasts in adjacent positions differentiate into eye, muscle, and intestine in that order, although each one would otherwise have been capable of forming any of the other tissues had their relative positions differed. Thus, not only does each tissue type inhibit the differentiation of more of itself in adjacent regions, but the quantity of each kind that is initally allowed to differentiate before the next type begins to form is carefully controlled by its own products. In this way, the proportions (not the absolute amounts) of various kinds of tissue masses are established within the whole.

The principle of self-inhibition has been restated more recently by Bullough (1962) as the primary extracellular factor operating in growth control. Tissue-specific chemical messengers (chalones) capable of inhibiting mitosis are believed to be produced by the reacting cells and to be disseminated systemically. It is contended that cells normally retain their embryonic tendencies to proliferate even into adult life, but that they come increasingly under the control of inhibiting substances. Hence, hyperplasia is viewed as a release from inhibiting influences, without the requirement of exogenous stimulation. It is the expression of an opportunity when the innate propensity to divide is unchecked. Therefore, Bullough's (1962) view avoids altogether the necessity of identifying mitotic stimulators. The operation of the hypothetical mitotic inhibitors by which the growth and size of tissues and organs are determined may, he suggests, be related to cell differentiation. Adopting Swann's (1958) contention that mitosis is, in a sense, a form of cellular differentiation inasmuch as it requires the elaboration of specialized (though not tissue-specific) proteins, Bullough (1962) points out the difficulties of conceiving of tissue-specific stimulators for a process such as cell division which is essentially identical in all cells. But since differentiation is tissue-specific, it is considered possible that mitotic inhibitors might operate by promoting the synthesis of cell-specific proteins, which in turn would be expected to divert synthetic pathways away from the production of mitotic proteins. Conversely, when differentiation is not promoted, then a cell automatically reverts to its mitotic state.

Unlike the foregoing theories, which limit growth regulation primarily to the effects of extracellular inhibitors, the ingenious theory advanced by Weiss (1955) provides for the existence of both inhibitors and stimulators. In an elaboration of this hypothesis, Weiss and Kavanau (1957) distinguish between the differentiated portion of a cell or tissue, which is concerned with specialized structure and function, and the generative part, which is normally engaged in molecular synthesis and, by extension, in cellular growth and reproduction. The latter constantly contributes to the former, since cells retain their generative potentialities throughout life, as expressed by increase in total size during periods of maturation and by homoeostatic maintenance of body and organ mass in adult organisms whose only growth is to replenish the cells normally lost by depletion. The mechanism by which growth is achieved in the generative mass is considered to depend upon tissue-specific catalytic molecules ("templates"). The rate of protoplasmic increase is proportional to the active concentration of these compounds in the cytoplasm. Complementary molecules, called "antitemplates", are also produced by cells. It is their function to inactivate the template and thereby to exert a constraining influence on cell growth and reproduction. Like the templates, the antitemplates are continually being degraded and replaced and are specific for the kind of cell from which they are produced and in which they are active. They differ from templates, however, in that they may be released from their cells of origin, circulate freely throughout the body, and penetrate other cells of the same kind. In this way they can gain access to the entire population of templates of their own complementary types. The fraction of templates thus inactivated is proportional to the bodily concentration of antitemplates. Hence, the ultimate mass of a particular type of cell, tissue or organ represents the amount of growth that is permitted commensurate with the ratio of intracellular templates to intra- and extracellular antitemplates.

The major advantage of this theory is that it is amenable to experimental testing, and accordingly has provided the rationale for numerous investigations of growth regulation aimed at proving the existence of templates or antitemplates. Clearly, any experimental intervention that upsets the normal equilibrium between templates and antitemplates will affect the growth of the tissue with which they are associated. A relative increase of templates over antitemplates will enhance growth while the reverse situation will suppress it. Partial extirpation of an organ will, of course, reduce the total number of templates in the system as a whole, but this by itself does not inhibit growth in homologous parts because there is no direct way in which the magnitude of the total template population can be measured by residual cells. Thus, the loss of tissue can only be detected by the ensuing decline in the concentration of extracellular antitemplates. Since these can diffuse in and out through cell membranes, the drop in their intracellular concentration will naturally equilibrate with their depleted systemic concentration, and hence will accurately reflect the actual tissue loss. The balance can only be restored by cellular proliferation until the original mass of tissue is re-established. Theoretically, it should also be possible to cause hyperplasia by decreasing the antitemplate concentration in other ways, such as by loss or dilution of blood plasma, although all tissues should react to these procedures. By the same token, artificial increases in the concentration of antitemplates, as in the case of plasma injections, or as a result of restricted fluid intake in order to concentrate the plasma, should suppress growth or even bring about atrophy in every tissue subject to this type of growth control.

It has been predicted that the addition of extra amounts of a given tissue to the body could have either inhibitory or stimulatory effects on the growth of homologous cells depending on the extent to which the implanted cells are intact or disrupted. If maintained in a fully viable state, grafted cells would produce supplementary antitemplates which would suppress the growth of homologous tissues. Disrupted cells, however, would be expected to release quantities of templates into the host system which would stimulate homologous tissue growth either by direct action within cells or by combining with and inactivating complementary antitemplates in the circulation thereby reducing their overall concentration in the system.

Considerable experimental effort has been focused on the key points of the above hypotheses in attempts to demonstrate the existence of the various stimulators and inhibitors that have been postulated. As will be seen in the reviews of this work in the chapters to follow, there is no dearth of evidence in favour of the various points of view that have been proposed. Yet unless the experimental data are carefully selected, it is apparent that the supporting evidence is far from unanimous. Indeed, the weight of inconsistent and negative results is enough to cast serious doubt on the validity of most of our existing theories. It would appear, therefore, that either our assay techniques are not adequately refined to reveal the answers that are sought, or the theoretical models being tested are oversimplifications of reality.

Proponents of the functional demand theory of growth regulation (e.g. Swann, 1958; Wright, 1958) have not translated their ideas into the relatively simple but hypothetical chemical concepts used to illustrate the foregoing theories relating to size determination. Attempting to correlate functional demands with cell growth and division, Wright (1958) speculates that the increased metabolism of excessively active cells results in the fragmentation of larger molecules into smaller ones in order to yield more energy. This accumulation of small molecules leads to a rise in the intracellular osmotic pressure, and therefore to excessive inward diffusion of water. The resulting tumescence of the cell is accompanied by dilution of its cytoplasmic entities, a shift in intracellular balance that accelerates synthetic activities and re-establishes cytoplasmic equilibrium by bringing about cellular hypertrophy. In view of the limitations of cell and nuclear sizes imposed by area-volume relationships, mitosis will eventually occur as a direct result of this unstable hypertrophic condition, thus restoring the optimum cell size and nuclear : cytoplasmic ratio. As far as it goes there could be some truth in this proposal, especially in view of the support afforded by other studies indicating the importance of cell size in triggering mitosis. But the ultimate decision on these matters must await more conclusive cytological and biochemical evidence concerning the immediate stimuli of cell division.

Of equal importance, however, is the intercellular communication by which the incidence of mitosis is controlled. In the case of the functional demand theory, it becomes difficult to think in terms of specific molecules playing the role of stimulator or inhibitor, except perhaps with reference to the endocrine glands in which function is nearly equivalent to the hormone molecules secreted. Systemic communication between homologous tissues would presumably involve a complex series of reactions with other tissues and organs which are normally associated physiologically with the tissue in question. Ordinarily subjected to mutual physiological influences, various body tissues would affect each other's functioning by virtue of physiological feedback mechanisms. These not only call forth or turn off organ functions in accordance with the rules of supply and demand, they may also indirectly stimulate or inhibit growth. There is abundant evidence that such a correlation exists, as reflected in the many pathologically and experimentally induced conditions in which hypertrophy results from excess demand for function. Whether or not the hypertrophy which compensates for partial ablation is likewise a consequence of overwork is not yet clearly established. Nevertheless, it is difficult to resist this conclusion, especially since tissue loss unquestionably imposes a functional burden on remaining parts. The latter, by virtue of their physiological margins of safety, are generally capable of doing two or three times as much work as they are normally called upon to perform. Thus, in an effort to conduct business as usual despite serious handicaps, most kinds of cells can exhibit, at least temporarily, remarkable degrees of physiological compensation. This, however, is only a stopgap measure which must eventually be rectified by tissue growth. Compensatory hypertrophy, then, can logically be regarded as an accommodation for functional overload, which is in turn an adaptation to tissue loss. If this approaches the truth, then the most obvious candidate for the position of growth regulator would be the functional activity itself, or the demand for same. The products of physiological activity or functional sufficiency would tend to decrease demand and accordingly to inhibit growth. The opposite situation would, through the usual channels of physiological feedback, create a need for more function, or the products thereof, and concomitantly would stimulate growth.

The specificity of such reactions would reside in the functional activities of each cell type, and therefore would be related to the products of a cell's differentiation. Thus, growth regulation would be functionally specific and not necessarily tissue specific, with the result that deficiencies in one tissue would occasionally produce effects in others with related functions. Furthermore, the degree to which a tissue exhibited compensatory hypertrophy would be related to the extent to which the loss of a part affected the physiology of other parts, that is, to the extent of its physiological sphere of influence. Systemic influences could cause compensatory responses anywhere in the body; local effects would result only in wound healing or morphogenetic regeneration.

According to this theory, growth is probably not controlled by specific molecular types with the sole function of inhibiting or stimulating mitosis. The degrees of specificity would equal the number of different functions, not necessarily the number of different cell types. The nature of the humoral communication would not necessarily involve one specific kind of chemical agent for each cell type, but would be represented by a more general change in the condition of the body, perhaps involving numerous chemical and physical factors, the complexity of which would depend on the function affected.

This approach to the problem of growth-controlling mechanisms is not without its disadvantages. It necessitates, for example, the precise definition of what a particular organ's function is, which is something that is not readily apparent in all cases. Many cells and organs perform more than one function, in which case it will be necessary to determine whether growth is governed by one or by all such functions collectively. Yet the theory has the advantage of being put to the experimental test, for example, by manipulating tissue mass and function independently. It cannot be expected in all cases to yield to the chemical isolation of growth-regulating molecules, but it is this very difficulty that has been responsible for the growing dissatisfaction with other hypotheses.

IV

Normal Development

ACCORDING to Weiss and Kavanau (1957), growth may be defined as "the net balance of mass produced and retained over mass destroyed and otherwise lost". If interpreted in negative as well as the usual positive terms, this definition is an especially fitting one inasmuch as it permits the inclusion of ageing processes as retrogressive instances of growth. The qualitative aspects of growth, i.e. the determination of the kinds of mass to be produced, are represented by the process of differentiation. The rate at which new protoplasm is produced, and the factors which influence it, constitute the quantitative aspects of growth. Superimposed on these two basic parameters (differentiation and reproduction) are such derivative phenomena as tissue induction, cell migration, and physiological gradients which when operating in co-ordination with an organized developing system are collectively expressed as morphogenesis.

It is possible to classify the various kinds of growth into certain commonly recognized categories, not the least of which is the rapid, progressive, and complex growth of the developing embryo. This growth gradually attains a state of equilibrium in the adult organism, the dynamic nature of which is manifested in the molecular and cellular turnover of its parts. Sometimes the homeostatic harmony of the post-embryonic organism is disrupted by developmental upheavals as when hormonal factors initiate such events as metamorphosis, puberty, or reproductive cycles. Inevitably, however, the balance between constructive and destructive events becomes increasingly difficult to maintain. Ageing continues until some crisis, too severe for the declining adaptive capacities of the animal to withstand, precipitates degenerative changes that are irreversible.

With the possible exception of this final crisis, the foregoing events can be considered as "natural" developmental phenomena. Other occurrences, of special interest to the student of growth regulation, are initiated by extrinsic causes and are usually classified as experimental or pathological growth. Examples of the former include such

familiar phenomena as wound healing, regeneration, and compensatory hypertrophy. The only real difference between these and
pathological forms of growth is that the latter are initiated accidentally
rather than intentionally. In either case, an understanding of the
adaptive reactions of cells and tissues to unnatural circumstances is
of great importance in elucidating the mechanisms by which the
normal equilibrium is maintained.

Differentiation

Development is the sum total of growth and differentiation, neither
one of which is embryologically meaningful without the other. The
classic problem of cellular differentiation is currently defined as one
of the synthesis of specific molecules, especially proteins. These
specific molecules are diagnostic for each cell type, not only as patterns
of enzymes involved in specialized functions, but also as structural
molecules built into the microscopically visible criteria by which
various histological types are distinguished.

Inasmuch as different kinds of cells exhibit varying rates of proliferation, the generality is often expressed that mitotic activity is
inversely proportional to the degree of cellular specialization. This is
only partially correct, as Dawson (1940) and Swann (1958) have
emphasized, for specialization is a relative term depending on the
function for which a cell may be differentiated. In a sense, a fibroblast is just as specialized for mediating collagen synthesis as a neuron
is for transmitting nerve impulses, and value judgments as to which
function is the more important or intricate are as precarious in the
field of cell biology as they are in human endeavours.

Alternatively, specialization can be interpreted in terms of division
of labour. A cell that devotes itself almost entirely to one principal
function (e.g. muscle contraction, transmission of nerve impulses)
may be considered highly specialized in contrast to one capable of
manifold functions. Yet such versatile cells as those in the liver or
the renal nephrons rarely divide under normal conditions although
their capability to do so is well known. Nevertheless, it must be
admitted that so long as a cell's function is not incompatible with
mitosis it will tend to retain the capacity, be it latent or expressed, to
divide. Should these two processes become mutually exclusive, the
specialized function a cell performs invariably takes precedence.
Thus, nerves, muscles, and retinal cells, for example, presumably
have sacrificed the ability to proliferate in adult organisms in order

to attain the high degree of structural specialization requisite to the performance of their particular physiological activities. Other kinds of tissues achieve specialization without losing mitotic competence by constantly renewing themselves through divisions among undifferentiated stem cells. In these cases (epidermis, erythrocytes, spermatozoa) the specialized end products of differentiation are of course incapable of further mitotic proliferation.

Differentiation, as usually defined, refers to the production of stable structural attributes of a cell. The stability of such structures, however, varies from one kind of cell to another. Some cell types are actually quite labile, as in the common conversion of fibroblasts to chondrocytes or osteocytes. In other instances, the pathway of differentiation may be deflected from one direction to another. This phenomenon, often referred to as metaplasia, is clearly illustrated by the formation of mucoid cells instead of keratinized cells by the basal cells of the epidermis differentiating under the influence of vitamin A (Fell and Mellanby, 1953; Weiss and James, 1955). In the strict sense, however, this is not an example of true metaplasia inasmuch as the affected cells are not yet fully differentiated. The term metaplasia should be reserved for those instances in which a differentiated cell becomes transformed via dedifferentiation to some other type. Proven examples of this phenomenon are encountered in certain regenerating systems, such as the production of blastema cells in regenerating newt limbs by the dedifferentiation of muscle fibres and other histological entities (Hay, 1959). Though existing techniques do not permit categorical conclusions as to the extent to which the future redifferentiation of such blastema cells is dictated by their past histories, there is an even chance, at least, that they may become something different from what they were originally.

Perhaps the most striking cases of metaplasia, however, are to be found in the regeneration of the lens and retina of newt eyes. The former develops from the pigmented epithelium of the dorsal iris (Reyer, 1954), while regeneration of the neural retina proceeds from residual cells of the pigmented retinal epithelium (Stone, 1950a,b). In either case, pigmented cells undergo depigmentation and proliferation prior to their redifferentiation into lens cells or elements of the neural retina. How the process of depigmentation occurs has been studied by Eguchi (1963) and Karasaki (1963), who have found that pigment granules are phagocytized following their extrusion from the regenerating cells. Such occurrences testify to the potential instability of at least some highly differentiated intracellular entities.

Swann (1958) has contended "that cell division should probably be regarded as a form of differentiation". If one accepts this view, then other aspects of cells, including those involved in such generalized activities as respiration and protein synthesis, should also be elevated to the status of differentiated characteristics, in which case the analysis becomes more semantic than scientific. Nevertheless, Swann (1958) reaches the apparently valid conclusion that the antagonism between mitotic activity and degree of differentiation may be the result of a competition for materials and space. This view has been amplified by Fell (1957) with reference to her observations on mitosis, migration, and differentiation of cells in tissue culture. It was pointed out that proliferation is most characteristic of colonies of cells which, owing to their migratory propensities, have a relatively low population density. Differentiation, however, is promoted in more dense aggregates of cultured cells. "Sometimes measures which restrict both mitosis and emigration," she wrote, "encourage differentiation, not because they reduce mitosis, but because they restrict emigration."

Swann (1958) has emphasized that the mitotic armamentarium of a cell is represented by many highly specialized proteins which must be synthesized in the same manner as are other differentiated products of the cell. Moreover, when a cell divides most of its other activities are interrupted, and the energy used cannot be otherwise expended. Be this as it may, the fact remains that the majority of cell types are capable of division despite the broad spectrum of differentiated states that are represented. Only in extreme cases do the differentiated features of a cell make mitosis impossible.

Turnover

The nature of the proliferative activity (or lack of same) indulged in by various kinds of cells has long been recognized as a basis for tissue classification. Credit for the original contribution along these lines is owed to Bizzozero (1894), who proposed the existence of three categories of tissues according to whether they (1) multiply throughout life (*elementi labili*), (2) proliferate only in growing individuals but seldom in adults (*elementi stabili*), or (3) fail to exhibit mitosis altogether once they have differentiated (*elementi perenni*). Years later, Cowdry (1942) suggested a similar classification of tissues, which he referred to, respectively, as "vegetative intermitotic cells", "reversible post-mitotic cells", and "fixed post-mitotic cells". Subsequent technical refinements, based primarily on the use of tritium-labelled thymidine, have led to a number of recent modifications of this fundamental system of classification (Messier and Leblond, 1960; O'Steen and Walker, 1960; Schultze and Oehlert, 1960). Allowing for the usual refusal of biological systems to conform completely to man-made classifications, there is general agreement as to which tissues belong in each of the three major categories.

Autoradiographic techniques have permitted a more precise distinction to be made between "renewing" and "expanding" cell populations, as defined by Messier and Leblond (1960), than was previously possible by counting mitotic figures. Cells labelled with tritiated-thymidine can be followed for prolonged periods of time, while a mitotic figure can be detected only during the brief interval of its existence. Therefore, in a renewing tissue the label eventually disappears as the cells are lost or destroyed, while in an expanding system the labelled cells persist and only lose their radioactivity by dilution during subsequent divisions. Hence, renewing and expanding tissues differ in two essential respects, namely, whether or not cells are regularly lost, and whether new cells are derived from special germinative tissues or from the population at large (figure 13). Alternatively, renewing tissues may be regarded as those whose end products are whole cells. Dempster (1954) has referred to the epidermis, for example, "as a holocrine gland whose main function is the elaboration of keratin". Other renewing tissues (e.g. red blood-cells, gametes, intestinal mucosal epithelium) could be viewed in the same perspective. The end products of expanding tissues, however, are usually molecules which can be released without destroying the cells that produce them, thus minimizing turnover at the cellular level.

Static tissues represent a special case of expanding systems in which growth by cell division is restricted to early stages of development, though it may continue by cellular hypertrophy during later periods. Even in these instances, however, there are occasional reports of mitosis in neurons (Altman, 1962) and muscles (Messier and Leblond, 1960). Moreover, a tissue which may be classified as mitotically static in higher vertebrates, may be capable of proliferation in some lower vertebrates, as in the regeneration of parts of the central nervous system. Because the tendency of some tissues to

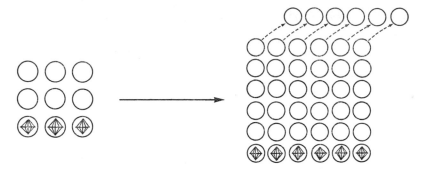

RENEWING CELL POPULATION

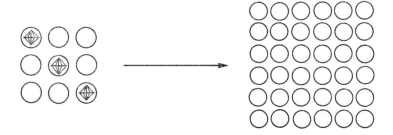

EXPANDING CELL POPULATION

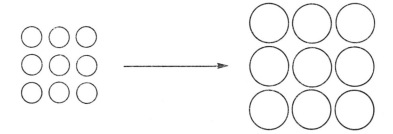

STATIC CELL POPULATION

Figure 13. Diagrammatic distinction between modes of growth in renewing, expanding, and static cell populations. In renewing populations, cells are constantly being lost or destroyed, and are replenished by proliferation of stem cells restricted to a "generative" zone. Expanding populations grow by diffuse proliferation, which ceases once the adult size of the organ is attained. Static populations grow by cellular hypertrophy except during early developmental stages.

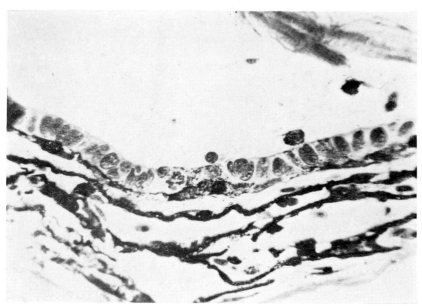

Plate 6.1. Neural retina regeneration in the eye of adult *Triturus viridescens* two weeks after retinectomy. Dedifferentiated retinal pigment cells have formed a single layer of proliferating cells. 314 ×.

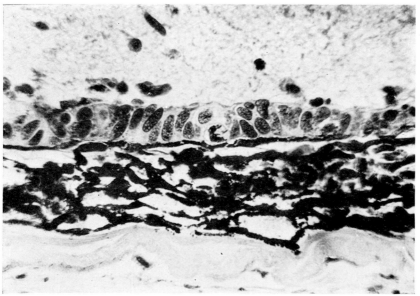

Plate 6.2. Similar eye eighteen days after removal of neural retina. The regenerating cells are becoming stratified. 314 ×.

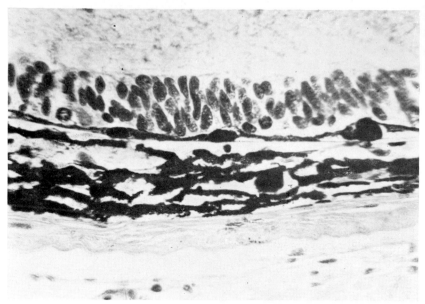

Plate 6.3. A three-week retina regenerate showing the accumulation of undifferentiated cells into multiple layers. 314 ×.

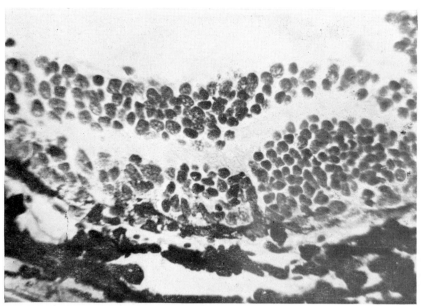

Plate 6.4. Twenty-six days after retinectomy, the differentiating cells have become organized into the principal layers of the retina. 314 ×.

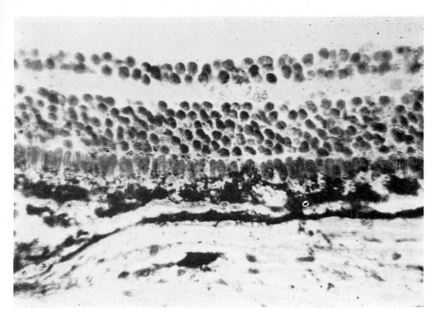

Plate 6.5. Normal adult newt retina. 314 ×.

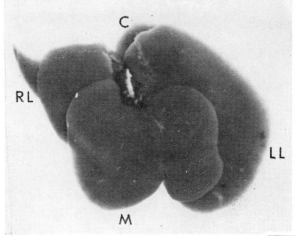

Plate 7.1. Normal liver of intact rat. C, caudate lobe; M, median lobe; LL, left lateral lobe; RL, right lateral lobes.

Plate 7.2. Appearance of liver immediately after removal of median and left lateral lobes, leaving only the two right lateral lobes (RL) and two caudate lobes (C).

Plate 7.3. Regenerated liver in rat of the same size three weeks after partial hepatectomy. The remaining lobes have hypertrophied to restore the normal mass of liver tissue.

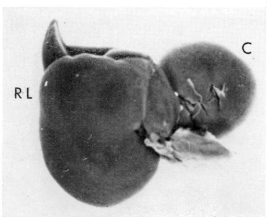

Plate 7.4. Compensatory renal hypertrophy. Upper kidney is from a rat which was uninephrectomized three weeks earlier. It is clearly larger than are the two control kidneys from a rat of the same size.

expand may gradually approach zero as proliferation ceases, a clear separation of expanding and static cell populations is impossible. Therefore, tissues such as striated muscle fibres and nerve-cells, which exhibit mitotic activity to negligible extents, have arbitrarily been included among static cell populations in the itemization of histological systems presented below.*

Renewing Cell Populations	*Expanding Cell Populations*
Epidermis (and derivatives)	Liver
Endodermal epithelium	Kidney
Endometrium	Exocrine glands
Transitional epithelium	Endocrine glands
Gonadal germinative cells	Lens
Haemopoietic tissues	Connective tissues proper
Skeletal tissues (in part)	Skeletal tissues (in part)

Static Cell Populations
Striated muscle
Neurons
Neural retina

One can only speculate as to the explanation for these different modes of growth in various cell systems, but the most obvious answer is that they represent adaptations which ensure maximal functional efficiency. Thus, in many renewing tissues the fully differentiated and functional cells are not only incapable of division but have relatively short life spans (e.g. erythrocytes, gametes). Indeed, some such cells are apparently most useful to the organism only when they are dead, as in the case of the fully keratinized epidermal cell. Evidently many kinds of differentiation are incompatible with indefinite survival of cells, perhaps because the mechanisms of repair have been sacrificed for the sake of specialization. In renewing cell populations, therefore, equilibrium is maintained because loss and replacement are in balance. The mechanism by which the rates of these two opposing processes are regulated remains to be determined.

It is conceivable that the rate of cell loss or destruction is governed by the rate at which new cells are produced. Were this to be the case, the control mechanism would be independent of either the mass or function of the end product, a situation not likely to be represented by the equilibrium between cell populations so characteristic of most

* Compiled and modified from data of Messier and Leblond (1960), O'Steen and Walker (1960), and Schultze and Oehlert (1960).

E

renewing histological systems. In some growing tissues, however, cell proliferation goes on at a fixed rate (e.g. epidermis and some of its appendages) regardless of how much end product is formed, though secondary fluctuations in this basic rate may be attributable to alterations in function or quantity of the differentiated tissue. In certain other systems, presumably subject to hormonally controlled growth rhythms (e.g. hair growth cycles, estrous cycles), the periodic secretion of hormones appears to be influenced by factors other than the mass or function of their target organs.

In general, it is more plausible that the rate of cell production in renewing systems is regulated by the rate of cell loss, in which case there must exist some means by which the differentiated tissue is constantly monitored and the information communicated to the generative cells. Which attributes of the differentiated end products are responsible for regulating production rates in this way are not known in most instances. Conceivably, the mass *per se* could affect the rate of proliferation, although this would have to be mediated by some hypothetical growth regulating compounds. Alternatively, the generative tissue could be sensitive to the rate at which the differentiated mass is depleted of cells. This kind of mechanism could work well in cases involving internal destruction of cells (the products of cell degeneration acting as mitotic stimulants to bring about their own replacement), but it would be difficult to comprehend how such a mechanism could operate in tissues which shed cells from the body. Desquamated epidermal cells, for example, are out of communication with the body and no longer available to participate in feedback mechanisms. It seems more rational, therefore, to seek an explanation for the regulation of growth rates in renewing tissues in terms of features correlated with both the mass of end product and the rate of cell removal. Functional activity fulfills these criteria, and would constitute a logical means of regulating growth in renewing tissues inasmuch as it is directly proportional to the mass of differentiated tissue, which in turn bears an inverse relation to the rate of cell loss. Thus, the reduction of the physiologically active mass of differentiated tissue by cell loss would diminish its functional output. This would be expected to create a demand for added functional activity on the part of the differentiated mass. Were the generative tissues sensitive to these demands, such that their growth rates might be stimulated under these conditions, the differentiated mass would be replenished, thus providing more cells to satisfy the need for greater functional activity.

In theory, though not necessarily in practice, the cells of expanding tissues survive indefinitely, their proliferative rates representing only that growth required to keep up with the general body growth. When the latter ceases, mitotic activity in these tissues is normally reduced to nil. Nevertheless, the degree of differentiation in such cells is not so specialized that the capacity for subsequent mitotic activity is precluded. Under conditions of reduced tissue mass or in certain abnormal physiological circumstances the cells of such organs often exhibit remarkable proliferative responses. Therefore, despite their mitotic inactivity in adult organisms, expanding tissues are actually in a state of dynamic equilibrium. Presumably, there are factors operating to maintain such organs at definite sizes in allometric proportion to the magnitude of the total body. If the body grows larger, or if the organ is reduced in mass, then proliferative activity ensues until the original relative weight is restored. The nature of the regulatory mechanisms responsible for such phenomena, whether associated more directly with mass or function, can be elucidated only through experimental investigations.

Cells in mitotically static tissues, among which are included neurons, retinal rods and cones, and striated muscle fibres, theoretically live as long as the organism does. It is the very highly specialized state of differentiation exhibited by these cells that is usually blamed for the fact that cell division is either impossible or extremely unlikely. Yet in such realms of speculation a strong argument could be advanced in support of the possibility that these tissues are nonproliferative because of their extreme importance in ensuring survival. Few organs of the body are more directly concerned with the immediate welfare of an animal than the nervous system, sense organs, and muscles. To jeopardize their functional competence by occasional cell divisions might have constituted a competitive disadvantage strong enough to have selected against such individuals during evolution. Instead, individual nerve fibres and muscle fibres have retained the ability to undergo varying degrees of cellular regeneration following direct injury. Except in lower vertebrates such cells cannot be replaced if lost.

Aside from the obvious anatomical difficulties, cell division in the central nervous system may be incompatible with important psychological factors which must not be abolished or seriously altered in the course of mitosis. If memory, for example, is coded in terms of complex molecules within neurons, the dangers of erroneous replication during division may have outweighed the advantages of mitotic competence during vertebrate evolution. In point of fact, the importance of such consequences would have increased in proportion to intelligence and mental complexity, thus paralleling the progressive decrease in regenerative ability in the central nervous system which has occurred during vertebrate phylogeny.

Ageing
The many degenerative changes which contribute to the general phenomenon of ageing may be regarded as indirect consequences of the body's homoeostatic depreciation. The normal integrity of the body is maintained by the operation of sensory mechanisms which detect deviations from the norm, and effectors by which these disturbances are corrected. These homoeostatic mechanisms have physiological and morphological consequences, both of which are reflected in the changing capacities of many parts of the body to grow and to repair damages at progressively older ages. In the young animal, disturbances such as a reduction in organ or tissue mass are promptly compensated by increasing the amount of residual homologous tissues. In older animals there appears to be a gradual but slight decline in the efficiency with which these responses are implemented.

Following partial hepatectomy, for example, Norris, *et al.* (1942), Bucher and Glinos (1950), and Aub (1950) have noted a slower rate of regeneration of the remaining liver of older as compared with younger rats, although the discrepancy is not always great (Cameron, 1952). This effect is probably associated with delays in the mitotic peaks of regenerating livers, which occur on the first post-operative day at 1 month of age, on the second day in 4- to 6-month-old rats, but not until the third day at 16 months of age (Marshak and Byron, 1945). This is consistent with the observations of Bucher, *et al.* (1961) that maximum DNA synthesis occurs 22 hours after partial hepatectomy in 24 to 27-day-old rats, at 25 hours in adult rats weighing 200 to 250 gm., and at 32 hours in year old animals (350 to 400 gm.). Comparable declines in restorative powers have also been described following loss of blood (Boycott, 1934) and unilateral adrenalectomy (Verzár, 1954).

Perhaps the most revealing histological changes with advancing age, however, are to be encountered in the kidney. Loss of weight in the ageing kidney (MacKay and MacKay, 1927; Kennedy, 1958) is accompanied by a marked decrease in the number of glomeruli to levels two-thirds or less that of the original number present at maturity (Arataki, 1926; Roessle and Roulet, 1932; Kennedy, 1958). This loss of nephrons is not retarded by excision of one kidney (Moore and Hellmann, 1930). The dimensions of the remaining glomeruli are variable in old age, partly because some of them are in the process of atrophy while others appear to have undergone hypertrophy in compensation for earlier losses (Kittelson, 1917; Arataki, 1926). Korenchevsky (1961) has noted that enlargement of the remaining renal convoluted tubules is characteristic of senescent kidneys and emphasizes that "with ageing, two opposite main processes, atrophic and hypertrophic, are simultaneously active in the tubular and glomerular tissues of the kidneys". In view of these observations, it is not surprising that the ageing kidney should preserve much of its capacity to undergo compensatory hypertrophy following unilateral nephrectomy. Although Verzár and Hügin (1957) noted the full retention of hypertrophic abilities in the kidneys of old rats as compared with those of young ones, other investigators (Carnot, 1913; Jackson and Shiels, 1927; MacKay, et al., 1932; Kennedy, 1958; McCreight and Sulkin, 1959) have consistently reported retardation in the rates of compensatory renal hypertrophy with increasing age. According to Shock (1962), "changes in the internal metabolism of a cell damages its capacity for self-repair and reproduction", which may account for the foregoing observations. In spite of such intrinsic changes in cells, it is also possible that because the kidney normally hypertrophies throughout adult life to make up for the steady loss of its nephrons, by the time uninephrectomy is performed in old age it may be approaching a theoretical upper limit of its hypertrophic capacities. This limit may represent the physiologically optimum size of nephrons below or above which functional efficiency diminishes. In other words, compensation for tissue deficits may occur only when hypertrophy represents a physiological advantage.

Many other changes associated with ageing are not accompanied by compensatory growth. This is particularly true of static cell populations which lack the powers of proliferation, namely, the nervous and muscular systems. Shock (1962) mentions that in ageing human beings the loss of weight of the brain is accompanied by a 27 per cent decrease in the number of nerve cells, and that muscles decrease 30 per cent in weight due to degeneration of muscle fibres which are not replaced. Taste buds, which are composed of cells that are constantly being lost and replaced (Beidler, *et al.*, 1960) decrease markedly in number during an animal's life span. This could be attributed to an accelerated degeneration of taste cells, or to a decline in their rate of differentiation. The fact that their disappearance as a result of temporary denervation is normally followed by regeneration argues in favour of the latter alternative as an explanation of their eventual loss in senescent animals. Conceivably, this could be a secondary effect of the aforementioned loss of nerve cells, some of which might have innervated taste buds. It has been established that other epidermal cells decline in their regenerative powers also, as evidenced by the dilatory wound healing typical of older organisms (Du Noüy, 1936; Gourevitch, 1951). These cases may thus represent special instances of the general phenomenon of ageing, which as Johnson (1963) has pointed out, may be causally related to the gradual depletion of redundant tissue and therefore of physiological reserves in the ageing body. The inability to compensate for such degenerative changes is the cause of senility.

V

Wound Healing

THERE are compelling reasons for classifying local wound healing as a special case of the innate growth phenomena discussed in the previous chapter. In both instances, the same basic processes occur, to wit, migration, proliferation, and differentiation of cells. It is possible that the factors responsible for the initiation of wound healing may be identified, in exaggerated form, with those operating in the normal growth processes evident in expanding and renewing cell populations. The conceptual advantages of reducing such diverse phenomena to a common denominator are obvious. Therefore, it is important to explore the nature of the intrinsic and extrinsic stimuli to localized growth as exemplified by normal cell turnover and induced tissue repair, respectively. By examining the concatenation of events between the initial cause of wound healing and the final result, our understanding of normal tissue growth may be enriched.

All living tissues in the body heal local injuries in much the same way. Many examples of this have been surveyed in the review of Johnson and McMinn (1960). Following a lag phase after injury (which is probably more degenerative than regenerative), there occurs an activation of near-by cells in preparation for their subsequent migration into the wound site. Presumably the activated cells are those close enough to the wound to have been exposed to sublethal influences. What is actually meant by activation, however, remains as obscure as it is provocative. Depending on whether the injury is minor or severe, infected or sterile, external or internal, etc., these early events may be accompanied by varying degrees of leukocytosis and phagocytosis. Concomitantly, there is a migration of cells from adjacent areas into the wounded region. Here they accumulate prior to redifferentiation into the tissues which replace in whole or in part those that have been lost. The degree to which replacement occurs largely determines whether the process is called wound healing or regeneration. The distinction in some cases is not easily recognized, which testifies to the arbitrary nature of our terminology. The

71

following examples of reparative responses in a few selected tissues and organs illustrate the regenerative aspects of wound healing.

Skeletal Wound Healing

Fractures of bones are invariably repaired by the deposition of new ossified tissue between the two fragments. The degree to which the fracture gap can be spanned differs with respect to dermal *v.* endochrondal bones. Inasmuch as the former lack the ability to give rise to cartilage (reflecting their intramembranous ontogeny), their regenerative abilities are seriously limited, as in the case of the cranium. Endochondral bones readily heal fractures across relatively short gaps, but if the separation is too great the broken ends fail to unite. Normally, however, injury to a bone is followed by migration and proliferation of ostoblasts derived from the periosteum adjacent to the damaged area. These cells multiply until a large mass of undifferentiated callus tissue is formed in the breach between the two bone stumps. Following the migratory and proliferative phases, differentiation results in the conversion of the callus into an extensive mass of cartilage. This in turn undergoes some provisional calcification, cellular hypertrophy, and eventual destruction as it is replaced by ossified tissue. Subsequent consolidation and remodelling of the ossified callus is responsible for the final unification of the broken bone. Thus, the component processes of fracture healing closely recapitulate the ontogenetic mechanisms by which the original bone developed. They may also be regarded as exaggerated manifestations of the normal histological reorganization that is responsible for the dynamic maintenance of bone by structural and chemical turnover.

Aside from the morphogenetic complexities that are responsible for remodelling the ossified callus, two basic problems of fracture healing have engaged the attention of experimental biologists. These relate to the nature of the initial stimulus and the source of callus cells. Speculation about the former problem has prompted many experimental attempts to demonstrate the existence of hypothetical factors capable of promoting osteogenesis. Reinforced by such interesting phenomena as ectopic bone formation in tissues normally not associated with osteogenesis, belief in bone stimulating agents (see review by Lacroix, 1951) has led to the testing of various extracts of bone on non-osseous tissues. Although Levander (1938) demonstrated that alcoholic extracts of bone injected into muscles resulted in ectopic ossification or chondrification at the injection site, other investigators were either unable to induce bone formation by similar methods (Stephenson, 1952), or succeeded in causing osteogenesis in muscles injected with alcohol alone (Heinen, *et al.*, 1949). In spite of the occasional induction of osteogenesis among fibroblasts, there is no convincing evidence that this is attributable to specific substances derived from bone. Indeed, instances of apparent assimilative induction of osseous tissue under the influence of bone transplants may not involve true metaplasia of fibroblasts. This interpretation is supported but not categorically proved by Goldhaber's (1958) studies on the behaviour of bony tissue within diffusion chambers. While ossification readily occurred within the diffusion chamber, none was observed outside of the membrane.

Evidence in favour of bone induction by metaplasia, however, derives from the original discovery by Huggins (1931) that urinary bladder tissue grafted to the rectus abdominis muscle was able to induce ossification in the surrounding connective tissues. By testing the various layers of such bladder grafts, the conclusion was reached that the inductive capacity resides in the transitional epithelium. This has been confirmed by Johnson and McMinn (1956) who noted that bladder grafts underwent encystment by the migration of epithelium from the edges of the original transplant. Intramembranous bone formation (in the absence of prior chondrification) was subsequently restricted to the surrounding connective tissues adjacent to recently migrated transitional epithelium (figure 14). Bone was never observed in association with the graft proper, where the epithelium was separated from tissues of the host site by a layer of bladder connective tissue. This would suggest that this phenomenon represents a true instance of inductive metaplasia, a conclusion substantiated by the observation that although homografts are capable of inducing ectopic ossification, the "newly formed bone does not appear to be involved in the immunity reaction" through which the destruction of the homograft is brought about (Johnson and McMinn, 1956). These authors concluded, therefore, that there is an inductive substance that diffuses into the neighbouring connective tissue from the epithelial component of the bladder graft. Whether or not a similar mechanism accounts for orthotopic ossification remains problematical.

This general problem, therefore, relates to the origin of the osteogenic cells which participate in fracture callus formation. Were such cells activated by a hypothetical bone-specific substance, it might be possible that cells other than the periosteal osteoblasts could

ADAPTIVE GROWTH

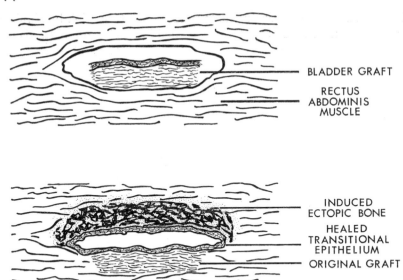

RECTUS
ABDOMINIS
MUSCLE

BLADDER GRAFT

INDUCED
ECTOPIC BONE

HEALED
TRANSITIONAL
EPITHELIUM

ORIGINAL GRAFT

Figure 14. Ectopic ossification induced by bladder tissue transplanted to rectus abdominis muscle. Above, schematic appearance
of bladder at time of grafting. Below, the healing transitional
epithelium has formed a cyst which has induced bone formation
only where epithelium is in direct contact with surrounding tissues.
The non-epithelial tissues of the bladder graft do not induce ossification. (After Johnson and McMinn, 1956.)

be similarly stimulated. To determine if injured bone releases such a
stimulant, and if so, whether or not normally non-osteogenic cells
would respond to its influence, Cooley and Goss (1958) undertook to
isolate bone injury from normal fracture healing in order to disclose
effects of the former, if any, on surrounding musculature and connective tissues. Advantage was taken of the fact that the exposure of
appendicular bones in the mouse to X-ray doses of 3,000r completely
precluded healing of the subsequently inflicted fractures. Moreover,
bones in the mouse can be successfully transplanted elsewhere in the
body without interfering in their normal reparative responses to
injury. When non-irradiated ulnae were transplanted into the musculature of irradiated thighs, normal healing occurred after these bones
were fractured. Conversely, when irradiated ulnae were grafted to
non-irradiated thigh muscle, fracture healing consistently failed to
take place despite the ready availability of ample healthy tissue. On

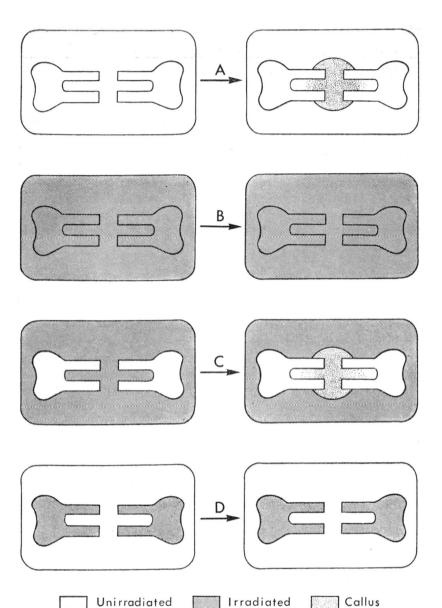

Figure 15. Effects of X-irradiation and transplantation on fracture healing in the mouse ulna. A, normal callus formation in a transplanted, fractured bone. B, Absence of callus in fractured, irradiated (3,000r.) bone. C, normal fracture callus produced by unirradiated bone grafted to X-rayed location. D, reciprocal experiment in which irradiated bone has failed to give rise to a callus even though transplanted to healthy site.

the basis of these results, summarized in figure 15, one cannot completely rule out the possible incorporation of neighbouring connective tissue cells into the calluses of normally healing fractures; but it can be concluded that if they are involved their role is passive. Furthermore, these results do not lend support to the theory that substances, in the nature of wound hormones, are released from fractured bones into surrounding soft tissues where osteogenic induction occurs. Obviously, the essential ingredient in the formation of the fracture callus is the participation of cells normally associated with the injured bone itself. Therefore, the fracture callus is largely, if not exclusively, derived from pre-existing osteoblasts. The exact mechanism of their activation in the vicinity of an injury remains an enigma.

Repair in the Uterus

Extensive regeneration may be noted in the course of repair of many internal organs, especially those which are tubular or hollow. The mammalian uterus is a case in point. Normally undergoing the familiar regressive and reconstructive changes associated with the female reproductive cycle, not to mention its hypertrophy resulting from the distentions of pregnancy, this organ has been found to be capable of considerable regenerative competence in response to mechanical injury. This may manifest itself in several ways, one of which is the healing that ensues surgical incisions (Selye and McKeown, 1934). If a uterine horn is bisected transversely, the severed portion is not replaced but a local healing response will take place at the site of wounding. This usually involves the convergent migration of serosal and endometrial epithelia until the underlying connective tissues and musculature are enclosed. When the uterus is cut longitudinally, however, healing often involves the extensive deposition of new tissues in the breach. The prompt migration of endometrial stroma from both sides of the cut not only serves to fill in the gaps but also forms a substrate across which the epithelia can migrate. If the opening in the uterus is too large, the probability that the inner and outer epithelia may heal to each other is increased, thus making it impossible for the uterus to complete its circumference. When this does not happen, however, the myometrial layer is eventually reconstituted in the regenerated segment, apparently by the *de novo* formation of smooth muscle fibres. Moreover, new endometrial glands develop in the inner epithelium after healing is completed.

Perhaps the most remarkable example of uterine response to traumatization is the local development of a deciduoma from the endometrial stroma at the site of irritation. Characteristic only of the progestational uterus, this exaggerated hyperplastic response to wounding is believed to simulate what normally occurs in association with the implantation of the ovum. In the latter case, growth of the endometrium represents the maternal contribution to placental development. In the experimental production of a deciduoma, the endometrium is doing the same thing in the absence of embryonic co-operation. Eventually the endometrium regresses to normal proportions.

Regeneration of the Gut

Another tubular organ which exhibits wound healing responses that are akin to regeneration is the digestive tract. As in so many other organs, here there is an especially rapid turnover of cells in the lining epithelium. The average life-span of the cells in the constantly re-generating mucosal epithelium of the mouse small intestine, for example, has been calculated by Quastler and Sherman (1959) to cover only 50 to 70 hours from their genesis in the crypts of Lieber-kühn to their eventual loss from the ends of the villi. The rapid migratory ability of these cells is also reflected in the rate of wound healing after destruction of the gastric mucosa by brief exposures to 50 or 60 per cent alcohol or 1 per cent acetic acid. Grant (1945) observed that the denuded mucosa was covered after only one to five hours by epithelial cells derived from the residual portions of gastric glands. The healing of more extensive lesions in the digestive tract, involving loss of the mucosa and part of the submucosa, has been reviewed by Ivy, et al. (1950) and Johnson and McMinn (1960). Numerous investigators have described the reconstitution of the gastric glands in the stomach, and the regeneration of new villi in the small intestine. Except for the failure of the muscularis mucosae to be restored, wound healing in the inner layers of the gut is accompanied by complete regeneration of its various histological components.

The most remarkable examples of intestinal regeneration have been observed in amphibians by Goodchild (1956) and O'Steen (1958, 1959). Following various kinds of transections of the digestive tract the several different tissues of the gut wall adjacent to the injury undergo disorganization, often accompanied by oedema, leukocytosis,

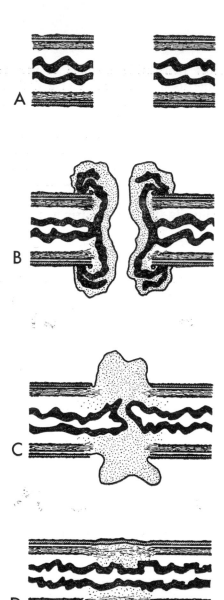

Figure 16. Diagram of successive steps in the reconstitution of the transected newt intestine. The severed segments (A) close over their ends (B) by healing of the epithelium (black) and by the formation of a blastema (stippled). Fusion of adjacent blastemas may occur (C) followed by re-establishment of continuity of the lumens and redifferentiation of submucosa and muscularis layers (D). (After O'Steen, 1958.)

and adhesions. Subsequently, the cut ends become closed over as a blastema of undifferentiated cells accumulates terminally (figure 16B). The latter may then adhere to the blastema of the opposite portion of the severed gut (figure 16C), or to the uninjured side of another segment. In either event, the two lumens eventually fuse and the normal histological structure of the region is reconstituted, the muscularis being the last to differentiate (figure 16D). Patency of the lumen may be established as early as two weeks after the operation in adult frogs (Goodchild, 1956), in one week in tadpoles (O'Steen, 1959), and in about 25 days in adult newts (O'Steen, 1958).

In addition to localized wound healing and regeneration, compensatory hypertrophy has been observed in the intestine. Flint (1910) removed 54 to 70 per cent of the small intestines of dogs and noted that among those that survived until autopsy 110 to 451 days later, the residual portions of the intestines had become enlarged. The same result was obtained when 73 per cent of the small intestine was isolated by partial resection. This empty, short-circuited segment remained intact, but did not become hypertrophic. The functional portions of the foreshortened intestines were found to have increased in diameter but not in length. The individual villi grew larger, though their numbers did not increase (figure 17). Histologically, the muscular layer of the intestine was also hypertrophic (especially the inner circular layer), whereas the mucosa was not affected. The cells of the mucosal epithelium, however, had become 30 to 50 per cent taller and contained larger nuclei than in normal intestines. The crypts of Lieberkühn had elongated and were dilated to four or five times the normal diameter. Thus, hypertrophy of the intestine occurs in those parts subjected to the greatest functional demands.

Bladder Regeneration

Two final examples in which healing and regeneration of internal organs are represented are the gall bladder and the urinary bladder. These two organs show some interesting similarities and dissimilarities in their responses to various kinds of trauma. Histologically, they both have a layer of enveloping musculature, but the gall bladder is lined with a simple epithelium (which may be columnar or low cuboidal in configuration, depending on the degree of distension), while the urinary bladder is lined with stratified (transitional) epithelium (which may be thick or thin under varying conditions of contraction or expansion, respectively). Although mitotic activity is

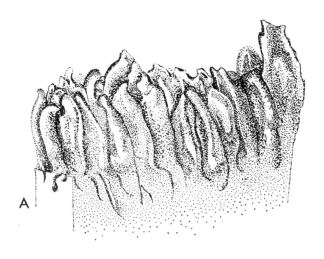

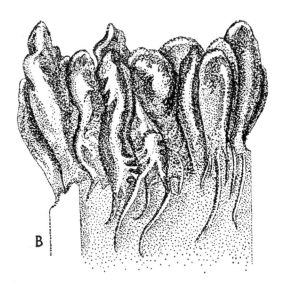

Figure 17. Reconstructions of intestinal mucosae of dogs showing
the normal villi in control animal (A) and the hypertrophic villi (B)
in a dog subjected to partial excision of the intestine. (After Flint,
1910.)

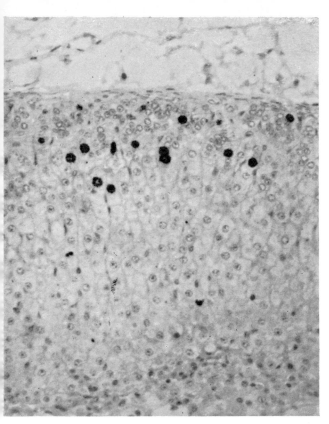

Plate 8.1. Adrenal cortex of mouse three days after subcutaneous administration of CCl$_4$ to stimulate proliferation. Cells labelled with tritiated thymidine are confined largely to junctional zone of the inner zona glomerulosa and the outer zona fasciculata at the time of labelling. 115 ×. (Plates 8.1 through 8.4 by courtesy of Dr. Robert M. Brenner (1963), with permission of the Wistar Institute Press.)

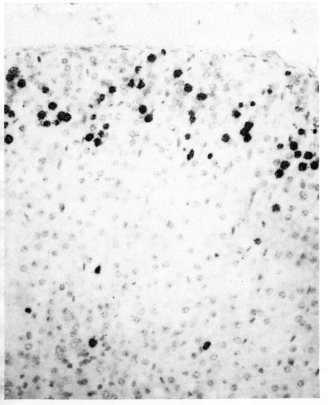

Plate 8.2. Distribution of labelled cells one week after treatment with tritiated thymidine. Cells are beginning to migrate inward and outward from original zone of proliferation. 115 ×.

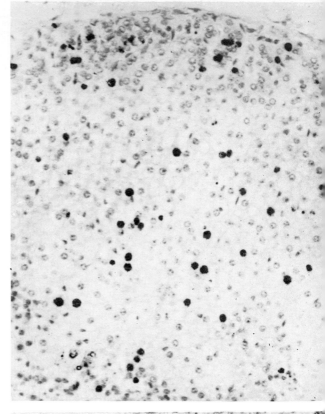

Plate 8.3. Four weeks after administration of label, cells from original zone of proliferation have migrated centripetally through the zona fasciculata. The frequency of paired, labelled cells attests to the occurrence of occasional cell divisions in the zona fasciculata. 115 ×.

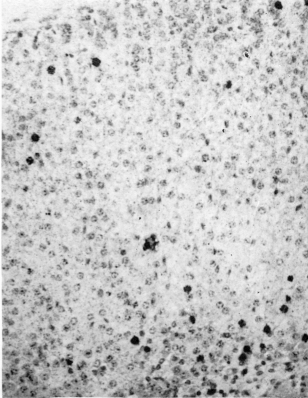

Plate 8.4. At the end of six weeks, most of the labelled cells have accumulated at the boundary between the zona fasciculata and the degenerating X zone at the extreme bottom of the photograph. Here the labelled cells disappear during succeeding weeks. 115 ×.

normally present in the epithelia of both organs, it is more common in the gall bladder mucosa (Jacoby, 1953, 1959) than in the transitional epithelium of the urinary bladder (Brauer, 1926; Leblond, et al., 1955; Walker, 1959). When a wound is inflicted in either kind of bladder, mitotic activity is stimulated, as is to be expected. However, unlike integumentary wound healing, the pattern of mitotic activity is not restricted to the regions peripheral to the wound margin.

In the healing of the gall bladder (McMinn and Johnson, 1957) and of the urinary bladder (McMinn and Johnson, 1955), mitoses are also encountered among the actively migrating epithelial cells in the area of the wound proper. Moreover, McMinn and Johnson (1957) reported that in the gall bladder there was an exceptionally early mitotic response to wounding, detectable as early as 24 hours postoperatively. This is corroborated by Jacoby's (1953, 1959) observations on the effects of experimental distention of the gall bladder in guinea pigs by common bile duct ligation. Following an 18-hour period of below-normal mitotic activity, proliferation in the epithelium increased to a maximum of about 16 times control levels by 24 hours and then gradually declined to normal by about the fifth day. Other tissues were similarly affected, but they attained mitotic peaks at different intervals after duct ligation. Connective tissue cells and vascular endothelium exhibited maximal responses on the third day, while smooth muscle did not reach its mitotic peak until the fifth day.

Jacoby (1959) interprets these results not in terms of the effects of mechanical distention, but as examples of functional overload. One function of the biliary epithelium is to concentrate the bile by reabsorption of water. Distention of the bladder with bile presumably puts a functional strain on the epithelial cells, which together with increased metabolism and hypæmia, may be responsible for the resulting hyperplasia which enables the epithelium again to become a simple columnar type. The sequential functional reactions of the different tissue types to bladder distention may account for the temporal variations in their maximal mitotic responses.

The mechanical effects of distention per se were tested by Jacoby (1959) on gall bladders of guinea pigs by using liquid paraffin to cause swelling. No increased mitotic proliferation occurred so long as the cystic duct and common bile duct remained ligated. But if the bile was allowed to enter the artificially distended gall bladder, mucosal proliferation resulted. From these observations, Jacoby concluded that the mitotic stimulus in gall bladder epithelium is due to functional

F

demands, not mechanical pressures. This interpretation will be of some consequence when the effects of bile duct ligation on hepatic proliferation are considered.

In contrast to the gall bladder, the urinary bladder is not known to influence the concentration or composition of its contents. As a simple storage organ, it is capable of considerable extremes of contraction and distention. Within the normal range, these vicissitudes apparently do not seriously affect its growth, but when artificially stretched beyond its normal limits of distention, the bladder is capable of enlargement by active growth. Thus, by injecting increasing amounts of fluid into a dog's bladder via a tube in its side, Carey (1921) was able to induce excessive bladder enlargement over a period of weeks until the bladder could eliminate up to 50 litres in 10 hours. Parenthetically, it should be noted that the original smooth musculature of this bladder became transformed into striated muscle capable of rhythmic contractions under tension.

The regenerative ability of the urinary bladder has been repeatedly demonstrated (Schiller, 1923; Bohne, et al., 1955; Liang and Goss, 1963). Its clinical importance is surpassed only by its experimental and theoretical interest, for the factors responsible for inducing the total regeneration of the urinary bladder after its nearly complete extirpation are not clearly understood. Under normal conditions, however, removal of most of the bladder is followed by wound healing at the site of injury. Provided the ureters and urethra remain connected, there gradually occurs an enlargement of the healed portion until a new bladder has eventually been formed (figure 18A). This kind of regeneration, therefore, does not involve the development of a blastema but appears to proceed by the expansion of preformed tissues under the influence of pressure from the urine. Thus, with progressive regeneration the animal becomes increasingly continent. In view of Jacoby's (1959) conclusions with reference to the gall bladder, it was especially important to determine if urinary bladder regeneration is due to some inductive influence of urine, or just to the hydrostatic pressure it exerts. To resolve this issue, Liang (personal communication) performed cystectomies on rats and deviated both ureters away from the urethra to the abdominal wall where they were allowed to drain to the outside. When by-passed in this way, the bladders failed to regenerate (figure 18B). However, when fitted with a catheter and repeatedly subjected to perfusions of saline several times a day over a period of several weeks (figure 18C), bladder

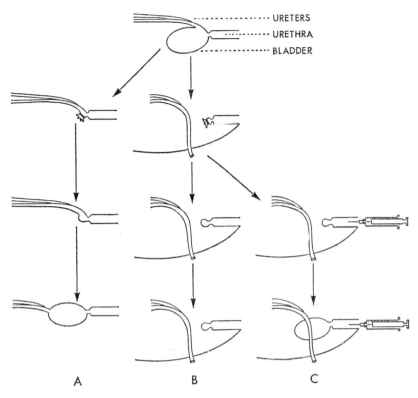

Figure 18. Experimental plan of Liang's investigations (personal communication) of urinary bladder regeneration in the rat. A, normal regeneration of bladder following cystectomy. B, absence of bladder enlargement following deviation of ureters. C, promotion of bladder regeneration, despite deviated ureters, following hydrostatic pressure increases by repeated injections of saline.

regeneration was successfully induced. This experiment conclusively proves that urine is not chemically necessary for bladder regeneration, but exerts its influence only through the tension it creates. It is also evident that the size of the bladder must be directly related to the physiological requirements placed on it, and will not regenerate unless functionally stimulated to do so. Whether or not a normal bladder, rendered functionless by deviation of the ureters, would regress beyond the normal contracted condition has not been experimentally tested.

Wound Hormones

What it is about an injury that stimulates a healing response is not known. The reason for our ignorance lies in the difficulty of separating experimentally the two basic attributes of a wound, namely, tissue loss and tissue destruction. Tissues cannot be removed without damaging adjacent cells, nor can tissues be injured without eventually bringing about their removal. Therefore, the various alternative theories of wound healing have not as yet been resolved.

One school of thought attributes healing responses to the influence of wound hormones produced at the site of injury which diffuse out into adjacent tissues thereby stimulating centripetal cell migration and hyperplasia. Alternatively, the wound could be regarded as somehow removing or inactivating growth inhibitors normally present in the surrounding tissues, thus bringing about the growth of the latter. The possible existence of stimulating or inhibiting substances capable of mediating local reparative responses has prompted many experimental attempts to isolate such hypothetical agents. Unhappily, these endeavours have usually failed even to prove the existence of such factors in animal tissues.

As indicated in Davidson's (1943) review of the subject, there is convincing evidence for the existence of wound hormones only in plant tissues. The various demonstrations that injured plant cells release substances capable of stimulating growth of uninjured tissues in their vicinity have culminated in the isolation of traumatic acid, a compound capable of inducing cell proliferation even when applied in minute quantities.

$$HOOCCH = CH(CH_2)_8COOH$$
Traumatic Acid

In tissue cultures, the growth-promoting properties of various tissue extracts (especially embryonic) have long been recognized, though the exact nature of the active ingredient(s) has remained obscure. The difficulties of distinguishing between general nutritive effects and specific stimulations when dealing with such unrefined extracts are obvious. Similar objections relate to the attempts to investigate wound hormones *in vivo*. It has been demonstrated by Lorin-Epstein (1927) and Young, *et al.* (1941) that there are factors released into the blood of wounded animals that can accelerate the healing of subsequently inflicted wounds. Auerbach (1952), however, noted slower healing in second wounds made a week after the first ones. Therefore, if systemically distributed stimulatory or inhibitory substances actually exist, little is known concerning their source, chemistry, specific action, or even whether they normally play a role in promoting wound healing.

Inasmuch as wound healing is a localized phenomenon, it is logical to look for growth regulating substances in the immediate neighbourhood of the wound itself. Accordingly, a number of investigators have studied the effects on rate of wound healing of various substances locally applied to wounds. McJunkin and Matsui (1931) reported a possible tissue-specific effect when epidermal healing was accelerated by the topical application of aqueous epidermal macerates, but not by those of liver or tail tendon. Carnot and Terris (1926) were able to stimulate the rate of cutaneous wound healing by the direct application of extracts of regenerating skin or of embryos, and suggested that substances ("cytopoïétines") in actively growing tissues were able to stimulate growth in other systems. Doljanski and Auerbach (1944), however, failed to cause accelerated healing in the skin of rats following localized treatment with extracts of chick embryos or of adult chicken hearts. Tier and Nystrom (1962) reported that skin wounds healed faster when rats were given intraperitoneal injections of new-born rat skin homogenates (but that other tissues were not effective). Local subcutaneous injections of saline extracts of various kinds of tissues around the edges of wounds in rabbit ears caused varying degrees of accelerated healing, the greatest effect (twice the normal rate) being elicited by extracts of skin (Nettleship, 1943). The results of the foregoing investigations were judged according to "rates of healing", interpreted to mean the rate at which epidermal cells migrate over the wound surface. Such a criterion, however, is subject to the interfering effects of wound contraction, which may in part account for the variable results.

This objection has been avoided by Wigglesworth (1937), who studied the hemipteran insect, *Rhodnius prolixus*, whose integument does not contract during wound healing. Small perforations in the simple epithelium of the abdominal integument normally results in the development of activated cells (with chromatin-rich nuclei) in a circumscribed radial zone around the site of injury. Beyond this there is a circular zone of mitotically active cells. Wigglesworth found that autolysed epidermal cells applied to such wounds caused a considerable increase in the radius of the activated zone six days after wounding, as well as a rise in mitotic activity in more peripheral regions.

Although heated preparations were generally less effective, almost any kind of degraded protein elicited a response. Certain other tissue preparations, administered beneath uninjured regions of the integument, likewise elicited a local accumulation of cells. Though interpreted as a healing response in the absence of mechanical injury to the epidermis, this should perhaps be regarded as a reaction to a chemical injury resulting from the effects of non-specific toxic materials derived from the degenerating tissues. Thus, these results, as well as those obtained in vertebrate systems, are all subject to the same objection, namely, that tissue extracts applied to wounds all undergo degeneration. This causes the release of degradation products which may have injurious effects on the cells exposed to them, thus substantially increasing the extent of the original wound. It could be argued, therefore, that this kind of experiment can prove no more than that healing responses occur in reaction to chemically as well as mechanically inflicted wounds.

Migration Stimulus

Aside from tissue degeneration, the one other attribute characteristic of all wounds is the loss of tissue that inevitably results. Since the single most important achievement of wound healing is the replacement of lost parts, it is fitting that the local consequences of tissue removal be considered in some detail. Replacement of the missing tissues is the first overt constructive event of wound healing. This may involve the migration of epithelial cells, the development of granulation tissue, the invasion of fibroblasts, the accumulation of osteoblasts, or the participation of whatever other cells may be in juxtaposition to the traumatized area. The actual mechanisms by which these cellular migrations occur is an important problem, although it is beyond the scope of the present account. The stimuli, control, and consequences of such processes are, however, very pertinent. To say that an epithelium cannot tolerate a free border is a statement of fact but not an explanation. The same is true of other tissues of the body in the sense that they react to discontinuities in their organized structures. Presumably, a cell next to a wound undertakes a polarized migration because the forces normally responsible for its spatial stability are disturbed. This could involve a kind of chemotaxis attributable to products of tissue destruction present in the wound, but this is unlikely since such factors would probably not be distributed throughout the wound in a gradient comparable to the centripetal migrations of healing cells. Cell degeneration is evenly dispersed over a wounded region and the only gradient is at the edges where the injured and uninjured tissues are contiguous.

If one concludes that cells migrate into a wound site not because of a chemical attraction there, but because they are no longer constrained to remain stationary, it must follow that cells have a natural propensity for migration that is normally held in abeyance. The innate restlessness of cells is abundantly obvious to anyone who has observed them as they appear in time-lapse cinematography. Thus, it is important not to be deceived by the static impression of cells one gets from the usual histological preparations.

It is not known what influences are responsible for maintaining the unstable equilibrium of cells as they are normally incorporated in tissues, but it is probably the physical presence of neighbouring cells. When present in sufficient concentrations, the cells would be mutually inhibited from excessive movements in any particular direction. In the event of localized cell loss or destruction, the intact cells at the periphery of the wound would be less inhibited on that side, and they would naturally tend to migrate into the wound. For similar reasons, other cells a little farther away from the wound edge would then follow. The cells would advance in the direction of the less crowded population until the depleted cell density is restored to normal.

Since such an equilibrium could not be re-established by cell rearrangements alone, the quantitative loss of cells caused by the wound must be restored by proliferation. As in the case of the control of cell movements, it is possible that cell division might likewise be regulated by mutual influences amongst the cells in a tissue. Again, the exact nature of such influences can only be surmised, but it is probable that they are in some manner related to the density of cell populations in tissues. Thus, when the original number of cells is decreased by injury, the remaining cells diminish their own population density in the process of repairing the damage. Fell (1957) has called attention to what is perhaps an analogous situation *in vitro*. She states that, "conditions which favour very active mitosis also favour very profuse cell migration". Presumably, the extent of cell dispersal outweighs whatever antagonism might exist between migration and mitosis.

Proliferation

If the original number of cells is to be restored after wounding, proliferation rates must be elevated above those normally occurring in renewing or expanding populations of cells. It is theoretically convenient to think in terms of hypothetical inhibitory materials emanating from the cells in a given population, such that above a predetermined threshold concentration of inhibitor their normal mitotic tendencies are mutually suppressed. Bullough and Laurence (1960a,b) have advanced such a proposal with reference to the epidermis, and there is little reason why it could not be applied to many other tissues as well. Other things being equal, the proliferative activity should be inversely proportional to the cell population density. This, however, is not the case in a healing skin wound, for mitotic activity is maximal not in the wound itself, but just around the periphery among the non-migratory cells. It must be assumed, therefore, that cell migration is antagonistic to cell division, and that not until the healing cells become sedentary again can mitotic activity be resumed (Ivy, *et al.*, 1952). Indeed, the studies of Abercrombie and Ambrose (1962) suggest that until the motile cells in a healing wound again become stationary as a result of contact inhibition, their mitotic propensities are temporarily suspended.

It is significant that hyperplasia is largely restricted to cells situated in the region from which other cells have recently emigrated. Here is the only location where there is both a lowered population density and stationary cells, a combination of circumstances conducive to hyperplasia. Despite the apparent logic of such an interpretation, the crucial experiment remains to be performed. Therefore, it is still not known whether the proliferation that accompanies wound healing is the result of the centrifugal diffusion of stimulatory substances (wound hormones) or to the depletion of pre-existing mitotic inhibitors.

If one assumes that chemical agents derived from degenerating tissues in the wound site may be responsible for initiating reparative processes, it becomes necessary to determine to what extent they may be tissue-specific. Are all tissues, regardless of their type, within a given radius of a wound stimulated to undergo migration and proliferation, or is healing restricted to cells of the kind directly subjected to injury? Apropos of this, Abercrombie (1957) compared local *v.* systemic growth responses, noting that the latter are attributed to widely dispersed stimulants to which only specific homologous tissues react, as in the many cases of compensatory hypertrophy. In spatially restricted responses, in contrast, "the stimulant is predominantly local, the responding cells being not so much those sensitive to as exposed to stimulation".

In attempts to resolve this problem, Bullough and Laurence (1960a) have undertaken selectively to remove one histological component in the skin without doing violence to contiguous ones of differing types. This was achieved by resecting a flap of mouse skin, excising from beneath a thickness of the panniculus carnosus, hypodermis, and lower portion of the dermis, and then replacing the flap together with the undamaged epidermis (and upper dermis). Under these experimental conditions, healing responses were restricted to those layers of the skin directly injured; the overlying epidermis exhibited no increase in mitotic activity compared with control areas. Conversely, selective injury to the epidermis caused by plucking hairs resulted in epidermal mitotic responses in the absence of hypodermal proliferation (Bullough and Laurence, 1960b). Indeed, the same authors have also noted that in wounds involving all layers of the skin, epidermal hyperplasia occurs sooner than does that in the hypodermis, a result not consistent with a non-specific stimulation. It appears from these studies that a healing reaction occurs only in those tissues whose integrity has been directly or indirectly disturbed. Judging from such evidence, either the proposed humoral agents responsible for stimulating healing must be tissue-specific, or the concept of wound hormones which has been so generally (though tentatively) assumed must be seriously reconsidered.

In addition to the hyperplastic response of epidermis to a local wound, Argyris and Argyris (1959) have noted that in the mouse there also occurs an activation of nearby resting hair follicles. This curious stimulation of hair growth does not become evident until almost two weeks after injury, and appears to be propagated centrifugally from the wound site. It was suggested that such an effect might be brought about by tissue-specific influences emanating from the nearby hyperplastic epidermis, rather than necrosis of injured tissues, for example. It is also quite possible that the contraction of the wound could give rise to secondary effects through mechanical tensions exerted on the neighbouring tissues. Whatever the ultimate explanation turns out to be, the activation of hair growth, whether spontaneous or experimentally stimulated, will help to shape our future ideas about the regulation of growth.

By far, the most important experiments along these lines have been the ingenious attempts by Bullough and Laurence (1960a) to determine whether epidermal hyperplasia in the neighbourhood of a wound is caused by the diffusion of mitogenic agents or the depletion of mitotic inhibitors. Having demonstrated that the mitotic activity accompanying a healing wound is located in a zone approximately one millimetre wide around the healing edge, and recognizing that in the mouse ear the epidermal epithelia on either side lie within this distance of each other, these investigators carefully wounded the skin on one side of the ear and after an appropriate interval examined the opposite undamaged epidermis for mitotic activity. Two days after wounding, this epidermis was found to be hyperplastic, as was that adjacent to the wound itself (figure 19). The latter zone of mitotic activity extended the usual one millimetre from the edge of the wound, while on the unwounded side of the ear the area of epidermal proliferation was somewhat smaller, as would be expected if allowance were made for the thickness of the ear. Moreover, the proliferation in the opposite undamaged epidermis was greatest over the centre of the wound rather than around the edges, indicating that it was not stimulated by degenerating epidermal cells. As healing proceeded, both the amplitude and the extent of proliferation on the other side of the ear became progressively diminished. Clearly, such proliferative activity is causally related to its proximity to the unhealed wound.

Is this due to the effects of injury that necessarily attend all wounds, or to the absence of the epidermis? To test these alternatives, Bullough and Laurence (1960a) carefully peeled off layers of epidermal cells by the Sellotape stripping method. They found that unless all of the epidermis is removed, the epidermis on the opposite side of the ear remains mitotically low. If all of the epidermis is removed, however, there is heightened proliferation in the opposite epidermis, despite minimal injury to the dermis. Since other experiments had indicated that injury per se was not sufficient to stimulate epidermal mitosis, the authors' interpretation that epidermal hyperplasia results from a depletion of mitotic inhibitors in denuded areas appears justified.

Another approach to the problem of determining whether epidermal mitosis next to a healing wound is stimulated by wound hormones or by epidermal migration from peripheral areas has been to isolate these two attributes of wound healing from each other. Inasmuch as migration cannot be induced in the absence of tissue removal or destruction, which of necessity involves the infliction of an injury, it remains only to preclude cellular migration in areas subjected to

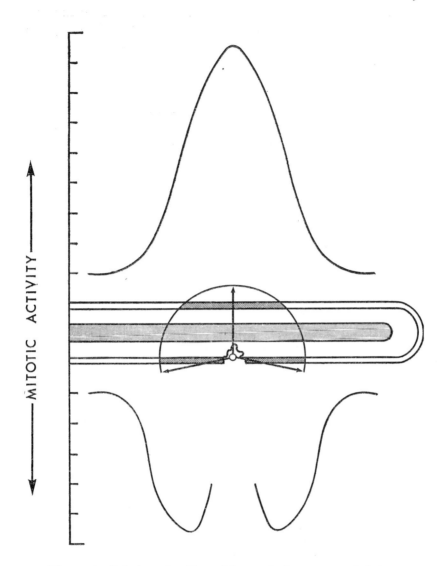

Figure 19. Relation of epidermal hyperplasia to a wound. Injury
inflicted on one side of a mouse ear (centre) causes proliferation
in adjacent epidermis as well as in that on opposite side of ear
(shaded) within a radius of about one millimetre. Patterns of epidermal mitotic activity are therefore bimodal (below) and unimodal
(above), respectively. (After Bullough and Laurence, 1960a.)

injury. Such an approach has been attempted in two different ways. The most direct method has been to study epidermal hyperplasia associated with wounds of varying sizes, on the theory that more extensive cellular migration would be expected to accompany the healing of larger wounds, thus affecting the rate and/or the area of proliferation. Bullough and Laurence (1960a) noted that over a wide range of wound sizes the *area* of epidermal hyperplasia remained fairly constant, i.e. restricted to a zone extending slightly over one millimetre from the margins of the wound. However, when the length of cut was reduced from $1 \cdot 3$ mm. to $0 \cdot 6$ mm., there was a definite decrease in the area of adjacent mitotic activity. Concomitant with these changes, there also occurred a reduction in the *intensity* of the mitotic response in proportion to the length of wound inflicted. Indeed, when the cut was only $0 \cdot 1$ mm. in length, no increase in cell division over the control rate was detected. This confirms the earlier observations of Wilbur and Chambers (1942) on the absence of mitosis in the healing of micro-wounds in the epidermis.

Still another line of evidence bearing on this problem derives from the studies of Weiss and Matoltsy (1959) on the very curious absence of wound healing occasionally observed in the skin of chick embryos less than 10 days old. Though this phenomenon is a variable one, when it does occur it presents a very unusual opportunity to observe whether or not proliferation will be stimulated next to an injured area that does not become healed by epidermal migration. Though this aspect of the problem was not specifically studied by Weiss and Matoltsy (1959) they did note that there was "no crowding of mitotic figures in the vicinity of the wound". Should this be confirmed by more detailed investigations, it would constitute compelling evidence that epidermal emigration from the area adjacent to a wound is causally related to proliferation in that region. That this relationship involves a decline in the population density of the cells around a wound is best illustrated when the process of wound healing is observed in a two dimensional system.

The insect integument, consisting of a single layer of epidermal cells, represents one system that approaches the two dimensional condition. Wigglesworth's (1937) studies of wound healing in nymphal *Rhodnius prolixus* have emphasized the correlation between mitotic activity and concentration of epidermal cells around a wound. In the two to three days following injury the cells lying within $0 \cdot 2$ mm. of the wound become "activated", i.e. they exhibit cytoplasmic basophilia, and the amount of chromatin in their enlarged nuclei increases. As a result of centripetal migration, these cells accumulate at the edges of the wound and after two days they begin to spread over the injured area itself. These movements result in the creation of a "hinterzone" beyond the 0·1 mm. wide region of closely packed activated cells at the very edge of the wound. This zone consists of residual activated cells which have not migrated from their original locations as did many others. It is in this region that mitotic activity is most prevalent (although cell division may be observed infrequently among cells which do migrate into the wound). According to Wigglesworth, "the sparseness among activated cells is the factor which determines cell division". This view was further substantiated by observations that mitoses are extremely rare around wounds inflicted on unfed nymphs, whose epidermal cells are so crowded that their population density is not significantly diluted by healing migrations.

The lens epithelium also presents a two dimensional view of wound healing (Harding and Srinivasan, 1961). Normally devoid of all mitotic activity (except at the equatorial margins of the lens), this monolayer of cells has been shown to burst into proliferative activity when a small wound is made in it. Harding and Srinivasan (1961) have succeeded in following the course of hyperplasia by visualizing the patterns of mitosis and DNA synthesis in whole mounts of rabbit lens epithelium previously treated with tritiated-thymidine and subsequently autoradiographed. The spatial and temporal correlations of these sequences are illustrated in figure 20. Judging from the uptake of tritium, there is a lag of at least 12 hours before the cells in the vicinity of the wound begin to synthesize DNA. The zone of labelled nuclei (figure 20, zone c) gradually expands outward from the wound site. Mitotic figures were not detected before 24 hours after injury, the earliest ones occurring nearest to the margin of the wound (figure 20, zone D). Thereafter, evidence of these two processes was found at increasingly greater distances from the centre, the band of labelled nuclei being outside of, and therefore preceding, that of mitosis. These concentric zones of DNA synthesis and cell division represent an expanding wave of proliferation propagated from the wound at an average rate of 17μ/hr. Within the band of mitotic figures is an area of cells which have recently completed division (figure 20, zone A[1]). Approximately 24 hours after initiating their first division cycle, these cells again synthesize DNA in preparation for a second wave of cell

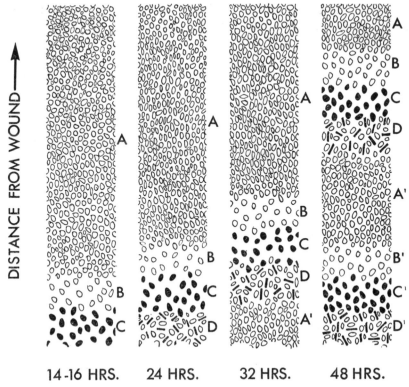

14-16 HRS.   24 HRS.   32 HRS.   48 HRS.

Figure 20. Spatial sequence of events in rabbit lens epithelium, semi-diagrammatically illustrated in surface view, at successive intervals (left to right) after infliction of a wound at lower margin. Zone A, unaffected epithelium. Zone B, area of diffuse cell population density. Zone C, region of DNA synthesis; cells labelled with tritiated thymidine are black. Zone D, mitotic proliferation. Zones A^1, B^1, C^1, D^1 represent second wave of reaction two days after injury. (After Harding and Srinivasan, 1961.)

division. Thus, in favourable preparations fixed two days after wounding, a single injection of tritiated-thymidine labels two concentric zones of nuclei.

The centrifugal propagation of mitotic waves away from a wound does not, in itself, help to resolve the problem of what initiates and perpetuates hyperplasia. Either the outward diffusion of a wound hormone or the progressive inactivation of mitotic inhibitors could explain the facts equally well. In favour of the latter alternative, however, is the existence of a zone of decreased cell concentration ahead of, and therefore occurring earlier than, the zone of labelled cells (figure 20, zone B). This decrease in population density, unquestionably the result of centripetal cell migrations, may logically be regarded as a significant antecedent to DNA synthesis. Hence, an incomplete sequence of events leading from injury to healing may be outlined: Loss of tissue (by removal or degeneration) creates a deficit which is overcome by the prompt migration of marginal cells into the wounded area. The partially depleted peripheral region then begins to synthesize DNA in preparation for the mitotic proliferation which will ensue. The combined processes of cell migration and replacement continue until the lost tissues are replaced.

Two principal steps in this sequence remain to be fully explained. One relates to the mechanism by which a wound "activates" neighbouring cells to become migratory. The other concerns the relation between decreased population density and mitotic activation. Both of these can most reasonably be interpreted in terms of the release of cells from influences, derived from their own numbers, which normally act as constraints antagonistic to migration and mitosis. It is probable that such influences are represented by tissue-specific, labile molecules that are constantly being resynthesized. Their chemical characterization will constitute the future focus of research in this area.

VI

Lens Regeneration

UNIQUE among regenerative phenomena is the replacement of the lens in the eyes of certain urodele amphibians. The mechanism by which this is achieved is clearly different from that by which the original lens develops by induction from the ectoderm overlying the optic cup of the embryo. It is not accomplished in the same way that the lens, once formed, grows to keep pace with the enlarging eyeball, that is, by proliferation of lens epithelium cells around its equator. Nor can it be classified as wound healing, since its regeneration can be elicited in the absence of a local wound.* If it were an example of true compensatory hypertrophy, one might expect a contralateral response to unilateral lentectomy but this does not happen. Because it is none of these things, though related to them all, lens regeneration occupies a very strategic position in the spectrum of compensatory modes of growth. In other respects, the lens also offers singular opportunities for investigation, for in addition to the classic role it has played in the elucidation of phenomena of embryonic induction, the lens has continued to be a tissue of such exceptional qualities that it has served as a model *par excellence* for the biochemical analysis of histological structures in general. With the possible exceptions of cartilage, erythrocytes, epidermis, and sperm, few other tissues in the body are available in as pure a form as is the lens which is naturally uncontaminated by a blood supply, innervation, or the ubiquitous fibroblast. These important conveniences have facilitated the immunological investigation of its antigenicity, and the electrophoretic separation of many of its specific proteins. Coupled with over 70 years of experimental investigations of amphibian lens regeneration, these properties render the lens an organ worthy of special consideration.

The histological process of lens regeneration is deceptively simple. Following a latent period after extirpation of the original lens, the dorsal region of the iris undergoes a thickening next to the margin of

---

* Reyer (1950) has reported lens regeneration from the dorsal iris in eyes experimentally prevented from developing embryonic lenses.

the pupil (figure 21B). The outer layer of iris cells are heavily pigmented, and concomitant with the initial tumescence of the dorsal iris is a depigmentation of some of these cells. Depigmentation, however, is not essential to subsequent lens regeneration. Ogawa (1962a) produced pigmentless larvae of *Triturus pyrrhogaster* by treatment with phenylthiourea, and found that they could still regenerate normal lenses.

Eguchi (1963) has recently completed an electron microscopic study of the mechanism of depigmentation in the iris during the early stages of lens regeneration in *T. pyrrhogaster* adults. By the third day after lentectomy, he observed that the nuclei of the dorsal iris cells become swollen, and their pigment granules move towards the periphery of the cell. Meanwhile, the inner and outer laminae of the iris separate to give rise to an "interlaminal space". By this time, amoeboid cells, possibly derived from the circulatory system, migrate around the inside and outside of the iris, as well as into the interlaminal space, and for the next week phagocytize the pigment granules of the iris cells. This is achieved by virtue of numerous, thin pseudopodia which characterize the invading amoeboid cells and by which they established contact with the surfaces of the pigmented iris cells. The extruded pigment granules are thus engulfed by the amoeboid cells in which they eventually disintegrate.

In addition to these morphological evidences of incipient lens regeneration, biochemical changes have also been detected. Takata (1952) showed that the cells of the dorsal iris become increasingly basophilic during lens regeneration, thus indicating enhanced RNA and protein synthesis. Yamada (1962) also found that the rate of RNA synthesis in the iris is increased and remains elevated until regeneration is well advanced. Of special interest, however, are the differences between the dorsal and ventral halves of the iris during the early stages of lens regeneration. Eguchi (1963) has observed that the dorsal iris cells may be distinguished from those of the ventral iris by the occurrence of clusters of mitochondria in their cytoplasm. Biochemically, it has been shown (Eguchi and Ishikawa, 1960) that the dorsal iris incorporates increased amounts of P^{32} as soon as two days after the loss of the lens. Although the ventral iris also exhibits an early acceleration of P^{32} uptake, after the fourth day the dorsal iris utilizes increasingly greater amounts of phosphorus while the ventral iris returns to pre-operative levels. Other studies by Eguchi and Ishikawa (1963) have demonstrated similar changes with respect

G

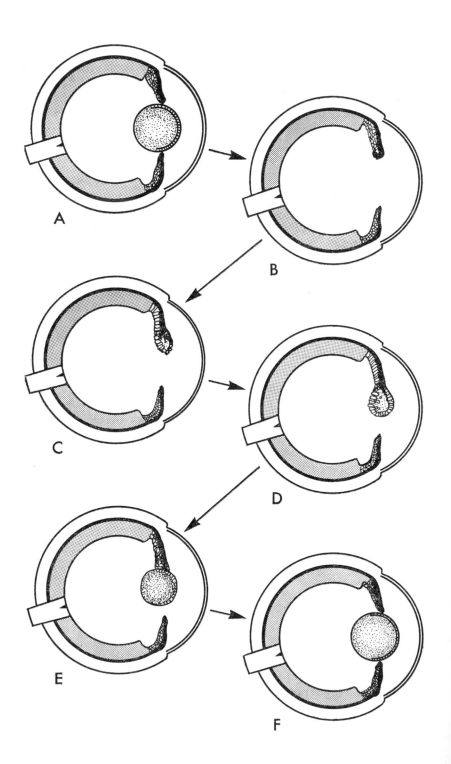

to alkaline phosphatase. From these studies it was concluded that "alkaline phosphatase plays an important role in the phosphorus transfer system and the increase of its activity is closely related to the lens-regeneration from the iris".

During the early stages of lens regeneration there is a marked acceleration of mitotic activity among the dedifferentiated iris cells. Since lens regeneration can be retarded by appropriate doses of X-rays (Politzer, 1952), proliferation would appear to be necessary for lens formation. Continued growth gives rise to a hollow vesicle formed of proliferating and reorganizing cells from the iris epithelium (figure 21C). As this lentoid enlarges, the posterior cells begin to elongate into rudimentary lens fibres, while the anterior layer of cells remains as the cuboidal lens epithelium (figure 21D). Once this polarity of the young lens is established, further development consists primarily of increase in size through continued proliferation and differentiation (figure 21E). Eventually the new lens becomes detached from the dorsal iris and occupies the position of the original lens in the pupil (figure 21F). Such a straightforward developing system as this is especially amenable to experimental interrogation. The answers should have general relevance to many other examples of growth.

Role of the Lens

First and foremost, the fundamental question posed by lens regeneration concerns the controlling mechanism(s) by which the process is initiated or inhibited. As Reyer (1954, 1962) has pointed out in his comprehensive reviews of the subject, there are two chief theoretical approaches to the problem. One of these contends that lens regeneration from the dorsal iris is normally prevented by the mechanical presence of the old lens. Admittedly, pressure against the dorsal iris by various non-living implanted objects intended to simulate the living lens will occasionally cause some interference in

Figure 21. Successive stages in the process of lens regeneration in the adult newt eye, as seen in schematic sagittal sections. A, normal eye. B, slightly swollen dorsal iris within a few days after lentectomy. C, depigmentation and proliferation of dorsal iris cells giving rise to a small lens vesicle, about two weeks after operation. D, differentiation and enlargement of regenerating lens, which consists of an anterior lens epithelium and posterior lens fibres during third week. E, F, continued growth and differentiation resulting in the eventual formation of a lens of normal dimensions.

lens regeneration, but will usually not inhibit it altogether. This effect, therefore, may be considered non-specific. Thus, by the process of elimination we are compelled to adopt an alternative explanation of lens regeneration, namely, that the cells of the dorsal iris are ordinarily deterred from developing into a lens by chemical influences, either positive or negative, associated with the presence of the original lens. Apropos of this, it has been shown that in order to exert such an influence the pre-existing lens must be sufficiently mature, for lens regenerates less than 25 days old failed to inhibit regeneration when implanted into the lentectomized eyes of *Triturus viridescens* adults (Stone, 1952). This nearly coincides with the age at which the lens becomes detached from its iris; beyond this age they possess inhibitory powers. On the other hand, if the lens is caused to degenerate either by direct injury or as a result of ocular ischaemia (as in transplanted eyeballs), the onset of regeneration is delayed. Although the competence of the dorsal iris to produce a new lens is restricted to the genera *Triturus* and *Salamandra*,* the capacity of the lens to inhibit this process is apparently not specific. Not only will lenses of various species of *Triturus* prevent regeneration when exchanged, but even lenses from non-regenerating genera such as *Amblystoma* (but not *Rana*) are likewise inhibitory (Stone, 1945). It is conceivable, therefore, that potential inhibitory influences in association with the lens are more widespread than can be demonstrated within the limits of transplantation experiments. If so, then the influence may be of a non-specific nature, perhaps related to the normal metabolic activities of lenses.

Stone and Vultee (1949) and Stone (1963) postulated that the lens normally produces inhibitory substances which are released into the aqueous humor bathing the iris and are thus capable of holding in abeyance the natural tendency of the dorsal iris cells to regenerate a lens. To test this hypothesis, aqueous humor derived from intact eyes of adult newts was injected daily into the anterior chambers of lentectomized eyes replacing equivalent amounts of fluid that were removed at each operation (Stone and Vultee, 1949; Stone, 1953, 1963). This procedure successfully inhibited lens regeneration in the operated eyes for periods up to 97 days, while saline-injected lentectomized eyes regenerated lenses normally. Upon cessation of aqueous

---

* Freeman and Overton (1961) noted the regeneration of lenses from cornea epithelium in *Xenopus laevis*. Occasional reports (e.g. Van Deth, 1940) of lens regeneration in the chick embryo have not been substantiated by McKeehan (1961).

humor injections, lenses regenerated in the experimental eyes. These results would appear to validate the hypothesis that lens regeneration represents the release of the dorsal iris cells from the influence of inhibitory agents produced by the original lens. If true, this would be an ideal system in which to analyse the nature of a tissue-specific growth-inhibiting substance. It would be intriguing to determine to what extent the inhibitory factors might be species-specific, and to subject them to the spectrum of physico-chemical tests by which they could be analysed for such properties as thermolability, antigenicity, electrophoretic mobility, molecular weight, and ultimately perhaps, chemical characterization. Recognizing the potentialities of this system, other investigators therefore attempted to confirm the original results of Stone and Vultee (1949).

Takano, et al. (1957) were the first to undertake this task. Commencing seven days after lentectomy in adult *Triturus pyrrhogaster*, eyes were injected daily with aqueous humor from intact eyes of *Triturus* or *Rana nigromaculata*. Controls were similarly treated with physiological salt solution. It was found that except when the iris was injured, lens regeneration in experimental and control eyes was essentially normal. In other experiments, aqueous humor from mouse eyes was injected into lentectomized *Triturus* eyes, starting on the third post-operative day, again with normal results. Even when injections were begun the day after lentectomy, no inhibition was noted. Neither did injections of lens extract adversely affect regeneration. In view of these results, Takano, et al. (1957) concluded that there was no reason to consider the lens as a source of inhibitory materials. Rather, they favoured the interpretation that so long as the old lens was present it metabolically "consumed" an inducing agent, possibly of retinal origin, that is presumed to be continuously produced in the eye.

In still another endeavour to demonstrate whether or not the aqueous humor of intact newt eyes contains substances capable of suppressing lens regeneration, the foregoing experiments were repeated by Goss (1961). Accordingly, aqueous humor from normal adult *Triturus viridescens* eyes was injected daily (from the second day) in place of that previously removed from lentectomized eyes. Lenses were extirpated from behind the iris through a dorsal incision at the corneal-scleral junction in order to avoid possible injury to the iris when the lens was pulled through the pupil. The opposite control eyes were similarly lentectomized, but were injected with 0·9 per cent NaCl. Disregarding those eyes in which the iris was inadvertently injured, or which exhibited other extraneous disadvantages (e.g. rupture of the original incision, excessive haemorrhage in anterior chamber, opacity of cornea), no instances of lens inhibition were observed attributable to the aqueous humor which was administered through the nineteenth post-operative day, by which time a lens nearly large enough to fill the pupillary space had developed. Comparable experiments utilizing saline extracts of newt lenses, or rabbit anti-newt lens antiserum, yielded similar negative results.

Unfortunately, the truth of a matter cannot be decided by popular vote. In view of the considerable technical difficulties which must be mastered before newt eyes can be repeatedly injected without doing violence to their delicate organization, it is possible that the above discrepancies might be attributed to variations in technical competence. Nevertheless, the vain attempts to confirm the original observations do not encourage the hope that the aqueous humor might yield valuable information about lens growth-regulating substances. Lacking a conveniently repeatable assay system, further attempts to identify and characterize growth-controlling factors must be considered to be temporarily but effectively blocked.

Indirect approaches to the problem, however, continue to be productive. A particularly pertinent line of inquiry concerns the spatial relationships between lens and iris. Zalokar (1944) reported that lenses tended to be inhibitory only when in sufficient proximity to the dorsal iris; displaced lenses often permitted varying degrees of regeneration. It is not surprising, therefore, that Stone noted the occurrence of lens regeneration in lentectomized newt eyes which had been previously grafted "parabiotically" to other eyes possessing lenses, despite the fact that their pupils and ocular fluids were confluent. Summarizing existing evidence on the subject, Reyer (1954) emphasizes the difficulties of resolving discrepancies and of arriving at a definite conclusion concerning the action of the lens on the iris. "Whatever its nature," he concludes, "its action appears to depend on the size and physiological condition of the lens as well as on its distance from the reacting iris tissue."

Perhaps the most promising approach to this aspect of the problem will prove to be via biochemical studies of lens metabolism and its effects on the composition of the surrounding ocular fluids. Some studies along these lines have involved the administration of certain metabolites, such as amino acids and vitamins. Although Zalokar

(1944) noted no effect of glutathione, cystine, cysteine, or vitamin C on lens regeneration, Takano (1958) obtained slight inhibition of lens regeneration in newts injected subcutaneously each day with cysteine, but noted that similar treatment with cystine promoted lens growth. Tryptophan, arginine, and lysine were less effective in accelerating the growth of regenerating lenses. Histochemical studies indicated that cystine was present in the lens epithelium, while cysteine, as revealed by –SH groups, was localized in the secondary lens fibres. Neither was detected in the aqueous humor by chromatographic methods. Other amino acids (hydroxyproline, tyrosine, arginine, lysine) were found to be qualitatively similar in the aqueous humor of regenerating vis-à-vis intact eyes, but were slightly more concentrated in the former. Whether such changes can be regarded as a causal basis of lens regeneration, or simply as a correlated effect of a common cause, cannot be decided on currently available evidence. Nevertheless, Takano (1958) prefers the hypothesis that the lens may normally use up many metabolites from the aqueous humor, including amino acids, and that their quantitative increase following lentectomy might bring about lens regeneration. If this is true, then the difference between stimulatory and ineffective levels of such substances must be very small to be so easily unbalanced by displacement of the lens in the eye, an alteration often associated with the release of iris tissues from inhibition (Zalokar, 1944).

However this may be, the notion that varying levels of nutrient metabolites are responsible for regulating lens regeneration suffers from the objection that almost any such substance can be made to appear as a specific stimulating agent simply by rendering it deficient, in which case it automatically becomes a limiting factor (but not necessarily a specific stimulator). In view of the incomplete state of our present knowledge, probably the wisest policy is to regard the special metabolism of the lens as a general conditioning influence on the intraocular environment to which the dorsal iris cells may have evolved a sensitivity in those species capable of lens regeneration. This, at least, would explain how even nonregenerating lenses are able to exert inhibitory influences on competent iris cells.

Influence of the Retina
The manifold relationships between the lens and the retina are widely recognized. Aside from their obvious physiological association, not to mention their inductive relations during the embryonic

development of the eye, the regenerative phenomena of lens and retina exhibit some remarkable similarities. It is probably no coincidence that all amphibian eyes known to regenerate lenses can also regenerate neural retinae (although the reverse is not necessarily true). Indeed, in both cases the ocular pigment cell (retinal or iris) is the source from which the new tissues are derived. This is achieved by the dedifferentiation of these cells, together with their proliferation and redifferentiation, into either lens or neural retina.

In the regeneration of the neural retina, Hasegawa (1958) has emphasized that the *pars ciliaris*, in addition to the retinal pigment layer, is an important source of regenerated neural retinal cells. The layer of unpigmented cells thus produced in a retinectomized eye then undergoes rapid proliferation to give rise to stratified layers of cells that differentiate into the various retinal elements, as illustrated in Plates 6.1 to 6.5. Regeneration of nerve fibres along the optic nerve, and the re-establishment of central connections, make it possible for some of the lower vertebrates to recover their vision after retinal degeneration in consequence of eye transplantation.

Although the retinal pigment layer is normally involved in neural retina regeneration (Stone, 1950a,b), under special circumstances it may participate in lens regeneration. Stone (1955) has demonstrated that when the iris is extirpated it is regenerated from the layer of retinal pigmented epithelium, whereupon a lens develops from the regenerated iris. The capacity of retinal pigment cells to give rise to lenses directly has been investigated by Stone and Steinitz (1957), who noted lens regeneration from occasional intra-ocular implants of pieces of retinae obtained from the dorsal, but not the ventral, portions of the eyeball. Further experiments by Stone (1957) showed that the dorsal region of the retina can be induced to develop small lenses by the creation of a permanent aperture which apparently simulates a pupil with marginal lens-regenerating potentialities. This interesting property was maximal in the retinal pigment layer nearest to the dorsal iris, and decreased posteriorly and ventrally. Notwithstanding these examples of lens-forming competence on the part of the retinal pigment cells, it has not been possible to induce the cells of the iris to participate in retinal regeneration (Stone, 1959a).

The possibility that lens regeneration from the iris might be controlled by a stimulating factor from the retina instead of, or in addition to, an inhibiting agent from the old lens, has often been expressed (see reviews by Stone, 1959b, and Reyer, 1962). This is based on several lines of evidence, not the least of which are the investigations of Stone and Steinitz (1953) on eyes deprived of both lens and retina. Under these conditions, although both tissues regenerate simultaneously, the development of the lens is slightly retarded in comparison with control eyes. The natural conclusion from these observations, that lens regeneration depends upon the presence of the retina, must be tempered by the fact that the onset of lens growth occurs during the very early stages of retinal restoration. However, further experiments by Stone (1958a) in which retinal regeneration was selectively prevented by excision of the pigmented epithelium together with the neural retina in lentectomized eyes, proved that no lens develops in the total and permanent absence of the retina. The irises of such eyes, however, retained the latent capacity for lens regeneration as indicated by their regenerative responses when later transplanted into other eyes possessing retinae (but not lenses). A different approach to the problem (Stone, 1958b) consisted of segregating the dorsal irises of lentectomized eyes from the intact retinae by inserting pliofilm discs between the two tissues. When the separation was complete and permanent lens regeneration did not occur.

Transplantation experiments also confirm the apparent dependence of lens regeneration on the retina. Stone (1958a) tested the capacity of the dorsal iris to regenerate a lens in extraocular environments (e.g. subcutaneously or in the abdominal cavity) and noted the nearly complete absence of lens regeneration. But when part of the retinal pigment epithelium accompanied such grafts, diminutive lenses were usually regenerated when the margin of the iris was in close proximity to the retina. Judging from these results it is not surprising that intraocular grafts of dorsal iris will regenerate lenses, provided that the lens of the host eye has been removed (Stone 1952; Reyer, 1956). The usual result, as illustrated in figure 22A, is that both the resident and the implanted dorsal iris give rise to lenses simultaneously. Even intergeneric grafts of dorsal iris can produce lenses irrespective of whether or not the host species is itself capable of regeneration. For example, Reyer (1956) transplanted segments of dorsal iris from larval *Triturus viridescens* into the lentectomized eyes of larval *Amblystoma punctatum*, a species which cannot regenerate lenses. Yet the percentage of implants giving rise to lenses compared favourably with control series involving intraspecific grafts

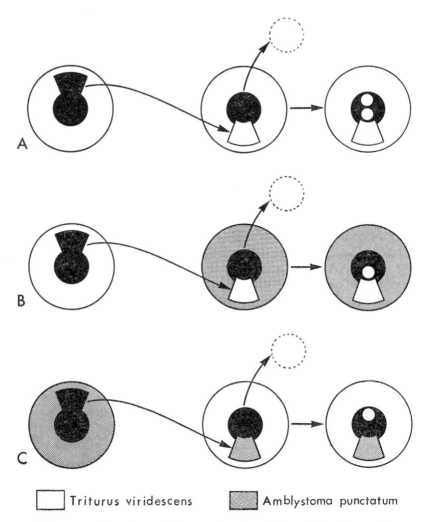

Triturus viridescens   Amblystoma punctatum

Figure 22. Experimental plan and results of Reyer's (1956) experiments on lens regeneration from transplanted segments of the dorsal iris. A, dorsal iris of *Triturus* transplanted to lentectomized eye of same species. Lens regeneration occurs from host and grafted iris. B, *Triturus* dorsal iris transplanted to lentectomized *Amblystoma* eye. Graft is still capable of lens regeneration even though host lacks this capacity. c, *Amblystoma* dorsal iris grafted to lentectomized *Triturus* eye. Graft fails to regenerate a lens although the host eye does so.

(figure 22B). Conversely, *Amblystoma* iris transplanted into *Triturus* eyes failed consistently to form lenses (figure 22C). Clearly, the lack of regenerative capacity in *Amblystoma* cannot be attributed to the absence of a retinal stimulating factor, nor to any other condition in the intraocular environment except the incompetence of its own dorsal iris.

Of special interest in this regard are the investigations of Stone and Gallagher (1958) on the behaviour of the newt iris *in vitro*. Such explants survived but never expressed regenerative tendencies even after several weeks. Nevertheless, when returned to recently lentectomized eyes some of these iris membranes then regenerated lenses, although this capacity had remained latent for up to 28 days at 18° C. *in vitro*. Thus far, attempts to culture retinae along with iris explants have proved unsuccessful.

Reaction of the Iris

The iris is the focus of whatever influences may emanate from the lens and the retina, and is thus inseparable developmentally from these other parts of the eye. Like the retina, it has the capacity in appropriate species to regenerate either itself or a lens, depending upon the nature of the experimental intervention. Iris regeneration *per se* has been investigated by Stone and Griffith (1954) and Stone (1955), who described its replacement following excision of partial segments or the entire circumference. This regeneration proceeds either from the cut edges of residual iris tissue, or from the retinal pigment layer in the vicinity of the ora serrata. If the lens is simultaneously removed, it will usually be regenerated from the still growing dorsal margin of the regenerating iris. In the intact iris of lentectomized eyes, lens regeneration normally proceeds from the mid-dorsal pupillary margin. However, various transplantation experiments of Stone (1952) have shown that this capacity also resides, in decreasing degrees, on the nasal and temporal sides of the mid-dorsal region. The regenerative potential does not extend ventral of the mid-lateral areas, nor can it be secondarily elicited or extinguished by exchanging segments of iris tissue from these different areas. But if the mid-dorsal region of the iris is removed or otherwise incapacitated in lentectomized eyes, lens regeneration usually occurs from the adjacent intact iris on either side of the defect, thus giving rise to double regenerates (Stone, 1954a). This regenerative ability is not restricted to the tissues at the margin of the pupil, for by creating permanent openings in other regions of the iris (Stone, 1954b) or nearby retina (Stone, 1957), lens regenerates have been induced along the dorsal margins of these artificial pupils. However, this occurs only in the dorsal parts of the eye.

Unquestionably, the most remarkable demonstration of the relationship between lens regeneration from the iris and the apparent influence of the retina thereon, relates to the polarization of the lens. Ordinarily, the lens fibres are posteriorly located behind the anterior lens epithelium. In an attempt to learn if this polarization of the lens is dictated by the orientation of the iris from which it develops, Stone (1954a) reversed the anterior–posterior polarity of the iris by removing a dorsal segment and grafting it in backwards. When the old lens was subsequently removed, it was replaced in some of the cases by regeneration from the reversed iris grafts. However, the lenses produced by such inside-out irises were normally oriented with reference to the eye as a whole. Analogous results have been observed in embryonic chick eyes with reversed lenses (Coulombre and Coulombre, 1963). Conceivably this is the result of a retinal influence, although the role of other parts of the eye cannot be excluded. Nevertheless, it is clear that the oriented differentiation of the lens occurs in response to subtleties in the micro-environment. It may be significant however, that the optimum location in the eye for lens regeneration, as determined by the incidence of regeneration from dorsal irises implanted in various positions, is in the pupillary space (Mikami, 1941). With increasing distance from this region the regenerative incidence declines. Thus, it is a curious and interesting fact that the spatial and axial orientations of regenerated lenses are so arranged as to be physiologically optimal with reference to the retina. Indeed, Reyer (1962) has compared the possible influence of the neural retina on lens regeneration to the trophic effect of nerves on limb regeneration. In both cases, functional significance of the developing structure is assured (cf. Chapter XV).

Specific Proteins of Developmentally Related Ocular Tissues
    It is hoped that there may be some significance to the distribution of specific proteins among the various tissues of the eye. Since analyses of such tissue-specific molecules have not as yet revealed their functions, it is impossible at present to predict to what extent (if any) they may be meaningfully related to regeneration and growth regulation. In the confident expectation that their physiological

significance will ultimately be revealed, and in the hopeful antici-
pation that this may explain some of the current enigmas of ocular
development, it is pertinent here to review the present status of our
knowledge concerning this aspect of chemical embryology.

More than any other organ, the eye has been intensively investigated for the presence of tissue-specific proteins. Prompted largely
by the technical advantages of utilizing lens tissue as a source of
antigens, immunological studies have yielded much information
concerning the comparative and ontogenetic chemodifferentiation
of various histological components of the eye, their chemical relationships to one another, and the developmental consequences of
treatment with specific antisera. Identifying antigenic lens protein
by reaction with anti-lens serum, various investigations have correlated the first appearance of lens-specific molecules with the early
developmental stages of visible lens differentiation. In the chick
embryo, the first indications of such proteins are to be detected at
the 11-somite stage (Langman, 1959) when the optic vesicle has
just made contact with the presumptive lens ectoderm. Since this
precedes any visible manifestation of lens differentiation, it constitutes convincing evidence that chemodifferentiation occurs before
histodifferentiation, or rather that differentiation is a matter of specific
protein synthesis. In this case, the earliest lens protein formed appears
to be α-crystallin. According to Maisel and Langman (1961) this
protein is present in the lens of the 72-hour chick embryo as well as
in the optic cup. Continued differentiation of the lens is characterized by the sequential appearance of β-crystallin in the lens fibres,
and finally by γ-crystallin. These proteins appear in the same sequence
in the embryonic chick iris (Maisel and Harmison, 1963).

Analysis of the distribution of lens antigens in other parts of the
eye has been made possible by immunofluorescent methods and
Ouchterlony's agar gel diffusion technique. Thus, Clayton (1954) detected lens antigens in the lens, ciliary process, and retina of seven
day old mouse embryos by means of fluorescent antibodies. Using the
same technique, Fowler and Clarke (1959) noted the localization of
fluorescent lens antiserum in the optic vesicle and brain of 7-somite
chick embryos. The lens ectoderm also reacted to these fluorescent
antibodies in 19-somite embryos. In their investigations of the distribution of α-crystallin by the Ouchterlony technique, Maisel and
Langman (1961) reported that this protein, already present in the
lens and optic cup of the 72-hour chick embryo, is also detectable in

the iris, pigmented layer of the retina, and cornea of older embryos or hatched chicks. β-crystallin is especially abundant in the lens fibres and can also be detected in the iris and retina, but not the chick cornea. The lens, iris, pigmented retina, and cornea of the chick all contain γ-crystallin. Without reference to the specific crystallins of the lens, Langman and Prescott (1959) were able to demonstrate the existence of lens antigens in the iris, cornea, retinal pigment layer, and aqueous and vitreous humors, but not in the neural retina, sclera, nor in other nonocular tissues of the body. When antiserum was prepared against chick iris, however, Maisel and Harmison (1963) found three antigenic types of molecules: one specific for iris alone, one also specific for serum, and one group identified with the α-, β- and γ-crystallins of the lens. Thus, there is an interesting correlation between the distribution of lens antigens among other ocular tissues and the capacity for regeneration. Indeed there is some evidence (Van Deth, 1940) that the chick embryo, like the newt, can regenerate new lenses, although this has not been confirmed by the studies of McKeehan (1961). However, in the chick iris, lens antigens are present in both dorsal and ventral regions, perhaps reflecting the fact that the dorsal iris in the chick embryo is not necessarily the source of new lenses (provided they can regenerate at all) as it is in the newt.

To what extent these lens antigens may be involved in developmental processes cannot be definitely determined. Some hint of their physiological importance, however, can be gained by exposing developing eyes to anti-lens sera. Guyer and Smith (1918) first attempted this by immunizing pregnant mice and rabbits against lens antigen and noting defects in the developing lenses of the offspring. Other investigators, notably Finlay (1924) and Huxley and Carr-Saunders (1924), were unable to confirm these observations in mice, rats, and rabbits. Flickinger, *et al.* (1955) tested the chick embryo in this respect, and found that when cultured in anti-lens sera no developmental abnormalities occurred. Fowler and Clarke (1959), however, cultured optic vesicles from 4 to 7-somite chick embryos (before lens antigens develop) in lens antiserum and obtained a marked reduction in their capacity to induce lenses when subsequently combined with presumptive lens ectoderm. When optic cups plus presumptive lens ectoderm were cultured in antiserum (Langman, 1960a) lens formation was prevented prior to the 17-somite stage but not thereafter.

In vivo studies, in which anti-lens serum was directly applied to developing chick embryos, have confirmed the importance of age in the reaction of the eye to antisera. Fowler and Clarke (1960) demonstrated that exposure to anti-lens sera before the 10-somite stage caused reduction or total absence of eyes, while in 11 to 19-somite embryos the most drastic effects were restricted to the lens. Up to 25 somites, lens formation was normal, but minor abnormalities in the rest of the eye were noted. This decline in sensitivity to anti-lens serum has also been observed by Langman, *et al.* (1962) who exposed chick embryos to antisera against α-crystallin or whole lens. Treatment of 24 and 32-hour embryos (6 and 11 somites, respectively) caused serious disturbances to the developing brain and eye, but 42-hour embryos (19 somites) progressed normally. If these early inhibitions are due to the inactivation or destruction of lens antigens as soon as they are synthesized, which according to Langman (1960b) commences in the 11-somite stage, then they may actually be essential to the process of lens induction and differentiation. The decline in susceptibility to specific antisera during later developmental stages could be explained either by the inaccessibility of such specific proteins owing to their possible sequestration, or to a decrease in their vital importance once the eye has achieved a certain degree of maturation. The fact that fluorescent lens antibodies will become localized in the tissues of developed eyes argues in favour of the latter possibility.

The effects of lens antiserum on larval *Triturus pyrrhogaster* eyes has been studied recently by Ogawa (1964). Larval newts were immersed in a mixture of half-strength Holtfreter's solution (two-parts) and anti-lens serum (one part) for up to three hours. Their corneas were slit open to permit access of antibodies to ocular tissues. This treatment was very destructive to the lens during the following few days, but complete recovery was observed during the second week after exposure. Other tissues in the eye were not affected by the antisera, nor did normal serum exert deleterious effects on any parts of the eye, including the lens. When lentectomized eyes were exposed to anti-lens sera, the result depended upon the age of the regenerate. Immediately after lentectomy, none of the tissues of the eye was injured by the antisera, nor was subsequent regeneration adversely affected. Exposure at later stages caused damage to the lens-forming tissues, but was nevertheless followed by lens regeneration. Thus, the newt eye is evidently immune to the traumatic effects of anti-lens serum once its lens is extirpated and before new lens antigens have had a chance to form in the dorsal iris. Thereafter, it is susceptible to lens antibodies by virtue of the presence of lens antigens, but it can repair the damage by regeneration.

An increase in the number of specific antigens detectable with progressive age increments of the lens has been noted in foetal v. adult rabbits by Halbert, et al. (1957), and in the developing chick lens by Beloff (1959) and Maisel and Langman (1961). Papaconstantinou (1959, 1960) has analysed embryonic and post-natal bovine lenses and has likewise discovered that the number of different α-crystallins increases from two in the third month of gestation to four in calves and adults. He has also learned with respect to the γ-crystallins, that these proteins are more abundantly formed in embryonic lenses than in post-natal ones. Thus, an embryonic lens has substantial amounts of γ-crystallin throughout its fibrous structure, while in calves or adults this protein is largely concentrated in the hard nuclear core of the lens (representing the tissues laid down in the embryo) and is progressively less abundant in the cortical layers of lens fibres. The results obtained by Halbert, et al. (1957) on rabbits are consistent with this: an antigen first formed in the lenses of 10-day-old rabbits was generally restricted to the cortex of the adult lens.

Phylogenetic alterations in lens antigens have also been revealed by comparative Ouchterlony agar gel diffusion analyses and by immunoelectrophoretic investigations. Halbert, et al. (1957, 1958, 1960) found that some of the mammalian lens antigens are shared in common with amphibian lenses, and that only one occurred in the fish. (The squid lens was antigenically unrelated to those in vertebrates.) These results led to the generalization that during the evolution of vertebrate lenses the number of antigens increases by virtue of the addition of new ones and the retention of old ones.

This may not be entirely accurate, however, in view of Ogawa's (1962b) comparative studies of vertebrate lens antigens. He has shown that almost as many lens antigens can be demonstrated in the newt (seven antigens) as in the chick (eight antigens), but that only two of these are identical with each other. Antisera against both chick and newt lenses, however, exhibited varying degrees of cross-reactions with other vertebrate lenses (frog, mouse, rabbit, cattle), but neither reacted with lenses from the killifish. Thus, the number of antigens in the vertebrate lens may not have been reduced during evolution. They may only have lost their immunologically detectable similarities.

Lens antisera against ↓ / Lens antigens from →	INVERT	FISH			AMPHIBIAN		REPTILE	BIRD			MAMMAL				
	Squid	Dory fish	Menhaden	Killifish	Newt	Frog	Turtle	Chick	Turkey	Duck	Rabbit	Mouse	Cattle	Human, monkey, hog, fox, cat	Human cataract
Squid[1]	5	o			o						o				o
Menhaden[1]	o		4		3						3				3
Newt[2]				o	7	3	2				2	2	2		
Frog[1]	o		3			6					4				3
Chick[2]				o	2	3		8			4	4	4		
	α						α	α	α	α	α	α		α	
Chick[3]	—						—	β	β	β	β	—		—	—
	—						γ	γ	γ	γ	γ	—		—	—
Rabbit[1]	o	1				4					5				4
Human cataract[1]	o	2				4					5				7

TABLE 2. Tabulation of numbers of lens antigens detectable by comparing cross reactions of lens antisera with lenses of various vertebrate (and invertebrate) species. Highest numbers of antigens occur in lenses homologous to the antisera used. The number decreases in proportion to phylogenetic relationships.

[1] Halbert and FitzGerald (1958).   [2] Ogawa (1962).   [3] Maisel and Langman (1961).

As can be seen from an inspection of Table 2, there is no general reduction in the actual numbers of lens antigens when different vertebrates are compared. The variations that appear to exist are more probably explained by differences in detection techniques. Nevertheless, it is clear that the greatest number of lens antigens is always found when the antisera are reacted against the original kind of lens used to immunize the rabbit. When this number is compared with the number of antigens in the lenses of other vertebrates above or below the one against which the antiserum was manufactured, there is always a decline in the number of antigens shared in common. This means that at least some lens antigens may have persisted from the fish to the mammal, but others have lost their identities. Whether or not this has involved their replacement by new molecules during evolution, or their conversion to immunologically distinct types, cannot be decided on existing evidence.

With reference to the three groups of crystallin proteins, Maisel and Langman (1961) were able to detect chick α-crystallins in representatives of all five vertebrate classes. Inasmuch as this is also the first specific protein formed in lens ontogeny, it is regarded as the most primitive, if not fundamental, of the lens proteins. β-crystallin of the chick type is absent in fish and amphibian (frog) lenses, but is present in reptilian and avian ones. Apparently it did not arise in reptiles until after the mammalian ancestors evolved, for it is not found in the lenses of mammals. The phylogenetic distribution of γ-crystallin is more puzzling, for it occurs in the lenses of the amphibians (frog), reptiles, and birds, but not in fish and mammals. Detailed analyses of more members of these groups, especially the amphibians, are mandatory.

Whether or not the foregoing information relevant to the ontogeny, phylogeny, and anatomical distribution of specific lens proteins is pertinent to the problem of lens regeneration is for the future to decide. It will be imperative, of course, for many of the elegant investigations that have been conducted on chick embryos to be repeated on newts that are capable of lens regeneration. Thus far, however, the only studies along these lines have involved the immunological comparison of regenerated and original lenses in urodele amphibia. It has been shown by Titova (1957), Vyazov and Sazhina (1961), and Ogawa (1963) that regenerated newt lenses possess antigens identical with those found in normal lenses. This has been confirmed by the results of unpublished experiments by the author, in which a few hundred newt eyes were lentectomized to yield enough lenses to serve as a sufficient antigenic stimulus when injected into rabbits. The antisera thus obtained reacted against at least three distinct antigens in the saline lens extract against which they were produced. When tested with saline extracts of the new lenses regenerated by the same newts from which the original lenses had been taken, the immunological identity between the original and the regenerated lenses was clearly evident (figure 23). Thus, despite their diverse histogenesis, the lenses (new v. old) of newt eyes are both histologically and antigenically identical in so far as can be ascertained by these methods.

Further attempts to determine to what extent the lens may share its antigenic specificity with other tissues in the newt have revealed no such relationships with other ocular tissues, in contrast to what has been observed in the chick. When rabbit anti-newt lens anti-

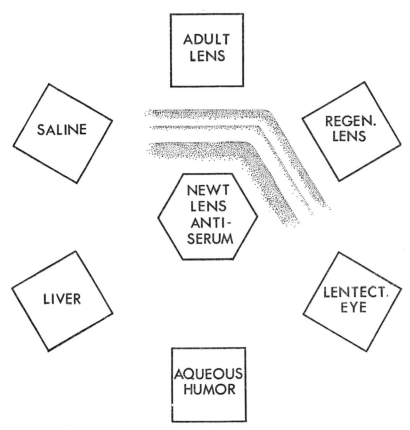

Figure 23. Ouchterlony plate showing identical reactions between newt lens antiserum (central well) and either the original or regenerated adult newt lens extracts (top and upper right wells). No reaction occurred with other parts of the eye, nor with various non-ocular tissues.

serum was reacted, via the Ouchterlony technique, against recently lentectomized eyeballs of newts, no precipitin bands could be detected, although reactions with newt lens was readily apparent. Nor was it possible to obtain a positive reaction with aqueous humor (undiluted, lyophilized, or pervaporated) from newt, frog, or bovine eyes. Finally, the same anti-lens antisera also failed to reveal lens antigens in saline preparations of extra-ocular newt tissues, including liver and abdominal body wall. These results are illustrated in figure 23. The implications of this evidence are that newt lens antigens are truly tissue-specific. Yet since they are present in the regenerated as well as the original lens, and inasmuch as the former is derived from the iris which normally lacks lens antigens, it follows that in the course of regeneration, lens antigens are synthesized anew. Presumably the competent cells of the iris (and pigmented retina?) possess the latent capacity to synthesize lens-specific proteins, but only when induced to regenerate lenses.

Titova (1957) has contributed to our understanding of this phenomenon by determining when lens-specific antigens appear in the course of lens regeneration from the iris. This was achieved by sensitizing guinea pigs to iris membranes from the eyes of *Triton taeniatus* which were either intact or which had been lentectomized five or 15 days before. Theoretically, any guinea pig that gave an anaphylactic reaction to extracts from frog lens (*Rana rudibunda*) would have been sensitized to newt lens antigen. No such reaction occurred in animals sensitized to irises from intact eyes, or from eyes lentectomized for five days. Only in the 15-day lentectomized eyes did the regenerating iris contain antigens capable of sensitizing guinea pigs to frog lens extracts. Therefore, between five and 15 days after lentectomy, the newt iris acquires detectable amounts of lens antigen.

More detailed analyses of this system by agar gel diffusion techniques have yielded more precise data along these lines. Vyazov and Sazhina (1961) found no detachable reaction five days after lentectomy, but noted a diffuse cloudiness in the agar when tissues from eyes lentectomized for seven days were tested. However, by the eleventh day the presence of a definite antigen was demonstrated. Fifteen-day regenerates yielded two antigens, whereas four were found after 30 days of lens regeneration. Thus, the appearance of tissue-specific antigens closely parallels the development of the lens. Indeed, the onset of antigen formation occurs at a time when visible manifestations of lens regeneration are barely perceptible. Takata, *et. al.* (1963) found that lens antigens in the regenerating newt lens are associated both temporally and spatially with the developing lens fibre cells. This is in general agreement with Langman's (1959) demonstration that the first evidence of lens antigen is detachable in the developing chick at the earliest stage of lens induction in the ectoderm (prior to overt lens development).

By using fluorescent antibodies against newt lenses, Ogawa (1963) has confirmed and amplified the results of the foregoing investigations. Irises from newt eyes zero or five days after lentectomy did not fluoresce when treated with fluorescent lens antibodies. On the tenth post-operative day, however, the iris gave a positive reaction that was restricted to the dorsal region where lens regeneration was commencing. Stronger reactions occurred in progressively more advanced regenerates. Correlative histological studies revealed that the earliest reaction between the fluorescent antibodies and the iris occurred at a time "when the iris cells swell or begin to lose the pigment" (Ogawa, 1963). In the process of lens regeneration, therefore, chemodifferentiation is an essential antecedent to histodifferentiation. The former is equivalent to specific molecular synthesis, which is induced by lens removal. Future research may reveal whether or not the inhibition of newt lens regeneration is causally related to the normal absence of lens antigens in the dorsal iris so long as the original lens is present.

VII

Gross Aspects of Hypertrophy

THE explanation of compensatory hypertrophy must be sought in the concatenation of causes and effects which link the original stimulus to the final result. The latter phases of growth, for which the phenomenon was originally named, are observable at the organ, tissue, and cellular levels of organization. Thus, organ hypertrophy is attributable in part to hypertrophy and hyperplasia of the constituent cells. These in turn may be related to alterations in nucleocytoplasmic ratios, and to increased rates of DNA synthesis. Perhaps these are the results of metabolic changes in the cells, associated with shifts in enzymatic activities. Traced back to their origins, the compensatory effects of partial organ ablation must lead to the extracellular mechanisms by which the loss of tissue is detected. These hypothetical antecedents, which exist in the realms of logical necessity rather than proven fact, are assumed to be going on during the lag phase which lies between the original operation and the earliest observed results. This is the period when the most important, and most elusive, processes are happening.

Hence, the criteria by which compensatory growth can be measured are numerous. Originally, the ultimate size attained by the growing organ was recognized as a reliable indication of compensatory hypertrophy. Efforts to analyse such end results in terms of contributing processes led to the utilization of cytological techniques, of which measurements of cell and nuclear dimensions and determinations of mitotic indices have proved the most useful. The latter have been amplified, with the advent of techniques for tritiated thymidine labelling, by determinations of the incidence of cells in a population that are synthesizing DNA. Other cytochemical techniques have yielded information on alterations in the occurrence of a variety of chemical constituents in growing tissues, and these data have been supplemented by occasional enzymatic analyses. Concomitantly, observations have been made on the physiological activities of compensating organs in order to learn to what extent they can make up for the functional deficit caused by partial ablation. Thus, many facts have been accumulated about compensatory growth, most of which can be arranged in a logical sequence. Others, however, particularly at the chemical level, cannot be meaningfully related to the overall growth process until more data are available. But only by filling in the many gaps that still exist in our knowledge of the constituent events making up the phenomenon of compensatory hypertrophy will the cause and control of growth eventually be understood.

The ultimate extent of hypertrophy realized by an organ and the time it takes to be achieved are subject to a number of important variables. Very few organs ever completely return to their original mass after partial ablation. Of those that have been sufficiently investigated, only the liver and blood-cells are generally recognized as being capable of total restoration, although the ovary may also fall in this category. The rate of regeneration is seriously affected by age and by species size, being slower to occur in older animals and larger species. In general, the more tissue removed in the original operation the longer the time required to make good the deficit. Additional factors that have been shown to influence compensatory hypertrophy include sex, endocrinological state, diet, and numerous other conditions affecting to varying degrees the physiological state of the organism and its organs.

Liver

These principles are illustrated in the case of liver regeneration. Being a vitally essential organ, there is a limit to the amount of liver that can be excised without jeopardizing survival. Extirpation of up to 70 per cent is routinely tolerated by experimental animals, but loss of more than 80 per cent is generally fatal (Bollman and Mann, 1936). Cameron (1952) reported that it took twice as long (3 weeks) to replace a 60 per cent loss of liver in the rat as was required to regenerate 30 per cent (10 days). Others, however, have noted even more rapid rates of regeneration following removal of substantial amounts of hepatic tissue. In the adult rat, as illustrated by Plates 7.1 to 7.3, partial hepatectomies of approximately 70 per cent are compensated in 1 or 2 weeks (Higgins and Anderson, 1931; Norris, *et al.*, 1942; Bucher and Glinos, 1950; Mangalik, *et al.*, 1954; Greenbaum, *et al.*, 1954). In the mouse, restoration is complete in 6 to 8 days (Yokoyama, *et al.*, 1953; Tsuboi, *et al.*, 1954). According to Fishback (1929), liver regeneration goes on for a period of 6 to 8 weeks in the dog. Thus, the time required to replace lost portions of the liver appears to vary in proportion to the size of the animal species.

A similar relationship holds for animals of different ages, for Norris, *et al.* (1942) and Bucher and Glinos (1950) have described a small but persistent delay in liver regeneration in old rats *v.* young ones. Indeed, these same authors report regeneration in excess of the original liver weights, especially in younger animals. Higgins and Anderson (1931) have also noted surplus liver regeneration two to four weeks after partial hepatectomy in the rat. This phenomenon, however, may be due in part to the failure to take into account the continuing growth of the rat during the regeneration process. It is important, therefore, to compare the restored weight of the liver not with the original weight but with that which the liver would have attained under normal conditions, which would, of course, take into account the changes in relative weight of the liver with increasing body size. This might explain in part the apparent inequity previously

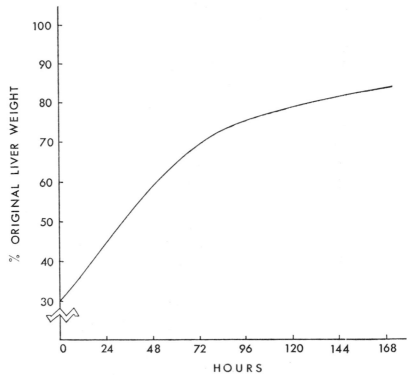

Figure 24. Rate of regeneration of liver mass in the rat is a function of time in hours after 70 per cent hepatectomy.

noted in the regenerative capacity of livers in young *v.* old animals. The complete recovery of the liver in relatively short periods of time is attributable to the rapid onset and fast rate of growth during the first few days following injury. Only 24 hours after 70 per cent hepatectomy, the residual portion increases to 45 or 50 per cent of the pre-operative weight (Higgins and Anderson, 1931; Brues, *et al.*, 1936; Greenbaum, *et al.*, 1954), as indicated in figure 24. Continuing regeneration restores approximately 60 per cent of the original mass in 48 hours (Brues, *et al.*, 1936) and about 70 per cent by the third day (Greenbaum, *et al.*, 1954; Mangalik, *et al.*, 1954). Thereafter, the growth rate begins to decelerate as complete restoration is approached.

Kidney

The kidney shares with the liver the common attribute of being essential for survival. Accordingly, total nephrectomy is inevitably followed by death within a few days, while loss of approximately 80 per cent of the total kidney tissue may sometimes be tolerated. Even greater losses may be sustained if operations on the two kidneys are not done simultaneously (Diaz and Levy, 1939; Morrison, 1962). Thus, two-thirds of one kidney can be removed, and a week later, all of the opposite kidney. Were it not for the intervening hypertrophy, this would have involved the loss of five-sixths (83 per cent) of the total kidney tissue. However, since the number of nephrons is reduced to this extent, a chronic renal insufficiency results that is responsible for the subsequent 50 per cent mortality (Morrison, 1962). For most experimental purposes relevant to compensatory hypertrophy, half of the total kidney tissue is removed by unilateral nephrectomy. Paired organs such as this offer obvious advantages over unpaired ones (e.g. liver) in that no direct injury need be inflicted on the residual tissue to be studied.

In contrast to the liver, the kidney is an organ that does not completely replace the original tissue mass after partial ablation (Plate 7.4). Jackson and Levine (1929) traced the increase in weight of the rat kidney after uninephrectomy to about 63 per cent of the combined weight of both kidneys in unoperated controls at the end of four weeks, while Addis and Lew (1940) reported 70 per cent restoration in 40 days. Apparently even greater hypertrophy can occur in the mouse, for Straube and Patt (1961) noted weight increases of 75 to 80 per cent of the original combined kidney weights 26 to 38 days post-operatively. In the rabbit, Addis, *et al.* (1924) recorded 58 per cent compensatory renal hypertrophy after 15 to 33 days, and a rise to 66 per cent after 106 to 126 days. These data collectively indicate a possible decline in hypertrophic capacity as one compares the kidneys of smaller animals with those of larger ones.

Endocrine Glands

Among the paired endocrine glands, none has been so thoroughly investigated as the adrenal cortex. Total adrenalectomy usually causes death within a week or so unless the animal is provided with an adequate source of NaCl. By removing both adrenals from rats and transplanting portions of them back into the systemic circulation, Butcher (1948) noted a 25 per cent survival rate when only 12·5 per cent of the total original adrenal tissue was present, but 60 to 69 per cent survival among rats with 25 per cent of the normal amount of adrenal cortex. Since in such experiments a proportion of the graft degenerates prior to adequate revascularization, it is probable that rats can actually survive on even less amounts of functional adrenal tissue than these studies would indicate. Unilateral adrenalectomy, however, is well tolerated and has constituted the technique of choice by which to demonstrate compensatory adrenal hypertrophy. The variability exhibited by the compensating adrenal is perhaps best illustrated by the results obtained by Bachrach and Kordon (1958) indicating a range of restoration of 64 to 94·5 per cent of the original combined adrenal weights in three weeks. However, the average of these figures (76 per cent) concurs in general with the consensus of other investigations. About 70 per cent replacement was noted in young rats by Horn and LoMonaco (1958) and by Addis and Lew (1940) after 15 and 40 days, respectively. Davidson and Feldman (1962) and Bernstein and Biskind (1957) report 77 and 78 per cent adrenal hypertrophy in rats after 9 and 150 days, respectively. In larger animals, such as the dog, enlargement of the remaining adrenal is not so great, as indicated by Swinyard and Bruner (1940), who reported only 57·8 per cent hypertrophy after 90 days.

The ovary is of particular interest since it expresses such remarkable powers of regeneration. This can be manifested either as repair and restoration of a partially removed organ or as the compensatory growth of the remaining intact ovary following contralateral ovariectomy. In either case the growth response is essentially the same since the reduction in ovarian mass is quantitative rather than qualitative.

Carmichael and Marshall (1908) reported that following removal of 75 or 90 per cent of rabbit ovaries, the remnants grew to at least the size of a normal ovary after six months. Regeneration of ovarian fragments has also been observed by Lipschütz, *et al.* (1922b) in the young rabbit, by Lipschütz and Voss (1925) in the cat, and by Pencharz (1929) in the rat and mouse. Unilateral ovariectomy is likewise followed by enlargement of the remaining ovary, sometimes to twice its normal size. In rats and rabbits, Carmichael and Marshall (1908), Stotsenburg (1913) and Hatai (1915) noted compensatory hypertrophy of residual ovaries to 75 to 100 per cent of the normal combined ovarian weights within several months, while 60 to 75 per cent restoration in the rat has been reported within shorter periods of time by Addis and Lew (1940), Horn and LoMonaco (1958), and Peterson, *et al.* (1962). In the opossum, Hartman (1925) observed a threefold increase in weight of the remaining ovary after unilateral ovariectomy.

It is possible that the degree to which the ovary undergoes compensatory hypertrophy is affected by age, for Arai (1920) observed only 70 per cent hypertrophy after unilateral ovariectomy in the rat before puberty, but 100 per cent restoration in mature ones. In view of other evidence, however, this effect is probably more the direct result of functional influences which are only secondarily related to age.

In 1906, Bond was the first to report the occurrence of compensatory hypertrophy after unilateral ovariectomy in the rabbit. As other investigators subsequently confirmed, he described enlargement of the remaining ovaries several months (and a few pregnancies) after operation. However, in rabbits isolated from males no compensatory hypertrophy occurred, a fact which was disputed by Carmichael and Marshall (1908) on the basis of only two experimental animals. One of these expressed hypertrophy of the remaining ovary to 83 per cent of the original combined weights after four months without mating, whereas the other, semi-spayed during pregnancy but not mated thereafter, underwent slight atrophy of the residual ovary in the following four months. Bond's original observation was eventually confirmed by Lipschütz (1928), however, who reported the absence of compensatory hypertrophy in fragments of ovaries in rabbits isolated from males before operation and for four and a half months afterwards. This phenomenon is peculiar to rabbits since they do not exhibit spontaneous ovulation as do most other animals. The nervous stimulation of mating is required to bring about ovulation by initiation of the secretion of luteinizing hormone, without which neither corpora lutea are formed nor compensatory ovarian hypertrophy allowed. Indeed, Khan (1962) has shown that compensatory ovarian hypertrophy is suppressed in rats treated with the tranquillizer, chlorpromazine, to inhibit the release of FSH from the pituitary. Such interesting exceptions to the general rule emphasize that the essential nature of compensatory growth in the ovary is the same as in normal ovarian growth during recurrent reproductive cycles, and perhaps in relation to sexual maturation as well. In all cases, the primary stimuli are gonadotrophic hormones, without which ovarian growth of any kind cannot be mediated. Thus, the correlation between function and growth in this organ is inescapable.

Lipschütz (1922) contended that the apparent testicular hypertrophy observed after unilateral castration was actually only an acceleration of development up to, but not beyond, adult dimensions. This conclusion was based upon observations of compensatory testicular hypertrophy in rabbits of various ages. Recalculating his data according to relative instead of absolute organ weights, it is found that in three-week-old pre-puberal rabbits subjected to semi-castration nine weeks before, the remaining testes had increased in weight 13·2 per cent above control levels. At four and a half months of age, rabbits similarly operated ten weeks previously possessed testes weighing 183 per cent more than controls. In six-and-a-half-month old rabbits the remaining testes (four months post-operatively) weighed 212 per cent more than controls, but by fourteen months of age and approximately a year after semi-castration, testicular hypertrophy was only 42·9 per cent above normal. From these data, it was proposed that in very young animals the testes may be completely incapable of compensatory growth. During subsequent growth, however, the testes become increasingly sensitive to unilateral castration by which they are stimulated to undergo accelerated development. Reaching its peak at puberty, this period is characterized by the capacity of the remaining testes to outgrow those in intact control animals but not to exceed adult limits. Thus, the testis at this stage is believed to be able to reach maturity faster. It follows, therefore, that as the animal itself approaches full maturity the capacity for compensatory testicular hypertrophy should decline eventually to zero. These relationships are expressed graphically in figure 25.

This may explain the reported absence of compensatory hypertrophy in the testes of mice (Rowlands, 1934) and dogs (Kyrle, 1911), both of which are animals that cease growing as adults. In contrast,

the rat characteristically exhibits compensatory growth in the remaining testis in accordance with its continued somatic growth throughout
life. Most of the studies on rabbits appear to have utilized animals
that were still growing. Thus, in the absence of compelling evidence
to the contrary, the theory advanced by Lipschütz (1922) may not be
incorrect, though it obviously needs to be more fully certified.

An interesting, but unexplained, phenomenon of uneven testicular
hypertrophy has been observed by Domm and Juhn (1927) in their
studies of the effects of unilateral castration in brown leghorn fowl.
When subjected to sinistral castration at 1 week of age, it was found
that the remaining right testis grew to a size that was 0·335 per cent
of the total body weight when the bird was 32 weeks old. However,
when the right testis was removed from a 1-week-old fowl, the left
remaining testis grew enough to weigh an average of 1·21 per cent of

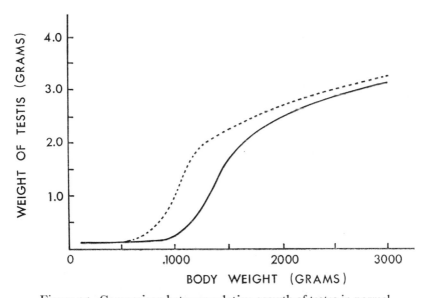

Figure 25. Comparison between relative growth of testes in normal
and unilaterally castrated rabbbits. In intact animal, weight of each
testis (solid line) is minimal during immaturity, increases rapidly
during puberty, and slowly approaches maximal dimensions in
adult. In semi-castrated rabbit (broken line) remaining testis
compensates by precocious enlargement, but cannot surpass the
adult size it would ultimately have achieved had rabbit remained
intact. (From Lipschütz, 1922.)

the body weight. This discrepancy apparently reflects in part the inequity normally evident in testis size in young birds, whose left testes are larger, as opposed to older ones in which the right testis is generally the larger one. Accordingly, unilateral castration in fowl 16 to 40 weeks old resulted in more nearly equal hypertrophy of residual left and right testes, although the left one still grew to a slightly larger average size.

Compensatory hypertrophy has been less thoroughly studied in the non-steroid endocrine glands, primarily because they are less amenable to partial extirpation,and also because the amounts of their remaining portions are not easily measured. Thus, virtually nothing is known concerning the possible regenerative potential of the partially removed pituitary, or of compensatory hypertrophy in remaining parathyroid glands.

The remnant of the thyroid following 75 per cent ablation is capable of enlargement, according to Loeb and Kaplan (1924) and Reichlin (1957). After hemithyroidectomy in the young rat, Horn and LoMonaco (1958) measured regeneration to 73 per cent of the normal thyroid mass in 15 days. Knigge (1961), however, found only 57·5 per cent restoration of the halved thyroid after 32 to 48 weeks in adult cats.

With reference to the islets of Langerhans, Allen (1922a) described the hydropic degeneration of β-cells starting 4 to 7 days after loss of large portions of the pancreas. Presumably representing cellular exhaustion due to hypersecretion, this phenomenon may be accompanied by the production of new islets of Langerhans derived by proliferation from the exocrine ducts of the pancreas. Creutzfeld (1951) has described the similar regeneration of new α-cells directly from the pancreatic ducts of partially pancreatectomized dogs, and Evens and Martin (1963) noted that in partially pancreatectomized rats there was 2·2 to 6 times as much islet tissue as in normal animals.

Exocrine Glands

Only fragmentary information is available on the gross aspects of compensatory hypertrophy in various exocrine glands, although the finer details of their growth have been more frequently studied. No data appear to have been reported on gross enlargement of seminal vesicles or avian salt glands, for example, following their reduction in mass, and studies of Cowper's gland (Shih, 1934) the prostate (Addis and Lew, 1940) and submandibular salivary gland (Alho,

1961) in the rat after 50 per cent ablation have revealed no definite indications of compensatory increase in weight of the remaining parts. However, reduction of the rat pancreas to an average of 61·5 per cent of the normal mass resulted in its restoration to an average of 74 per cent of control amounts after four weeks (Augustine, 1963). In mammary glands, Ribbert (1895) reported compensatory enlargement of the remaining organs in the rabbit after removing five or seven out of the eight available glands. Similarly, Linzell (1963) observed a twofold increase in the remaining mammary gland after unilateral mastectomy in the pregnant goat, but failed to detect any growth response under similar circumstances in the guinea pig. Investigations of the outer orbital glands of rats have shown that following total removal of the left gland and 50 to 65 per cent excision of the right one, regeneration of the latter occurred in 19 per cent of the cases, causing an average enlargement to 80 per cent of the size of control glands (Babaeva, 1961). What effect, if any, the removal of the opposite gland had on these results, was not revealed by these experiments.

Lymphoid and Haemopoietic Tissues

The lymphoid tissues are distributed among a variety of organs throughout the body. Though *de novo* regeneration of totally extirpated lymphatic organs does not usually occur (Sanders and Florey, 1940; Fukutani, 1959), Furuta (1947) described the occasional replacement of excised popliteal lymph nodes in young rabbits but not in adult ones. More commonly, however, the response to subtotal removal of lymphatic organs is manifest in other lymphoid tissues of the body. Thus, Turner and Hall (1943) showed that when approximately half of the lymphatic organs were removed from mice there was an increase in weight of the remaining lymph nodes in the next ten days. Similar observations were made by Fukutani (1959) following removal of approximately 85 per cent of the lymph nodes from rats. Splenectomy has comparable effects on lymph nodes (Whitney, 1928; Bracco, 1939). Partial splenectomy in mice and rats is regularly followed by enlargement of the remnant to the original size (Liosner, *et al.*, 1961) or to a portion thereof (Cameron and Rhee, 1959).

As in the case of the liver, the erythron is capable of 100 per cent regeneration following loss of erythrocytes by bleeding, or their haemolysis induced by phenylhydrazine. Moreover, the time required to restore completely the normal haematocrit is affected by age and body size. Boycott (1929, 1934) has shown that young rats and rabbits are capable of total red blood-cell replacement in five and thirteen days, respectively. In contrast, old rats and rabbits require about one and three weeks, respectively, to make good the loss. In humans, the average time required for restoration of lost blood is about seven weeks (Fowler and Barer, 1942). Since an old rat is approximately equivalent to a young rabbit in erythropoietic potential, apparent age differences are very possibly a reflection of size differences. Boycott (1929, 1934) has pointed out that little animals are more metabolically active than big ones, and that their red blood-cells have shorter life-spans. Thus, the turnover of erythrocytes in the rat, as reflected in the reticulocyte count, is faster than in the dog or human, for example. The phylogenetic rationale for this lies in the adaptation of erythro-poietic rates in inverse proportion to body sizes. "Wounds in nature," wrote Boycott (1929), "are not graded according to the size of the recipient animal, and they let out blood in absolute, not relative, volumes."

VIII

Histological Hypertrophy

IF there is a purpose to compensatory hypertrophy it is to increase the functional efficiency of organs and tissues. Since organs are composed of manifold functional units, it is these that are most sensitive and responsive to the demands for compensation. Where the constituent cells are capable of proliferation, hyperplasia is the method of choice by which functional efficiency is enhanced. Otherwise, cell enlargement must suffice. In either case, the functional units at the histological level of organization are inevitably enlarged. But increase in size *per se* does not necessarily promote functional efficiency, especially where surface-volume relationships are important. Accordingly, one would expect that if compensatory hypertrophy were actually a response to physiological demands, the increase in size of the functional units would be accompanied by alterations in structural proportions commensurate with the varying activities of different parts. This is essentially what has happened during evolution as anatomical structure had adapted to the changing requirements of increasing bodily sizes. Similarly, one sees alterations in histological proportions associated with ontogenetic growth, again reflecting the mechanism by which physiological efficiency is maintained. If compensatory hypertrophy has any functional significance, theory would predict that it should also be achieved by differential responses in the growth of organ parts in accordance with functional requirements.

Liver

The liver is a case in point. Inasmuch as the lost lobes are not replaced in liver regeneration, the remaining mass of hepatic tissue increases by proliferation of cells and in part by cellular hypertrophy. To achieve this, the hepatic lobules must either increase in size or number. Although Ponfick (1890) claimed that the individual lobules of the regenerating liver increase in size, subsequent investigators have shown that the diameters of lobules in regenerating livers are not appreciably altered. Fishback (1929) described the regeneration

I   129

of new lobules from bile ducts, and Bollman and Mann (1936) noted that the added lobules are of normal size and structure.

However, liver lobules are not the discrete, circumscribed structures they sometimes appear to be when seen in transverse section. Organized around bile ducts and blood vessels, they are a continuous system of branching, cylindrical structures which are themselves composed of numerous functional sub-units. The latter are the hepatic cords and their constituent bile capillaries. Inasmuch as they do not increase in length as the liver grows, it must be concluded that new ones are produced in the regenerating liver. This is presumably achieved either by budding from the bile ducts or even by branching from pre-existing cords. This apparently recapitulates the normal processes by which the liver enlarges in the growing organism, namely by the addition of new lobules which bud from pre-existing ones (Mall, 1906; Johnson, 1919). According to McKellar (1949) this process may occur by the bifurcation of central veins in order to give rise to two lobules by subdivision of the original one. If the method of liver regeneration is indeed histologically identical with that of normal hepatic growth, then it should be theoretically possible for the liver to regenerate indefinitely following repeated partial hepatectomies. Indeed, Simpson and Finckh (1963) have reported the persistence of nearly normal histology in regenerated rat livers after five successive partial hepatectomies.

Kidney

Such is not the case with kidneys, which are unable to form new functional sub-units (nephrons) except in immature stages (Kittelson, 1917; Arataki, 1926; Kennedy, 1958). In the new-born rat there are slightly more than 10,000 glomeruli, but the number steadily increases (at a declining rate) to almost three times as many in the mature animal (Table 3). Thereafter the number of glomeruli slowly diminishes to about half the maximum in senile rats (Roessle and Roulet, 1932; Kennedy, 1958). Although some of the early investigators mistakenly attributed compensatory renal hypertrophy to increases in the number of nephrons (see review by Arataki, 1926), the studies of Saphir (1927) revealed no augmentation of the normal number of glomeruli in the remaining kidneys of uninephrectomized rabbits. This has been convincingly illustrated in more recent studies by Hiramoto, et al. (1962), who treated rats with rabbit anti-rat kidney globulin in order to label their glomeruli (as revealed by the indirect

Age	No. of Glomeruli Kittelson (1917)	Arataki (1926)
Newborn	10,465	10,700
1 week	19,682	
2 weeks	24,061	
3 weeks	25,930	
7 weeks	28,583	
12 weeks	28,863	
ca. 100 days		31,000
500 days		20,000

TABLE 3. Relation of age to number of glomeruli in the rat kidney. Note that the number of differentiated glomeruli increases to early maturity, and declines with advancing age.

fluorescent antibody technique). Seven months after uninephrectomy in such rats all of the glomeruli were still marked, indicating that despite compensatory hypertrophy no new glomeruli had developed. Even when one kidney is removed from 1 to 3-day-old rats, when many new nephrons are actively forming, Moore (1929) showed that the number of glomeruli in the hypertrophic kidney 165 days later is not different from control values. Indeed, in the congenital absence of one kidney there is still the normal number of glomeruli in the solitary hypertrophic kidney. In a study by Boycott (1910) of one such case in a rabbit, the single kidney represented 0·58 per cent of the body weight, compared with 0·68 and 0·72 per cent for *both* kidneys in two normal control animals. The single kidney contained 291,000 glomeruli, while the controls had 605,000 and 559,000, respectively, per animal. It would appear, therefore, that the kidney can develop only a predetermined number of nephrons regardless of the size to which it may be required to grow.

Clearly, growth of the kidney must therefore involve enlargement of individual nephrons. This accounts in part for the normal increase in kidney mass in the developing animals. Both Kittelson (1917) and Arataki (1926) determined that the average glomerular diameter of new-born rats was 62μ, a value that doubles during subsequent maturation. The renal tubules also undergo enlargement with age. This has been described by Oliver (1942) in association with the nephrosclerosis of senescence, while Korenchevsky (1961) measured the total mass of individual renal tubules in young v. old rats and found a 45 per cent increase with age, attributable in part to cytoplasmic hypertrophy and in part to a 50 per cent increase in lumen size. Thus, the enlargement of nephrons is accounted for by changes in tubular diameter as well as elongation. As indicated earlier, this may well be a compensatory response to the normal decrease in the number of nephrons with advancing age.

Similar changes are encountered in kidneys undergoing compensatory hypertrophy following unilateral ablation. Although Moll (1955) could find no increase in glomerular or tubular diameters in compensating mouse kidneys, many other investigators have reported size increases in these structures in rats and rabbits (Boycott, 1910; Oliver, 1924; Saphir, 1927; Morrison, 1962). The consensus, therefore, is clearly in favour of glomerular and tubular dilation as a primary causative factor in renal hypertrophy. Certain pathological conditions also lead to similar changes. Oliver, et al. (1941) calculated that in a case of nephritis in the dog kidney, the proximal convoluted tubules increased 50 per cent in diameter and became almost three times as long, thus bringing about a considerable increase in tubule volume apparently to accommodate for the pathological degeneration of other parts of the nephrons. Thus, the response of the kidney is not specific with respect to the initiating stimulus. Hypertrophy may be induced by age, partial ablation, or pathological conditions, and in each case the dimensions of the nephrons are similarly increased. This hypertrophy, however, is largely restricted to the functionally most active parts of the kidney, namely, the glomeruli and convoluted tubules. Morrison (1962) reported that renal hypertrophy in the rat did not involve enlargement of the papillae, whose main job is the simple conveyance of urine.

In view of the mechanism by which renal hypertrophy occurs at the histological level, namely, enlargement but not addition of nephrons, it is obvious that this imposes limits on the extent to which the kidney can compensate for reductions in its substance. Residual nephrons can enhance their functional efficiency by enlarging their surface areas through elongation and increases in width. But because the surface area does not keep pace with volume changes, it is evident that beyond certain limits enlargement of nephrons should be more deleterious than beneficial. Presumably this accounts for the fact that large animals possess kidneys that are subdivided into lobes or renucli (figure 6), thereby permitting the necessary proportionate increase in renal mass without elongating the component nephrons beyond their physiologically optimum limits. In the experimental animal it is possible by stepwise operations to reduce the number of nephrons to a minimum. Experiments along these lines by the author have revealed the progressive compensatory hypertrophy of residual kidney tissue as illustrated in figure 26. This has also been achieved by Morrison (1962) who excised two-thirds of one kidney from young rats, and one week later removed the entire opposite organ. Although compensatory hypertrophy occurred in the remaining fragment, it was not enough to offset eventual renal insufficiency which accounted for the deaths of about half the animals. In such cases, each nephron enlarges in length and width, and each glomerulus expands in order to become more functionally proficient. Yet it is not known whether continuing physiological demands stimulate hypertrophy beyond the point of functional advantage or if growth automatically ceases when it becomes physiologically unrewarding. If the latter alternative were

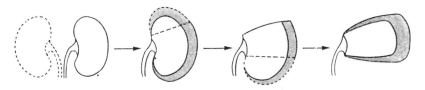

Figure 26. Extreme reduction in mass of kidney by stepwise operations at three week intervals in the rat. Broken lines indicate portion removed at each operation. Shaded areas show extents of hypertrophy over preoperative dimensions (unshaded).

not true, however, it would be expected on theoretical grounds that beyond its optimum size a nephron's efficiency would decline, creating even greater functional demands and in turn stimulating more growth. In the nature of a positive feedback, this situation is approached only by certain neoplastic growths.

Endocrine Glands

The histological problems confronted by endocrine glands stimulated to hypertrophy are less complex than those of the kidney because of their simpler functional units. Notwithstanding the varying degrees of histological organization exhibited by endocrine glands, each secretory cell is in general an autonomous unit dependent only on its proximity to a blood supply into which it releases its hormones, and by which its activities are regulated. With the exception of the thyroid, the significance of the histological architecture of endocrine glands is not understood and presumed to be of relatively minor importance except insofar as it may serve to distinguish various cell types with different secretory activities. The adrenal cortex is a case in point, for the zona glomerulosa is believed to be responsible for the secretion of mineralocorticoids, while the inner zones (fasciculata and reticularis) are associated with glucocorticoid secretion. In compensatory hypertrophy of the adrenal cortex following excision of the opposite gland, enlargement is attributed proportionately to all zones. More refined physiological disturbances, however, may cause selective hypertrophy or atrophy of the different zones. Deane, et al. (1948) showed that hypertrophy of the zona glomerulosa could be induced in rats by low sodium diets. In cats, Newmark, et al. (1959) described not only an increase in the width of the zona glomerulosa but also atrophy of the zona fasciculata under conditions of sodium deficiency.

Morphogenetic regeneration can also occur in the adrenal cortex. It reflects the method by which the adrenal cells are normally replaced. Various studies have indicated that the adrenal cortex is really a renewing organ, rather than an expanding one. By labelling newly divided cells in the mouse adrenal with tritiated thymidine, Brenner (1963) has confirmed that most mitotic activity occurs in the region comprising the inner glomerulosa and outer fasciculata (Plate 8.1). Such labelled cells can be traced during subsequent weeks as they migrate through the zona fasciculata (Plates 8.2 and 8.3). Although some may remain in the outer region of the cortex, most of the labelled cells end up at the boundary between the zona fasciculata and the degenerating X zone after about six weeks (Plate 8.4). Here they eventually disappear, presumably by degeneration.

The pattern of proliferation and migration in the regenerating adrenal cortex recapitulates that which occurs in the normal gland. When the inner zones of the rat adrenal are removed by enucleation, regeneration can occur from the residual tissues adherent to the capsule, but not from the enucleated inner portion of the gland (Ingle and Higgins, 1938). Even when the whole gland is transplanted elsewhere in the body, its regeneration occurs from the zona glomerulosa following degeneration of the inner zones (provided there is no other intact adrenal tissue in the body). Ingle and Higgins (1938) noted that under these circumstances regeneration begins as early as the third day by proliferation of cells in the capsule and zona glomerulosa and is complete at the end of five to six weeks when the original mass of cortical tissue is replaced. Investigations of regeneration from enucleated capsules left *in situ* in male rats deprived of their opposite glands (de Groot and Fortier, 1959) have revealed that regeneration commences by the end of the first week, and has restored nearly the total original cortical mass of the gland after six to eight weeks. Moreover, the zonation of such regenerated adrenals was completely restored to normal dimensions except for a slightly enlarged glomerulosa.

In the ovary, compensatory hypertrophy is largely the result of follicular growth. Although Hatai (1915) was of the opinion that the hypertrophy was due to increases in the amounts of interstitial tissues, his successors (Arai, 1920; Asdell, 1924) found no appreciable growth of the interstitial cells of the ovarian stroma following unilateral ovariectomy in rats and rabbits. Thus, it is the number of ovarian follicles that is increased in semi-spayed animals, as is exhibited in the litter sizes.

Some of the early investigators were interested in testing the hypothesis that sex might be determined by whether a given egg was produced from the left or the right ovary. It was noted that after one ovary had been removed, subsequent litters were of nearly normal size (and of mixed sexes). First reported by Hunter (1792) with reference to the pig, similar results have been observed in the rabbit (Carmichael and Marshall, 1908; Doncaster and Marshall, 1910; Hammond, 1925) and the rat (Arai, 1920). Even when all of one ovary and half of the other was removed from rabbits, Hammond (1925) noted that the number of offspring per litter still approximated normal. In the opposum, Hartman (1925) recorded that the single remaining ovary produced an average of 30·1 eggs, whereas in intact animals each ovary averaged 11·1 eggs. In this animal there is a normal loss of about half of all the ovulated eggs through degeneration or lack of fertilization, which may account for the super-fecundity of the semi-spayed opossum.

Apparently the number of ovarian follicles to develop depends upon the concentration of gonadotrophins secreted by the pituitary, and not upon the amount of ovarian tissue available. This has been experimentally demonstrated by Sato (1963), who stimulated the ovulation of supernumerary ova from mouse ovaries by injections of pregnant mare's serum followed by human chorionic gonadotrophin 44 hours later. As shown in Table 4, increasing doses of PMS induces the ovulation of progressively larger numbers of ova. Indeed, 10 i.u.

of PMS brought about the production of twice as many eggs as 5 i.u. This was more than six times the number maturing in the normal

PMS dose (i.u.)	HCG dose (i.u.)	Av. No. of eggs ovulated	Av. No. of foetuses developing
0	0	8·2	7·5
1	2	9·6	9·3
5	5	27·7	25·4
10	5	53·8	26·4

TABLE 4. Effect of pregnant mare's serum (PMS) and human chorionic gonadotrophin (HCG) on egg production and development in the mouse. Although the number of ova that mature increases with the dose of PMS, the number of developing foetuses plateaus at the maximum capacity of the uteri.

ovary. This, of course, puts a strain on the uteri which are nevertheless capable of accommodating more than three times the normal number of foetuses. If more eggs than this are ovulated, however, the excess are either not fertilized or fail to implant. These super-pregnant females seldom give birth to living offspring, and many of their embryos are resorbed.

The histological examination of solitary remaining ovaries in semi-spayed rabbits (Asdell, 1924) and rats (Emery, 1931) revealed an increase in the number of mature follicles and corpora lutea. These observations confirmed those on the mouse by Allen (1923), who determined that unilateral ovariectomy caused an increase in the number of ova maturing in the remaining ovary but brought about no change in the number of immature ova that differentiate. The promptness of this effect on the maturation of ova has been especially well illustrated by the studies of Greenwald (1962) on the hamster. This animal has a four-day oestrous cycle. Unilateral ovariectomy on the first two days of the cycle results in twice the normal number of ripe ova produced by the remaining ovary. The same results were obtained by operating at 9 a.m. on the third day of the cycle, there being an average of 11·6 mature ova formed. Unilateral ovariectomies at 4 p.m. and 10 p.m. of the third day resulted in the average ovulation of 9·2 and 5·7 ova, respectively, from the remaining ovaries. Clearly, the number of ova to be shed by each ovary becomes definitively determined late in the day immediately preceding oestrus, by which time the loss of one ovary is without effect on the opposite one.

An especially curious result of unilateral ovariectomy occurs in those birds which possess only a single left ovary. Removal of this ovary initiates development of the right rudimentary gonad which usually differentiates into a testis. According to the studies of Kornfeld and Nalbandov (1954) testes are produced by 98 per cent of the right gonads following left ovariectomy in the fowl, while ovaries develop in 2 per cent of the cases. Taber, et al. (1956) found testicular development in only 75 per cent of the poulards studied. Spermatogenesis was noted in 8 per cent of such testes by Taber, et al. (1955). Twenty-four per cent of the cases exhibited varying degrees of ovarian differentiation (Taber, et al., 1955), which reflects the incidence of cortical tissue present in the rudimentary right gonads of fowl. Thus, left ovariectomy apparently does not determine the percentages of testes and ovaries produced by right gonads. It merely initiates development, the direction of which depends on the relative amounts of cortical and medullary tissues already present in the rudimentary organ.

In contrast to the ovary, the testis usually exhibits very little compensatory hypertrophy, a fact which Lipschütz, et al. (1922b) attributed to the divergent relationships of male v. female gonads to their respective roles of gamete production and hormone secretion. In the ovary, both functions are performed by the ovarian follicles or their derivatives, with the result that hypertrophy in response to hormonal influences must of necessity involve heightened egg production as well. In the testis, however, the dual functions of spermatogenesis and testosterone secretion go on more or less independently. Thus, the organ can compensate for a deficiency in testosterone output by increasing its interstitial tissue without changing the mass of seminiferous tubules. For this reason, relatively modest extents of compensatory testicular hypertrophy following unilateral castration are usually encountered. Increases in weight to less than 60 per cent of the normal combined testicular weights have been reported by Nothnagel (1903), Hatai (1915), and Horn and LoMonaco (1958). But as Hatai (1915) has calculated, this would represent more than double the original amount of interstitial tissue if it is assumed that the latter normally represents approximately 10 per cent of the total weight of the testis. Lipschütz, et al. (1922a,b) noted increases in the amount of interstitial tissue in small testicular remnants (and even in testes subjected to injury but not loss). Thus, it would appear that testicular hypertrophy may be due to growth of interstitial tissue. Whether or not unilateral castration also leads to increases in the mass of seminiferous tubules remains to be determined, although there is reason to doubt that this would happen. Tubular elongation could not be easily detected histologically, but diametrical changes are easily detected and measured in histological sections. Edwards (1940) has found that only half the total normal number of sperm are produced after unilateral castration, which contrasts with the capacity of the ovary to double its egg production under comparable conditions. Therefore, seminiferous tubules probably do not compensate.

Nevertheless, it is well known that the diameters of seminiferous tubules can and do change according to the degree of spermatogenic activity. This phenomenon is especially noticeable in various animals with seasonally defined breeding cycles. In some cases, the seminiferous tubules may regress to diminutive structures lined with simple epithelia and showing no signs of spermatogenesis. Under the appropriate stimulus, however, the same tubules will undergo considerable enlargement commensurate with their heightened functional activities. Therefore, seminiferous tubules can exhibit hypertrophy (as well as atrophy) but there is little evidence that this is a significant factor in compensating for the loss of the opposite testis.

Other endocrine organs exhibit hypertrophy, but in most instances (e.g. parathyroid, islets of Langerhans) this involves hyperplasia without obvious alterations in the histological arrangement of their cells. The thyroid, however, has a very specialized micro-anatomy in which are manifested some revealing changes following partial thyroidectomy. First and foremost, one observes an increase in the height of the follicular epithelium, accompanied by vacuolation of the colloid and enriched vascularity (Marine, 1926; Magdalena, 1935). In the rat, the increase in epithelial height reaches a maximum ten days after removal of 50 to 75 per cent of the thyroid (Logothetopoulos and Doniach, 1955); in the dog it may become two to three times higher than normal a month or two after partial ablation (Houssay, *et al.*, 1932). According to Logothetopuolos and Doniach (1955), the compensatory responses of the thyroid involve neither an increase in the number or diameters of follicles, nor the number of nuclei per follicle. They did detect, however, an increase in the uptake of I^{131} as early as three days after partial thyroidectomy in the rat. Reichlin

(1957) likewise noted enhanced iodine incorporation in thyroid remnants. This reached levels 230 per cent above normal in the residual halves of cat thyroids two weeks after operation (Knigge, 1961) and was still 40 per cent above average after 32 to 48 weeks. Such changes are not unexpected in view of the well-known goitero-genic effects of iodine deficiency, thiouracil administration, or other conditions which create an increased demand for thyroxine. Few organs illustrate so well the interdependence between physiological needs and growth regulation.

Exocrine Glands

In the pancreas, in which partial ablation of necessity involves direct injury to the remaining tissue, new tissue regenerates from the severed ducts and soon develops into a new system of branching tubules (Kyrle, 1908) which differentiate terminally into normal acini replete with zymogen granules. Although these observations have been confirmed by Fisher (1924), there seems to be no definitive report concerning the possibility of *de novo* acinar development in regions removed from the area of immediate injury in the pancreas. Such a phenomenon would not be easily detected with existing tech-niques and may well have gone unnoticed. It would appear, however, that terminal duct regeneration is not sufficiently extensive to account for all of the pancreatic hypertrophy that occurs following partial ablation, which may implicate other forms of supplementary growth.

A comparable situation prevails with reference to the salivary glands. Direct injury to a gland results in the limited growth of new tubules from the severed ducts, together with the terminal formation of new acini (Milstein, 1950). However, in otherwise intact salivary glands induced to undergo hypertrophy by contralateral ablation, there is no direct evidence of increase in the numbers of acini. Under these conditions, as well as in enlarged glands following treatment with isoproterenol (Brown-Grant, 1961) or repeated amputation of lower incisors in the rat (Handelman and Wells, 1963), hypertrophy appears to be the result of acinar enlargement.

According to Babaeva (1961), who removed all of one outer orbital gland plus 50 to 65 per cent of the contralateral one in rats, the com-pensatory growth that ensued was a generalized response in the residual acini. There were apparently no indications of regeneration from the wound surface itself.

The histology of mammary gland hypertrophy following partial ablation has not been sufficiently investigated to permit a definite conclusion as to its mode of growth. However, the normal enlargement of mammary glands in association with lactation is very possibly identical with the growth that may be stimulated by other means. Thus, Ribbert (1895) has described the regeneration of a single mammary gland in the rabbit following the surgical removal of part of its mass. In this, as in other forms of growth (Smithcors, 1945), the mammary gland is capable of extensive elongation of its duct system and differentiation of new acini. Presumably it is this that accounts for the 10 to 30 per cent increase in milk yield per milligram of tissue that Linzell (1963) noted in the remaining mammary glands of lactating goats subjected to unilateral mastectomy.

The salt glands of birds (Plate 8.5) have not been investigated for compensatory growth capacities following unilateral extirpation. However, the striking enlargement which these glands undergo in birds maintained on salt water indicates that compensatory hypertrophy would probably occur if a sufficient functional demand were established. Be this as it may, the histology of salt gland hypertrophy parallels the normal method of ontogenetic growth. Ellis, et al. (1963) have described the histological and cytological changes occurring in salt glands of ducklings maintained on compulsory salt drinking water as compared with controls given access to fresh water. In the normal bird four days after hatching, rudimentary secretory tubules may be seen growing out radially from the central canals. In subsequent development, these slowly elongate as peripheral cells multiply and gradually differentiate into the principal secretory cells that make up the body of the gland. These processes are greatly accelerated in the salt loaded ducks, for after only three days the secretory cells differentiate, and effluent production begins on the fourth day of treatment. Thus, lobule hypertrophy, evident after three to four days on the salt regimen, is the result of increases in diameter and length of the secretory segments. This, in turn, may be attributed to the precocious and accelerated differentiation of increased numbers of secretory cells, as well as to the enlargement of such cells in association with their greater secretory activities.

Lymphoid Tissues

Lymphoid hypertrophy is essentially a matter of the enlargement of constituent lymph nodules. This is a major contributing factor to the hypertrophy of lymph nodes as well as spleens. Although growth of the latter after partial ablation may involve expansion of the tissues of the red pulp (Cameron and Rhee, 1959), increase in the amount of white pulp is especially conspicuous. This was recently described by Metcalf (1963) with reference to splenic grafts to splenectomized mice, in which the lymph nodules in the grafts enlarged seven to twelve times their normal dimensions.

A special case of splenomegaly occurs as a result of immunological reactions consequent upon exposure of chick embryos to grafts of adult spleens or other immunologically competent tissues. This remarkable enlargement of the embryonic host spleen involves many cytological and histological alterations (see review by DeLanney and Ebert, 1962). Although granulopoiesis is conspicuously stimulated, most of the reactions are degenerative in nature and include vascular destruction, deposition of mucopolysaccharides, and necrosis. Thus, splenic hypertrophy under these conditions is part of a syndrome that leads usually to the death of the chick.

Heart

Though it does not lend itself to experimental studies of the compensatory effects of partial ablation, the heart nevertheless exhibits an interesting sequence of changes during its normal growth from birth to maturity (and its abnormal hypertrophy as a result of hypertension). Since it is the left ventricle that does most of the work, it is this part of the heart that typically becomes enlarged under pathological conditions (Chanutin and Barksdale, 1933). Studies of normal cardiac growth in contrast to hypertrophy and atrophy of the heart have yielded important data on the relationships between the muscle fibres and their vascularization (Wearn, 1941; Roberts and Wearn, 1941).

From birth to maturity, it has been shown that there is essentially no change in the total number of cardiac muscle fibres. However, the cross-sectional areas of fibres increase sevenfold, to an average diameter of 14μ in the adult human (figure 27). Concomitantly, the absolute number of capillaries also increases. In the new-born human each capillary serves an average of six muscle fibres. As the latter enlarge during maturation the number of capillaries multiplies until the fibre: capillary ratio is approximately 1 : 1 in the adult. But because the entire system is enlarging, the concentration of capillaries per square millimetre of tissue remains constant at all ages. Wearn (1941) counted an average of 3,300 capillaries per square millimetre

at birth and 3,342 in the adult human. These principles are schematically illustrated in figure 28. In cardiac hypertrophy, the fibre width

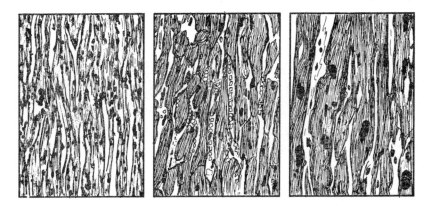

Figure 27. Growth of cardiac muscle fibres as seen in longitudinal
section. From left to right are illustrated muscle from new-born,
adult, and hypertrophic hearts. (After Wright, 1958.)

continues to increase, sometimes to an average of 20μ (figure 27).
However, no further capillary proliferation takes place, with the result
that the ratio of capillaries to fibres remains constant (1 : 1) while the
concentration of capillaries decreases to as little as 2,483 per square
millimetre. The unhappy consequence of this is that fewer capillaries
are serving a larger total mass of muscle fibres (figure 28), and it is
the latter that suffer, sometimes to the point of heart failure. In
cardiac atrophy, the average fibre size decreases whereas the number
of capillaries does not change. Therefore, the capillaries become more
concentrated. According to Karsner, *et al.* (1925) the number of
fibres also decreases while the number of nuclei rises in human
cardiac atrophy.

Figure 28. Diagrammatic illustration of the growth of human
cardiac muscle fibres (open circles) in relation to capillaries (black
dots) as viewed in cross-section (based on data of Wearn, 1941, and
Roberts and Wearn, 1941). In new-born heart, the capillary : fibre
ratio is 1 : 6. In adult heart this ratio is 1 : 1, but individual cardiac
fibres have enlarged. In hypertrophic heart, fibres enlarge even
more, but number of capillaries remains unchanged, thus reducing
their concentration.

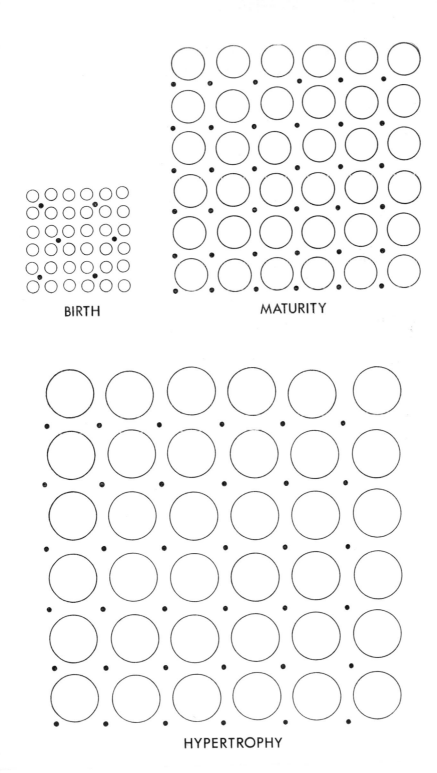

BIRTH

MATURITY

HYPERTROPHY

From the foregoing examples of the histological aspects of hypertrophy, it is clear that in some instances the mechanism of growth recapitulates normal ontogeny, but that in other cases this is not possible. The former category includes such organs as the liver, ovary, adrenal cortex, thyroid, parathyroid, islets of Langerhans, some exocrines, blood-cells, and lymphatic tissues. These are all characterized by the capacity to increase their total mass without seriously distorting their histological architecture. Consequently, there is no reason why, despite hypertrophy, they cannot function normally. As a result, their hypertrophy may be considered abnormal, but not pathological in the deleterious sense.

Owing to various developmental constraints, however, certain other organs cannot grow beyond normal adult dimensions without resorting to mechanisms somewhat different from those by which their normal growth had been achieved. The kidney can only enlarge its nephrons since their *de novo* formation in the adult is impossible. Some exocrine glands, perhaps unable to produce new secretory acini, may only be able to enlarge pre-existing ones. The heart exhibits a remarkable capacity to enlarge its individual muscle fibres when called upon to do so, and in this respect simulates normal cardiac growth mechanisms. But in the absence of capillary proliferation, hypertrophy of the muscle fibres leads inevitably to their progressive deprivation of oxygen and nutrients. These cases represent very limited attempts to compensate for deficiencies and are therefore vulnerable to serious pathological consequences should the functional demands exceed their powers of adaptation.

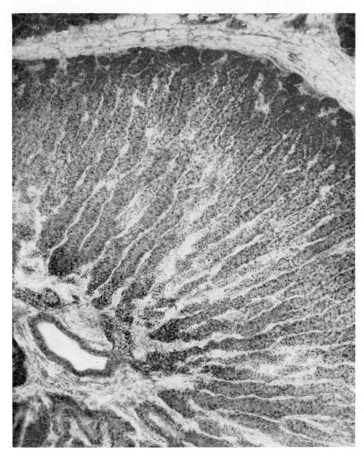

Plate 8.5. Transverse section through lobule of mature salt gland of sea gull. Secretory tubules radiate from central canal (lower left). The proliferative portions of the tubules are in the more densely stained periphery of the lobule, in contrast to the more lightly stained differentiated regions of the secretory tubules. 300 ×. (Courtesy of Dr. Richard A. Ellis.)

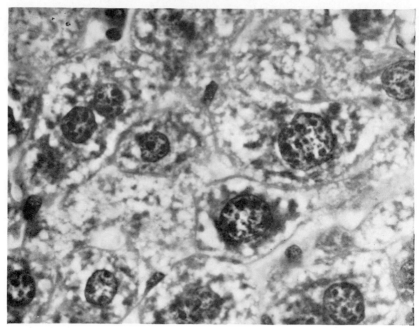

Plate 9.1. Normal adult mouse liver showing extremes in nuclear size ranges. 750 ×. (Courtesy of Dr. Elizabeth H. Leduc.)

Plate 9.2. Multinucleate cell in CCl$_4$-treated mouse liver, located immediately peripheral to degenerating central zone (right) of the lobule. 750 ×. (Courtesy of Dr. Elizabeth H. Leduc.)

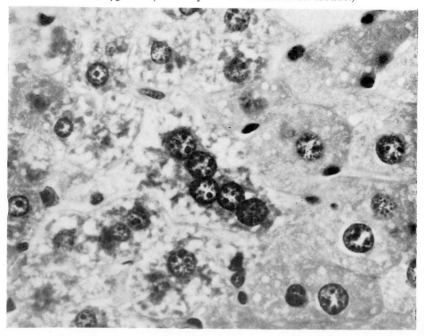

IX

Cellular Hypertrophy

AT the cellular level, growth is achieved by the complementary processes of enlargement and multiplication. The former is generally indicative of heightened synthetic activity within the cell in association with differentiation or function. It may even be causally related to cell division, perhaps by way of mechanisms correlating RNA and DNA activities. In distinguishing between these two facets of growth, Weiss (1959) wrote that "there are two types of machines, one is the machine that produces products like myofibrils or hemoglobin or melanin, and the other is the machine *to produce* the machine that will produce these various types of products. And these two types of machines apparently have different types of metabolic requirements. It is the primary machine (the one producing other machines) that requires the DNA; and the second machine, then, is the one that grows with protein synthesis and RNA". A similar idea has been expressed by Alho (1961) who stated that "RNA is thus the biochemical counterpart of hypertrophy and DNA that of hyperplasia". The compensatory hypertrophy exhibited by most tissues and organs is the combined result of both of these processes. But if functional overload is the primary cause of compensatory growth, and increased physiological activity results in cellular enlargement, then the latter should constitute one of the earliest visible indications that the reduction in tissue or organ mass has been detected and reacted to by the residual homologous cells.

Cell Size

Evidence for this is to be found in the case of liver regeneration. Stowell (1948) observed the earliest indications of volumetric cytoplasmic increases only six hours after partial hepatectomy. This amounted to 2·6 times normal after 18 to 24 hours, and declined thereafter. By 48 hours, cytoplasmic volume was still above normal. Unable to find a rise in cell volume during the first ten post-operative hours, however, Harkness (1952) recorded a maximum cell volume that was 63 per cent above normal at 24 hours. After 48 to 70 hours, the average volume of hepatic cells was still 40 per cent greater than in controls. In the regenerating mouse liver, de Burgh (1957) found an increase in cytoplasmic volume during the first day, whereas Hammersten (1951) recorded the maximum cytoplasmic volume at 48 hours in the regenerating rat liver. The observations of Wilson, *et al.* (1953), that cell size in regenerating livers was increased during the phase of greatest mitotic activity, are in general agreement with these other results.

Such a correlation between cell size and proliferative activity is also evident from data relevant to diurnal modulations in liver cells. Jackson (1959) showed that in normal rats the size of liver cells was greatest at 6 a.m. and least at 8 p.m., while mitotic activity was maximal at 8 a.m. and minimal in the afternoon and night. Jaffe (1954) noted a similar mitotic rhythm in the regenerating livers of rats, in which the greater activity occurred between 6 and 10 a.m., the least from 6 to 10 p.m. In the regenerating mouse liver, Barnum, *et al.* (1957) recorded mitotic maxima at 8 a.m. and 1 p.m., with minimal proliferation at 10 p.m. Wilson (1948) found the most mitoses between 5 and 9 a.m. in normal mouse livers and the least from 5 to 9 p.m. Thus, in regenerating as well as normal livers, cell enlargement coincides with, or slightly precedes, cell division, whereas decreased cell volume is associated with periods of minimal mitotic activity.

There is little direct evidence of permanent cellular enlargement in hypertrophic kidneys. However, the prompt increase in renal mass within 24 hours of unilateral nephrectomy, before the rate of proliferation begins to rise, bears indirect witness to the possibility of cellular hypertrophy in this organ (Schaffenburg, *et al.*, 1954).

Scattered reports in the literature indicate varying degrees of cellular hypertrophy in other tissues. Endocrine cells in general become enlarged when induced to overwork. Most prominent is the case of the heightened thyroid epithelium under the influence of thyrotrophic hormone. Comparable phenomena are characteristic of other endocrine tissues in which the state of secretory activity is correlated with the degree of hypertrophy or atrophy of the component cells.

The cells of exocrine glands evidently exhibit similar modifications under varying degrees of secretory activity. This is best illustrated by the salivary glands, in which hypertrophy is accompanied by enlargement of acinar cells, but not tubule cells, following administration of isoproterenol (Brown-Grant, 1961) or repeated amputation of the lower incisors (Handelman and Wells, 1963). Atrophy induced by dibenamine, an adrenergic inhibitor, was associated with reduction in the size of acinar cells (Handelman and Wells, 1963).

Nuclear Size

In view of the significance of nucleo-cytoplasmic relationships, it is not surprising that cells generally maintain a relatively constant ratio between the two. When a cell grows, however, there are two ways the nucleo-cytoplasmic ratio can be held constant, namely, by mitosis or by nuclear enlargement. There is evidence that the latter may occur with some regularity in the cells of certain organs. In the normal mouse liver, for example, Jacobj (1925) found that all nuclei were the same size in embryonic or new-born animals, but that in adults there were several nuclear volume classes (Plate 9.1). Several nuclear classes also occur in the kidney (Rossi and Campagnari, 1959). Doljanski (1960) described a decrease in nucleo-cytoplasmic ratio in rat livers at the time of weaning, possibly the result of the increase in hepatic protein content at that time.

Perhaps the widest array of nuclear size classes it to be found in the orbital glands of rats. In a careful analysis of these organs, Teir (1949) discovered as many as six different sizes of nuclei represented. Calculated according to nuclear volumes, these classes were found to be arranged in a geometric progression as multiples of the smallest in the series. The latter, believed to represent haploid cells, were rather rare, while nuclei twice this size were most abundant, and tetraploid nuclei were two-thirds as common as diploid ones. The largest nuclei, measuring 16 and 32 times as large as the smallest, were extremely scarce and in some glands were nonexistent. More common in the inner than the outer orbital gland, the theory was proposed (Teir, 1949) that enlarged nuclei resulted from the restriction of cell division owing to pressures exerted by the surrounding tissues of the orbit within which the inner orbital gland is confined. Teir (1951) also pointed out that the existence of different nuclear size classes may depend upon function, although their incidence and distribution were unmodified by various kinds of wounds inflicted on the orbital gland (Järvi and Teir, 1951).

In organs compensating for partial ablation, however, the sizes of nuclei are profoundly affected. In the regenerating rat liver,

Stowell (1948) noted that the nuclear volumes paralleled the increases and decreases in cytoplasmic volumes. The nuclei averaged 2·2 times the normal volume 18 to 24 hours after partial hepatectomy, and were returning to normal by 48 hours. According to Hammersten (1951) the liver nucleus reaches its maximum size 30 hours after hepatectomy. The earliest increase was observed by Harkness (1952) to occur ten hours after operation, when the average nuclear volume was 117 per cent of control values. At 24 hours, this had risen to 179 per cent and by 48 to 70 hours was 203 per cent. Wilson, et. al. (1953) reported that nuclear volume was decreasing five to seven days after partial hepatectomy in the rat. In contrast to these observations, de Burgh (1957) claimed that liver nuclei do not enlarge during regeneration.

In compensatory renal hypertrophy, nuclear size increases have been recorded (Sulkin, 1949). Schmiedt (1951) measured a 37 per cent increase in nuclear volume in residual mouse kidneys one day after contralateral nephrectomy, followed by a decrease in size on the second post-operative day. According to Fajers (1957a), there is a rise in nuclear volume for about 48 hours after uninephrectomy, after which the nuclei begin to return towards normal. Thus, in general the growth of at least some organs is achieved in part by transient increases in cell volumes with concomitant enlargement of their nuclei.

Binucleate Cells

Binucleate cells occur with varying frequencies in many organs (Enesco and Leblond, 1962), and may reflect the propensity of most cells to maintain a normal nucleo-cytoplasmic ratio during processes of growth. For example, binucleate cells are absent in the normal livers of new-born rats and mice, but are not uncommon in adult livers (Jacobj, 1925). Their numbers are substantially augmented in mouse livers at about the time of weaning (Wilson and Leduc, 1948), but are markedly reduced in three-day regenerating livers, at a time of great mitotic activity (Wilson, et al., 1953). Moreover, the incidence of binucleate cells rises once liver regeneration is complete. Under abnormal conditions multinucleate cells of remarkable dimensions may be encountered in the liver, as illustrated in Plate 9.2. With reference to other organs in the body, their occurrence has been reported in the rat pancreas (Jacobj, 1925), the orbital glands (Teir, 1949), and in normal and compensating kidneys (Sulkin, 1949).

Nucleoli

Studies of nucleoli in relation to compensatory hypertrophy have concentrated largely on the regenerating liver of rats. In this system, Stowell (1948) found a fourfold increase in nucleolar volume 18 to 24 hours after partial hepatectomy. By 48 hours, however, they had decreased in size to subnormal levels. According to Hammersten (1951), hepatic nucleoli reached their maximum sizes 30 hours after operation. Nevertheless, Wilson, *et al.* (1953) observed a marked increase in nucleolar volume on the fifth day after partial hepatectomy, and suggested that this might be associated with enhanced synthetic activities in liver cells at this time.

Role of Cell Hypertrophy in Normal Ontogeny

It is pertinent to compare some of these changes that occur in association with compensatory hypertrophy with the mechanisms by which some tissues and organs grow during the normal development of the organism. The comprehensive account of such phenomena by Enesco and Leblond (1962) has revealed that tissues (e.g. muscle, fat) follow a growth pattern different from that characteristic of organs (e.g. liver, kidney, pancreas, endocrine glands, etc.). Basing their conclusions in part on the calculated "weight per nucleus" of various tissues and organs, i.e. the quantity of protoplasm served by one nucleus, it was found that during approximately the first 17 days after birth in the rat most structures grow almost exclusively by cell multiplication, with little or no modification in cell dimensions. This phase of growth is followed by a period lasting several weeks during which the mitotic rate decelerates and cell size increases. Continued growth into adulthood is accomplished by the addition of new cells without further significant enlargement of cytoplasmic mass in organs such as the kidney, lung, pancreas, and adrenal. The liver, in contrast, exhibits a small but persistent increase in cell volume up to about 95 days of age.

The roles of cellular hypertrophy and hyperplasia in the growth of adipose tissue and muscle fibres in maturing rats differ from the pattern of growth in organs (Enesco and Leblond, 1962). Fat was found to grow in part by the addition of new cells, but largely by the continued intracellular accumulation of stored lipid (figure 29). Therefore, the dimensions of adipose cells vary directly with the age and size of the animal over a considerable portion of its growth. In muscular tissues enlargement with age is accomplished solely by

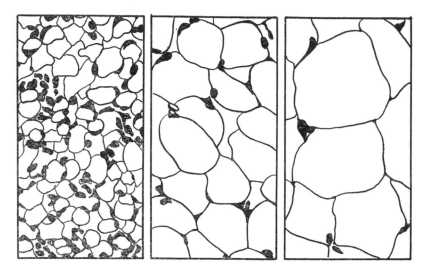

Figure 29. Histological comparison between adipose tissue from rats 17, 34, and 95 days old (left to right). Growth occurs largely by increases in individual cell sizes. 337 ×. (After Enesco and Leblond, 1962.)

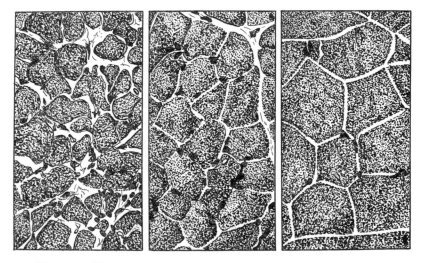

Figure 30. Transverse sections of skeleton muscle from 17-, 34-, and 95- day-old rats (left to right). Growth is achieved by hypertrophy of the muscle fibres. 337 ×. (After Enesco and Leblond, 1962.)

hypertrophy of the fibres. In heart muscle there is an increase in the number of nuclei up to about 48 days of age, after which growth is achieved almost exclusively by increases in the dimensions of cardiac muscle fibres. Thus, although the weight of cardiac tissue per nucleus rises progressively after the first two weeks of life, it increases even more after the seventh week. In skeletal muscles, represented by the gastrocnemius, there is a continual increase in the number of nuclei throughout growth, but hypertrophy of the fibres accounts for the steady increase in their diameters with age and the progressive rise in weight per nucleus (figure 30). Although the number of muscle fibre nuclei is known to increase with age, expansion of the cells occurs at a more rapid pace. In the gastrocnemius, for example, Enesco and Leblond (1962) calculate that between the ages of 17 and 95 days, the number of muscle nuclei increases 3·8 times while the fibre size (weight per nucleus) is enlarged by a factor of 5·5. The latter increase involves the differentiation of many new myofibrils, but this process is obviously limited by the increasing distances between the innermost fibrils and the extracellular blood vessels. In the absence of configurational changes in individual fibres, the hypertrophy of skeletal muscles must clearly be subject to definite upper limits. Smooth muscle fibres are likewise capable of considerable hypertrophy when conditions demand it, but in addition they are apparently able to augment their numbers by division or *de novo* differentiation under appropriate circumstances.

X

Cellular Hyperplasia

WITH the exception of tissues incapable of cell division, cellular hypertrophy following partial ablation or physiological strain is usually only a provisional measure eventually superseded by mitosis. The former provides for the augmentation of cytoplasmic mass, the latter for the increase in the number of nuclei. Since hyperplasia is the major factor in tissue and organ growth, the problem of growth regulation is essentially a matter of determining what controls mitotic activity. Normally occurring at variable rates depending on the kind of tissue involved, cellular proliferation is typically accelerated in most organs in which compensatory growth is occurring. Thus, few *in vivo* systems afford a better opportunity to analyse the factors governing rates of mitotic activity than do organs stimulated to undergo compensatory hyperplasia.

Methods

Numerous attributes of this response must be investigated if a complete understanding of compensatory hyperplasia is to be achieved. The conventional method for estimating the proliferative activity of a tissue is simply to count the mitotic figures in representative random areas of sectioned material and to calculate the average number of mitoses per hundred cells. The extremes of the mitotic process may be conveniently defined by the disappearance of the nuclear membrane in prophase and the occurrence of cytokinesis in telophase. If a sufficiently large amount of tissue is sampled, the unavoidable personal variability of the investigator can be minimized. Nevertheless, one can always expect considerable variations in the mitotic activities of tissues from individual animals subjected to identical experimental procedures. Even when as many variables as possible are controlled, including temperature, diet, sex, age, weight, time of day, genetic background, etc., individual variations persist and must therefore be taken into account. This can only be done by utilizing enough animals so that the discrepancies can be averaged out. Statistical methods are often necessary to determine if experimental results are significantly different from controls.

To amplify the incidence of mitotic figures, which is frequently very low, many investigators have used colchicine to arrest mitoses. Administered some hours prior to sacrifice, this drug prevents dividing cells from going through anaphase presumably due to a deficiency in the formation of spindle fibres. Thus, all cells entering upon mitosis during the interval between colchicine injection and sacrifice are accumulated as arrested metaphases. Instead of observing only those cells in mitosis at the moment of death, one can count all cells that started to divide over a period of several hours. This method is of value in facilitating the process of counting mitotic figures, although it does not alter the relative data obtained, if it is assumed that colchicine does not affect the incidence of cells entering mitosis. Since the latter assumption may not be warranted, and because most tissues exhibit sufficient mitotic activity to permit convenient and accurate counts to be made without arresting mitoses, the use of colchicine should be regarded as an unnecessary variable to be reserved for very special experimental circumstances.

In determining the mitotic response of a tissue to an experimental intervention it must be remembered that the induced proliferative activity is superimposed on a normal incidence of cell divisions associated with the natural growth and turnover of cell populations. Furthermore, this background proliferation is not a constant phenomenon, for mitotic activity invariably exhibits diurnal rhythms which can distort a mitotic response curve. Allowance is usually made for this variable by adhering to the same time schedules throughout the course of a series of experiments.

Other things being equal, mitotic activity can then be determined at intervals after such operations as partial ablation. It is thus possible to determine the onset, peak(s), and duration of compensatory hyperplasia. Of particular value is a knowledge of the time and magnitude of maximum mitotic activity, for it is upon the accuracy of these data that the validity of the experimental results depends, especially when comparing the responses to a series of stimuli. Hence, for any organ it is possible to construct a curve representing the degree of mitotic activity at varying times after operation. If enough data are available, various organs undergoing compensatory hyperplasia can be compared with a view to learning if the temporal and quantitative aspects of their respective mitotic curves show any significant differences from each other. Alternatively, it would be of value to compare the responses in one kind of organ to varying degrees of surgical reductions in mass. Confronted with the necessity of replacing differing amounts of tissue, to what extent does an organ alter the onset, peak, magnitude, and duration of the ensuing compensatory hyperplasia? And is there a minimum amount of tissue loss below which no compensatory response is elicited? Answers to these questions depend solely upon the accumulation of sufficient reliable data, together with their intelligent interpretation. Only in this way will it be possible to correlate the course of hyperplasia with the many other events taking place from the cellular to the molecular levels of organization. The ultimate goal will be an unbroken chain of causes and effects connecting the original tissue loss to its final replacement. Hyperplasia is only a single, but important, step in the sequence.

Liver Regeneration

The regenerating liver has become a model system in which to study compensatory hyperplasia by reason of the various advantages it offers, not the least of which is the very low rate of cell division normally occurring in the adult organ. Estimates of normal liver mitoses (see Plate 10.1) vary from less than 0·005 per cent (Brues and Marble, 1937) to 0·01 per cent (Abercrombie and Harkness, 1951) and 0·05 per cent (Hammersten, 1951). Thus, even small increments of proliferative activity are detectable above the scarcity of background mitoses. Nevertheless, the liver does represent a slowly expanding population of cells, especially in a constantly growing animal such as the rat. Mitoses are abundant in the livers of infant rats, particularly during the first three weeks after birth (Teir and Ravanti, 1953; Doljanski, 1960). They continue to occur with diminished frequency up to the eighth week of life, but are extremely uncommon thereafter (McKellar, 1949; Teir and Ravanti, 1953). By using the rate of P^{32} uptake in DNA as a criterion, Stevens, *et al.* (1953) estimated that the cell population in the livers of adult rats was increased at a rate of 0·71 per cent per day. It has been claimed that the continuing, albeit rare, occurrence of mitoses in the adult liver indicates a slow turnover of cells, with life-spans averaging in excess of 150 days (Swick, *et al.*, 1956).

Following partial hepatectomy, estimates of the earliest onset of mitosis vary considerably in the rat. The precision with which such an event can be determined depends on the frequency at which animals are sacrificed for mitotic counts. Glinos (1958a) detected the first post-operative proliferation among periportal hepatic cells after only 16 to 24 hours. Gurd, *et al.* (1948) found incipient hyperplasia after 18 hours, while a number of other investigators have reported increased mitotic activity 24 hours after partial hepatectomy (Brues and Marble, 1937; Stowell, 1948; Hammersten, 1951; Harkness, 1952; Zaki, 1954; Cater, *et al.*, 1956, 1957; Abercrombie and Harkness, 1951). Above normal proliferation has been noted after 30 hours in the rat by Christensen and Jacobsen (1949) and after about 36 hours in the mouse by Barnum, *et al.* (1957).

The timing of the maximum rate of mitoses in the regenerating liver cannot be precisely determined. Although it is customary to indicate an exact hour at which the mitotic peak may have been observed, such statements actually indicate only that mitotic activity is greater at that time than at the immediately previous and subsequent observations. Therefore, the validity of such data is inversely proportional to the duration of the successive intervals at which observations are made. Subject to these limitations, the earliest mitotic peak in the regenerating rat liver has been reported by Hammersten (1951) to occur only 24 hours after partial hepatectomy, but other investigators (Cater, *et al.*, 1956; Weinbren, 1959; Weinbren and Fitschen, 1959) have found the maximum to be at 28 hours. Still other reports indicate that the highest levels of proliferation are at 48 hours after operation (Christensen and Jacobsen, 1949; Jaffe, 1954; Zaki, 1954), and some contend that the maximum does not occur until the third day (Higgins and Anderson. 1931; Wilson, *et al.*, 1953). Barnum, *et al.* (1957) have noted a mitotic peak at 56 hours in the regenerating mouse liver.

To some extent, these discrepancies may be explained by the possibility of secondary mitotic peaks. Having observed increased proliferation after 24 to 26 hours, leading to a first mitotic maximum at 28 hours, Cater, *et al.* (1956) reported that activity had subsided 39 hours after partial hepatectomy, but rose to a second minor peak after 45 hours. This may be attributed in part to the fact that proliferation in the regenerating liver is necessarily superimposed on normal diurnal rhythms, as has been shown by Jaffe (1954) and Barnum, *et al.* (1957), who noted high rates of proliferation in the mornings and low ones at night. Therefore, the time of day at which experiments are begun and terminated may be very important. The variations in experimental results may also be related to age, for

Marshak and Byron (1945) found that although mitotic activity was increased on the first day after partial hepatectomy in rats of all ages tested, the maxima occurred on the first, second, and third days, respectively, in rats one, four to six, and sixteen months of age. Aside from these possible explanations, the apparent lack of precision in estimating the temporal relations of hyperplasia to partial hepatectomy may most logically be accounted for by the normally complex physiology of the liver which would be expected to exert variable but serious influences on mitotic activity.

One of the most remarkable features of liver regeneration is the tremendous increase in mitotic activity that occurs. As in other organs, the mitotic index of the normal liver is extremely low (though not non-existent). Abercrombie and Harkness (1951) estimate the normal rate of cell division to be 0·01 per cent. At the peak of mitotic activity in the one day regenerating liver, the mitotic index has been shown by various investigators to rise as high as 2·13 per cent (Brues and Marble, 1937), 2·87 per cent (Abercrombie and Harkness, 1951), 3·8 per cent (Cater, et al., 1956, 1957), 1·83 per cent (Weinbren and Fitschen, 1959), and 3·7 per cent (Weinbren, 1959). After two days, it declines to 0·97 per cent (Brues and Marble, 1937), 1·51 per cent (Abercrombie and Harkness, 1951), and 0·9 per cent (Weinbren, 1959). Thereafter, it gradually returns to pre-operative levels. Thus, allowing for the expected variations in experimental material of this kind, there is reasonably good agreement among different authors as to the magnitude of the mitotic response in regenerating livers.

The duration of hepatic hyperplasia may vary from less than two days to about a week, again depending on which reference is cited. Weinbren (1959), for example, reported a return to normal levels of proliferation only 40 hours after partial hepatectomy (at a time when other investigators claimed that mitotic activity was still rising). Hammersten (1951) stated that the rate of cell divisions was normal after 48 to 72 hours, whereas Gurd, et al. (1948) and Zaki (1954) found a return to pre-operative levels on the fourth day. Others have reported that hyperplasia subsides at the end of a week (Higgins and Anderson, 1931; Wilson, et al., 1953). This coincides with the approximate time required for the original weight of the liver to be restored.

The consensus is that the pattern of hyperplasia in the regenerating liver is characterized by a lag phase during the first post-operative day followed by a rapid rise to a mitotic peak variously estimated to occur some time during the second day, and a more gradual decline to nearly normal levels during the third to seventh days. As previously indicated, this pattern overlaps considerably with the volumetric changes, although the onset of the cell and nuclear enlargement appears to precede the early rise in mitotic activity (Harkness, 1952).

In livers induced to regenerate as a result of tissue destruction by administration of carbon tetrachloride, the course of repair is not unlike that following partial hepatectomy. Characteristically, necrosis of the central regions of the liver lobules, as seen in Plate 10.2, occurs during the first 24 hours after treatment (Lacquet, 1932; Hoffman, *et al.*, 1955; Myren and Oye, 1960). According to Myren (1956), carbon tetrachloride appears to damage the midzonal cells of the hepatic lobule directly, which in turn brings about the indirect destruction of the more centrally located cells as a result of circulatory disturbances. There is no increase in mitotic activity during this first 24-hour period (Cameron and Karunaratne, 1936; Leevy, *et al.*, 1959), but a rise has been detected after 36 hours (Leevy, *et al.*, 1959). Mitoses are common at the end of two or three days after treatment (Cameron and Karunaratne, 1936; Hoffman, *et al.*, 1955; Leevy, *et al.*, 1959) and are rare thereafter. Thus, the injuries inflicted by this toxic agent are largely repaired after only several days, although more subtle disturbances may persist, inasmuch as Hoffman, *et al.* (1956) have shown that repair is delayed in second injuries made up to eight weeks after the first.

Compensatory Renal Hyperplasia

Second only to the liver, the kidney has yielded valuable information concerning the hyperplastic response to partial ablation. The intact kidney normally exhibits more proliferation than does the uninjured liver, its mitotic index having been variously reported as 0·015 to 0·038 per cent (Franck, 1960), and 0·024 per cent (Goss and Rankin, 1960) in young adult rats. In very old rats, McCreight and Sulkin (1959) reported a decrease to about one third of the levels encountered in young animals. These values are known to vary according to the time of day, with the greatest number of mitoses occurring between 2 and 4 p.m. and the minima at 10 to 12 p.m. (Blumenfeld, 1938) or 6 to 8 a.m. (Williams, 1961). The latter author reported a twofold difference between the higher and lower values. These mitoses are predominantly located in the renal cortex or outer medulla. The differential mitotic counts of Williams (1961) have revealed that normal proliferation is highest in the proximal convoluted tubules, very low in the collecting ducts and distal convoluted tubules, and intermediate in the ascending loop of Henle. Thus, the mitotic incidence appears to decline in a proximodistal direction along the nephron. The possible functional significance of this is obvious.

Following subtotal nephrectomy there occurs a marked increase in the incidence of mitotic figures above the normal level in the residual renal tissues. As in the intact kidney, this hyperplasia is most common in the cortex (Carnot and May, 1938; Moll, 1955; Ogawa and Sinclair, 1958) and is virtually absent in the inner medulla (Carnot and May, 1938). Steuart (1958) and Franck (1960) reported no rise in the rate of cell division 24 hours after partial nephrectomy. This has been confirmed by Goss and Rankin (1960) who found only a small, but not statistically significant, increase in the mitotic index on the first post-operative day. With a few exceptions (Sulkin, 1949; McCreight and Sulkin, 1959; Semenova, 1961) all investigators have reported a substantial elevation in the mitotic rates of remaining kidneys 48 hours after operation (Rollason, 1949; Saetren, 1956; Steuart, 1958; Franck, 1960; Goss and Rankin, 1960; Rosen and Cole, 1960; Argyris, 1961). This is followed by a rapid decline after 72 hours (Goss and Rankin, 1960), although Sulkin (1949) and McCreight and Sulkin (1959) reported maximum mitotic activities at this time. Semenova (1961) claimed that hyperplasia does not occur until the seventh day after uninephrectomy in the mouse.

Other investigators have noted two mitotic peaks after partial nephrectomy, one at two days and another on the seventh day (Ogawa and Sinclair, 1958; Franck, 1960), the latter being one-half the magnitude of the former (Franck, 1958). Sulkin (1949), however, reported peaks on the third and tenth days. By far, the most accurate data on this subject have been furnished by the extensive observations of Williams (1961) who recorded the primary rise in mitotic index as occurring 40 hours after unilateral nephrectomy, to be followed by a secondary increase of lesser magnitude between the third and fourth days (figure 31).

Notwithstanding certain inconsistencies, there is little doubt that there is a rapid rise in the rate of cell divisions after the first day, reaching a peak towards the end of the second post-operative day, and declining thereafter. In comparison with the regenerating liver, then, the hyperplasia of the compensating kidney appears to be slightly retarded in its initiation and perhaps in the timing of its maximum response as well. Apparently the loss of part of the liver is felt sooner than is a reduction in renal mass. Otherwise, there is little evidence to indicate any significant difference in the general patterns of the hyperplastic responses in these two organs.

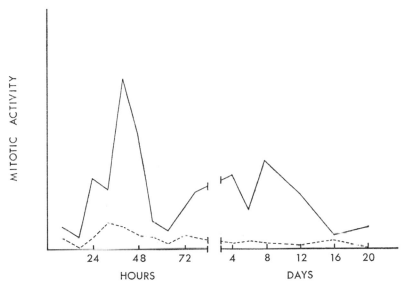

Figure 31. Compensatory renal hyperplasia in the rat after unilateral nephrectomy. Solid line indicates mitotic activity in the proximal convoluted tubules. Maxima occur at 40 hours and on fourth day. Broken line represents proliferation in distal tubules, with peak during second post-operative day. (After Williams, 1961.)

The magnitude of the maximum mitotic index attained in compensatory renal hyperplasia has been reported by Franck (1958) to reach three to five times normal levels. McCreight and Sulkin (1959) calculated an average sevenfold increase in young rat kidneys, while Goss and Rankin (1960) observed a sixfold rise in proliferation. Using colchicine to arrest mitoses in mice, Argyris (1961) found eight times as many figures 48 hours after unilateral nephrectomy as were present in control kidneys. Thus, there is general agreement as to the relative magnitude of the mitotic response in compensatory renal hyperplasia.

Endocrine Glands

In contrast to the liver and kidney, both of which have been exhaustively studied with reference to compensatory hyperplasia, very little has been learned about most other organs. In the adrenal cortex, for example, the normal pattern of proliferation has been abundantly investigated and shown to occur largely in the area between the zona glomerulosa and outer fasciculata (Hoerr, 1931; Hunt, 1940; Baxter, 1946; Mitchell, 1948). Yet the possible effect on mitotic activity of compensatory growth induced by unilateral adrenalectomy does not appear to have been examined. Nor has the pattern of hyperplasia been studied in the gonads after unilateral ablation, although proliferation unquestionably plays a major role in their growth.

In the thyroid, removal of half or more of the gland has been shown by a number of investigators to result in heightened mitotic activity in the remnant, although Hunicutt (1914) and Logothetopoulos and Doniach (1955) failed to report is occurrence. Nevertheless, Loeb (1919), Marine (1926) and Gray (1929) all detected extra proliferation in the remaining thyroid in the weeks following partial thyroidectomy. Since none of them examined their material for mitoses before the fourth post-operative day, it is not possible to tell whether or not the thyroid follows a pattern of hyperplasia similar to that of the liver and kidney. Gray (1929), however, noted that most mitoses were localized in the directly injured follicles of guinea pig thyroids five to nine days after operation, and that proliferation was not maximal throughout the rest of the gland until after nine to thirteen days. With reference to the mitotic aspect of compensatory growth after partial ablation in other endocrine glands (e.g. parathyroid, pituitary, islets of Langerhans), virtually nothing is known. But since the turnover rates of various hormones presumably differ from one another, one might expect variations in the temporal relationships of the compensatory hyperplasias of endocrine glands commensurate with how long it takes a hormonal deficiency to develop and be detected.

Exocrine Glands

Fortunately, more has been learned about the potentialities for compensatory hyperplasia in exocrine glands than in endocrine glands. The pancreas is a case in point. Normally exhibiting only rare mitotic activity, the exocrine portion of the pancreas is capable of both local and general regeneration. Proliferation occurs in the

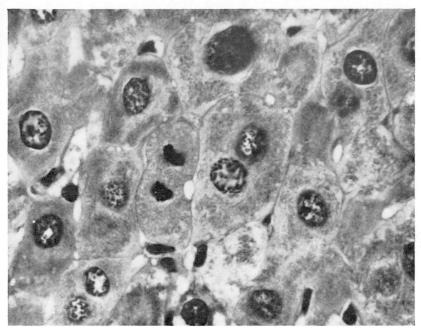

Plate 10.1. Normal telophase mitosis in mouse liver. 750 ×.
(Courtesy of Dr. Elizabeth H. Leduc.)

Plate 10.2. Selective necrosis (lightly stained areas) of central
zones of mouse liver lobules after treatment with CCl$_4$. 70 ×.
(Courtesy of Dr. Elizabeth H. Leduc.)

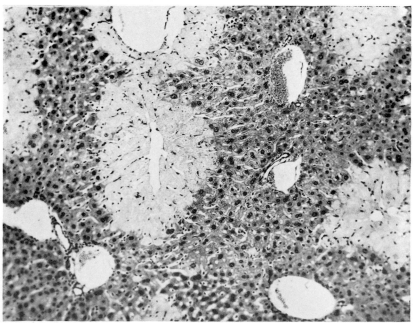

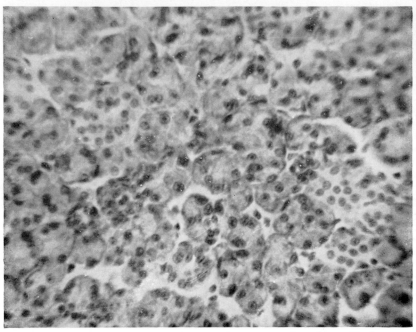

Plate 15.1. Appearance of normal, untreated submandibular salivary gland of the rat. 100 ×.

Plate 15.2 Hypertrophic submandibular salivary gland of a rat injected intraperitoneally with 50 mg. of isoproterenol daily for seven days. Acinar cells are conspicuously enlarged, and mitoses (arrow) are common. 100 ×.

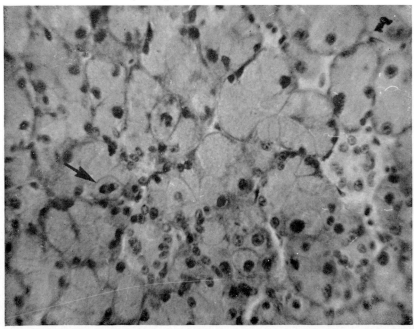

severed ducts in association with the regeneration of new acini (Kyrle, 1908), and the rate of mitotic activity is accelerated throughout the remnant of the gland following partial pancreatectomy (Augustine, 1963). The latter phenomenon reaches a maximum two days after operation in the rat, rising from a pre-operative average of 0·066 to 0·181 per cent, representing an increase that was 2·7 times normal after an average of 31 per cent ablation. This peak was slightly higher two days after extirpation of approximately half the pancreas. In contrast, mitotic counts revealed no significant difference between the rates of cell division in sham operated animals as opposed to those sacrificed one, three or four days following partial pancreatectomy. Thus, as has already been noted in the liver and kidney, the compensating pancreas undergoes a sharp rise in proliferative activity during the second day after operation, and then abruptly falls to nearly normal levels.

As examples of paired exocrine organs, the salivary glands can be subjected to unilateral excision in order to study the growth responses of the contralateral intact organ(s). Their reactions to direct partial ablation with or without contralateral extirpation can also be investigated. The latter phenomenon leads to cellular proliferation in the ducts and acini of the injured gland (Milstein, 1950) together with the regeneration of new acini. Alov and Semenova (1958) removed two-thirds of one submandibular gland from mice and found that after three days both glands were hyperplastic, the injured remnant more so than the opposite intact gland. Unilateral ablation also causes a definite increase in the rate of cell division in the opposite gland. Bizzozero (1903) performed this operation on the submandibular and parotid glands of rabbits and described heightened proliferation in the contralateral glands at various intervals between the third and tenth post-operative days. Repeating and extending this work, Alho (1961) has undertaken a detailed investigation of growth regulation in the salivary glands of rats and mice. He found that after removing one submandibular gland, the mitotic rate in the contralateral organ increased in acinar cells but not in the tubules. The mitotic index rose slightly on the first day, climbed to a maximum on the third day, and was still relatively high at the end of a week. Since data were not collected on the intervening days, however, the three-day peak cannot be regarded as necessarily precise.

Furthermore, Alho (1961) has noted that the amplitude of the mitotic index in compensating salivary glands was not as great as that

L

in hepatic or renal compensatory hyperplasia. The mitotic index of alveolar cells of normal submandibular glands was found to be 0·003 per cent. Three days after excision of the opposite gland, the rate of proliferation had risen to 0·018 per cent.

Of particular interest in this study, however, was Alho's (1961) discovery of the non-specific effect of unilateral salivary gland extirpation. Removal of one submandibular gland not only resulted in an increase in the mitotic index of the opposite submandibular gland on the third day but also brought about above normal proliferation in the major sublingual and parotid glands three days after operation. Other exocrine glands (e.g. outer orbital) showed no reaction under these conditions, indicating a specificity for salivary gland tissue but a lack of discrimination between the different kinds of glands within this category.

In view of the special opportunity provided by the orbital lachrymal glands of the rat for studying the importance of reduction in mass as opposed to functional overload in mediating compensatory hyperplasia, it is unfortunate that a more complete set of data is not available on these organs. Teir and Sundell (1953) removed the right outer orbital glands from a series of 2-week-old rats and determined the mitotic activity in the remaining inner and outer orbital glands at intervals thereafter. Since the proliferation rate in these glands is extremely high during the first few weeks of life and decreases to low levels by approximately the sixth week (Teir, 1952a,b) it is very difficult to detect significant effects on such an unstable background. Although no control values were listed, the results of these experiments showed no apparent influence of partial ablation on the mitotic activity or weight of the opposite outer orbital gland or on either of the inner orbital glands at any time from one day to four months afterwards. When the same operation was performed on young adult rats (Goss, unpublished) there was still no difference two days later between the mitotic indices of any of the remaining inner or outer orbital glands and those of sham operated controls. Though comparable data at other time intervals would be desirable, it is clear that all available evidence indicates the absence of contralateral compensatory growth in the outer orbital gland at a time when, judging from responses in other organs, the maximum effect might have been expected. This is logical from the functional point of view inasmuch as these glands service separate eyes. It is interesting, however, that the ipsilateral inner orbital glands also showed no mitotic response to excision of the outer glands, a fact which could best be explained by assuming that these two glands have separate and different functions despite their histological similarities. Whether or not this is actually the case may be revealed by the outcome of further experiments yet to be performed.

Renewing Tissues

In numerous other tissues and organs, hyperplasia is the fundamental mechanism by which growth, either normal or compensatory, is accomplished. In renewing, as opposed to expanding, tissues the rate of proliferation is adjusted to the rate of cell loss or destruction, the result being a dynamic equilibrium by which the active cell population is maintained constant. In such systems, the pattern of proliferation is inescapably associated with the process of cellular differentiation. Ordinarily, cell division is largely or entirely confined to a generative region of relatively undifferentiated cells. During the subsequent life histories of these cells, differentiation and division tend to bear an inverse relation to one another. Superimposed upon a pre-existing system undergoing mitosis and differentiation, compensatory growth in renewing tissues and organs could be achieved in a number of ways, any one of which might theoretically account for increases in the population of functioning cells.

Prolongation of cell life-spans, for example, would temporarily reduce the rate of cell loss and thereby increase the total mass of tissue, provided that the rate of cell production were held constant. Figure 32 illustrates this principle in the form of two hypothetically alternative cell populations, each with the same constant rates of reproduction. When the birth and death rates of individual cells are unaltered, but the life-spans of the cells in one population are double those in the other, then the number of cells existing in the former at any instant in time will be twice that in the latter.

Alternatively, if the rate of differentiation were accelerated, more functional cells would be provided in a shorter period of time than in a comparable population requiring longer to differentiate. These hypothetical possibilities, as outlined in figure 33, could therefore explain how the size of a population of cells might be regulated. Neither of these possibilities, however, has been conclusively shown to play a major role in sustaining the indefinite expansion of tissues or organs. Thus, the method of choice seems to have been to promote more rapid cell divisions in a population of cells that differentiates

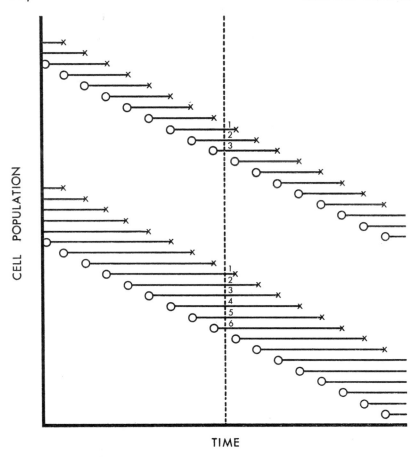

CELL POPULATION

TIME

Figure 32. Effect of life-span on size of cell population. Under
conditions of constant rates of birth (circles) and death (crosses)
the size of a population of cells is proportional to their average
life-spans. Thus, at any given moment (broken line) there are twice
as many cells in the long-lived population (below) as in the short-
lived one (above).

and ages at unmodified rates. Thus, when the intermitotic interval is
abbreviated, the number of descendants produced by a stem cell may
be greatly increased, as is schematically illustrated in figure 34.
Whether this involves more divisions during the course of maturation
of individual cells, or increases in the rates of stem cell proliferation
before differentiation commences, is not yet clear.

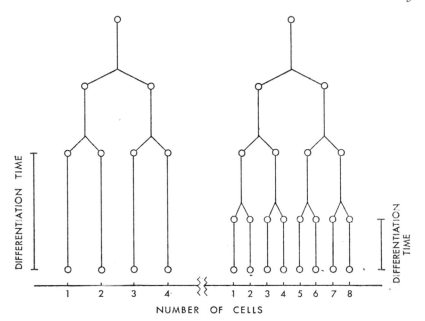

Figure 33. Hypothetical effect of altering the length of time required for differentiation in a population of cells with a constant rate of proliferation. By shortening the period of differentiation, more descendants can be produced by a stem cell in a given length of time (right) than when a longer time is required for differentiation (left).

The possible relationships between stem cells, differentiating cells, and mitosis have been reduced to two relatively simple models. In view of the necessity of not depleting the reservoir of stem cells, it has often been proposed that primary cell divisions might be unequal in that one daughter cell would remain as an undifferentiated stem cell capable of undergoing more primary divisions, whereas the other would undergo differentiation (which might or might not be accompanied by more mitoses) (figure 35A). An alternative possibility would involve the differentiation of both daughter cells resulting from the division of a stem cell, in which case provision must be made for the replenishment of the sacrificed parent cells. Conceivably, this could be achieved by differentiation of new stem cells from an exogenous source (figure 35B) or by occasional dedifferentiation of some of their descendants (figure 35C). Each of the above models is probably an

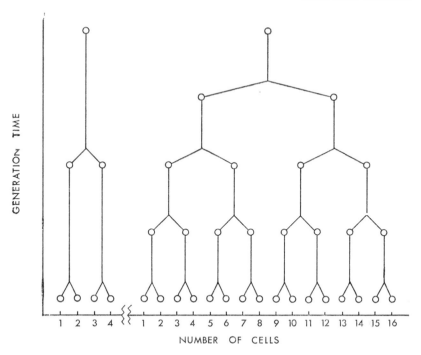

Figure 34. Regulation of cell populations by alterations in inter-mitotic intervals. When the generation time is long, a given stem cell may give rise to four (n) descendants (left). If the frequency of cell divisions is doubled, however, the same stem cell could multiply into 16 (n^2) progeny (right).

oversimplification of the actual kinetics of proliferation. It is quite possible that stem cells may occasionally give rise by division to daughter cells with different destinies, but they may at other times produce division products both of which might differentiate or both of which might remain as stem cells. The important thing is that on the average the rates of mitotic activity and cellular differentiation should remain in balance, and if the latter takes place at a constant rate, then growth must be governed by factors affecting cell division.

Epidermis

In a tissue such as the mammalian epidermis, in which there is usually only one division between the basal stem cell and the non-proliferative cell in the stratum Malpighii, the rate of renewal is

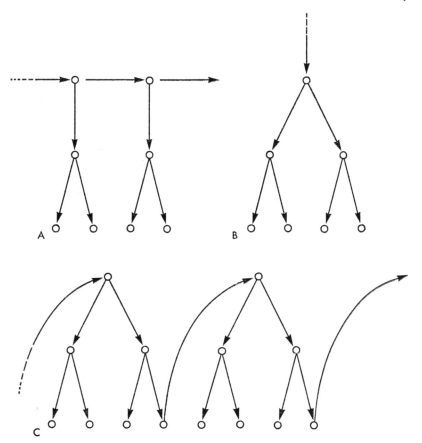

Figure 35. Alternative models by which differentiated end products of proliferation could be produced without depleting reservoir of stem cells. In A, division of undifferentiated stem cell gives rise to one daughter cell that differentiates and another that remains as a stem cell. If both daughter cells differentiate, then stem cells must be replenished either from an exogenous source, as in B, or by occasional dedifferentiation of some of their differentiated descendants, as in C.

obviously controlled by influences affecting the basal germinative cells. Indeed, when the epidermis is called upon to repair wounds, or to respond to the loss of the outer cornified layers of cells, it does so by hyperplasia in its basal layer. This in turn results in a quantitative increase in the number of differentiating cells and thereby contributes to the regeneration of the epidermis. Whether or not this effect is augmented by accelerated differentiation of individual epidermal cells has not yet been determined.

Erythropoiesis

Haemopoietic tissues are composed of a number of intermingled cell populations differentiating in lymphoid, myeloid, or erythroid directions. The last of these has been subjected to intensive investigation. Under normal conditions, erythropoiesis begins with the differentiation of haemocytoblasts into erythroblasts, distinguished by their smaller size and basophilic cytoplasm. Subsequent differentiation is characterized by the progressive synthesis of haemoglobin which gradually obscures the cell's basophilia as it accumulates in the cytoplasm, thus converting the cell into a polychromatophil erythroblast. When no more basophilia is evident the cell is referred to as a normoblast. Up until this stage of differentiation the cell goes through a number of successive cell divisions. Beyond this phase, the normoblast nucleus becomes pyknotic and is extruded from the cell. The resulting reticulocyte is then released into the circulating blood where it rapidly matures into a fully differentiated erythrocyte.

The state of erythropoiesis may be estimated in a variety of ways, the simplest being by calculating the haematocrit, or by direct counts of red blood-cells, to determine the mass or number of formed elements in the peripheral circulation. The rate at which these cells are destroyed can be learned by analysis of the concentration of haemoglobin breakdown products in the bile. The rate at which new cells are added to the blood is indicated by the concentration of reticulocytes (which are recognizable only during the first day of residency in the circulation). If haemoglobin synthesis is taken as proportional to red cell production, then the rate of erythropoiesis can be estimated by determining how much Fe^{59} is incorporated into the blood in a given time interval. In a process as complex as erythropoiesis, several different criteria of measurement are desirable, though each of the above techniques yields an indirect parameter of marrow hyperplasia. Enhanced erythropoiesis, whether the result of blood loss, haemolysis, cobalt administration, hypoxia, or injection of erythropoietin, could be achieved by the precocious release of reticulocytes into the circulating blood, the accelerated differentiation of erythrocyte precursors (as revealed by Fe^{59} uptake), the interposition of more cell divisions between haemocytoblast and normoblast, the deflection of a greater proportion of stem cells into red cell production, or a combination of these possibilities.

Inasmuch as erythropoietin appears to be the common mediator by which a wide variety of initial stimuli are translated into an increased rate of red cell production, it is important to ascertain its exact mode of action on the erythropoietic process. According to Matoth and Ben-Porath (1959), *in vitro* studies of bone marrow revealed increased mitotic activity upon exposure to serum containing erythropoietin. Erslev (1959) reported the results of bleeding rabbits and replacing the removed blood after a 20-hour anaemic interval. Regardless of various treatments after this period, the typical reticulocyte response occurred on the second day, indicating that the differentiation of stem cells into pro-normoblasts had been accelerated, but that beyond this phase the rates of proliferation and differentiation were not altered. Filmanowicz and Gurney (1959) also believed that erythropoietin exerts its effects on the earlier phases of erythropoiesis by increasing the numbers of young nucleated red cells without affecting the differentiation of later stages (e.g. normoblasts). In later experiments, the influence of erythropoietin on blood cell production in the spleens of polycythaemic mice was examined (Filmanowicz and Gurney, 1961). After 24 hours there occurred an increase in the pro-erythroblast population, and at 72 hours the number of normoblasts was maximal. Reticulocytes did not reach a peak until three and a half days. If erythropoietin operated on the latter phases of red cell production, a more premature formation of reticulocytes would have been anticipated. Stohlman (1961) held that erythropoietin stimulates the differentiation of greater numbers of stem cells into erythrocyte precursors and initiates cell division in the former only indirectly via the resulting depopulation of stem cells. So long as differentiation and division are so intimately associated in the process of erythropoiesis, it is going to be difficult to distinguish which is the target of erythropoietin activity.

Comparative Aspects of Hyperplasia

Having surveyed a number of specific tissues and organs for hyperplastic responses to partial ablation, some general considerations might be instructive. In comparing the mitotic reactions of such organs for which sufficient data are available, it is clear that the pattern of compensatory hyperplasia follows a generally similar course throughout. There is an initial lag of about a day or more before the rate of mitosis begins to increase. However, during this period the normal levels of proliferation are unabated, indicating that the heightened mitotic activity to follow does not represent the release from a temporary inhibition of cell division in the population of cells during the lag phase. Thus, the rise in incidence of mitoses during the second day is a true supplementation over and above normal levels and is not just making up for prior deficiencies.

With reference to the timing of the post-operative mitotic peak, there is reason to conclude that this varies only slightly from one organ to another. Within the limits of accuracy of the available data concerning the compensatory hyperplasia in the kidney (Goss and Rankin, 1960), pancreas (Augustine, 1963), and salivary glands (Alho, 1961), it is possible to conclude that the major proliferative responses coincide. The liver may reach a climax earlier than these other organs, but this may be related to the greater precision with which observations on liver regeneration have been made. Following these relatively brief mitotic episodes, the compensating organs return promptly to nearly normal levels, although they may well maintain a slightly elevated rate of proliferation for more prolonged periods until the final hypertrophic mass is attained. In view of the usual variations in mitotic activity regularly encountered, however, it may be impossible to detect such a sustained reaction as a statistically significant increase.

The amplitude of the mitotic indices in different normal organs varies considerably, and presumably determines their rates of growth and cell turnover. In the normal liver, this has been recorded as varying between 0·005 per cent (Brues and Marble, 1937) and 0·05 per cent (Hammersten, 1951), with 0·01 per cent (Abercrombie and Harkness, 1951) probably representing a fairly accurate estimate. In the kidney there is a slightly higher mitotic index, amounting to approximately 0·024 per cent (Goss and Rankin, 1960). The pancreas is still higher at 0·066 per cent (Augustine, 1963) whereas the submandibular salivary gland is only 0·003 per cent (Alho, 1961). Although the differences between these organs are not excessive it has been found that the heights to which their mitotic activities rise during compensatory hyperplasia may vary considerably (figure 36). The salivary glands exhibit small, but significant, rises in mitotic activities. Still greater increases are encountered in compensating kidneys in which a mitotic index of 0·148 per cent is reached 48 hours after uninephrectomy (Goss and Rankin, 1960). In the pancreas,

Augustine (1963) found approximately a threefold increase in the mitotic index (0·181 per cent) two days after removing an average of 31 per cent of the rat pancreas. In comparison with these figures, however, the heights to which the hepatic mitotic index climbs during regeneration are very impressive, indeed. Various investigators have reported maxima ranging from 1·83 per cent (Weinbren and Fitschen, 1959) to 3·8 per cent (Cater, et al., 1956, 1957).

Clearly, the magnitude of the maximal hyperplastic responses of various representative organs is not correlated with the normal mitotic levels under non-regenerating conditions. Conceivably, the discrepancies illustrated in figure 36 might be explained by such factors as relative organ size (the largest organ in the body exhibits the greatest outburst of proliferation) or differing susceptibilities to functional overload. Whatever the answer, the varying amplitudes of compensatory hyperplasia in different organs represent a major unsolved problem of growth.

Variations in Reduction of Organ Mass
Another factor which affects the magnitude of the mitotic reaction in compensatory hyperplasia is the amount of tissue removed. As the review of this subject by MacDonald, et al. (1962) has recently shown, few investigators have given this problem the serious attention it deserves. Some incidental observations by Drabkin (1947) on liver regeneration following removal of the median lobe (36·2 per cent) or of the median plus the left lateral lobes (68·4 per cent) revealed that after two weeks 56·7 and 73·9 per cent, respectively, of the amounts removed had been replaced. Actually, this is equivalent to the restoration of the liver remnants back to 84·3 and 82·1 per cent, respectively, of their original weights, which simply indicates that given enough time regenerating livers will grow to equal masses regardless of how much has to be replaced. Nevertheless, Cameron (1952) reported that it took ten days to complete regeneration following 30 per cent hepatectomy, but three weeks to do so after removal of 60 per cent. Similar studies in the frog by Liosner, et al. (1961) showed that regeneration was complete in two to three days after excision of one-third of the liver, whereas six days were necessary to restore the original mass after two-thirds of the liver had been removed. In shorter periods of time, however, smaller liver remnants regenerate more tissue than larger ones, as Levenson, et al. (1959) demonstrated by weight determinations 48 hours after 35 and 70 per cent hepatectomies

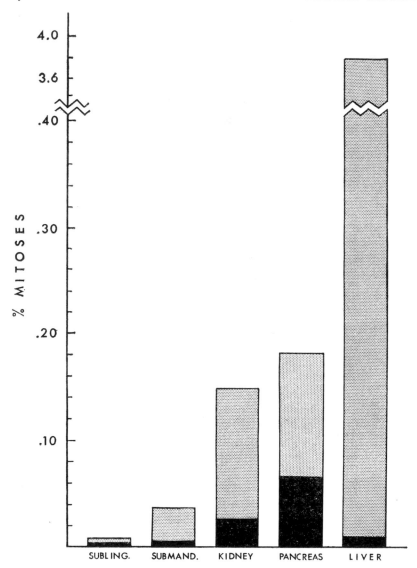

Figure 36. Comparison between approximate mitotic activities in normal (black) and compensating (shaded) organs at the peaks of their reactions. In the sublingual salivary gland, compensatory hyperplasia is only twice the normal low level of mitotic activity. At the opposite extreme, the regenerating liver may exhibit several hundred times as much mitotic activity as the resting liver.

in rats. In a study of the influence of age on liver regeneration in the mouse, Straube and Patt (1961) removed one, two, and three lobes of the liver. In two-, six- or eight-month-old animals, regeneration was complete in seven days in all cases. In ten-month-old mice, however, ten days instead of seven were required for the regeneration of the livers from which three lobes had been removed, and in mice eighteen months of age regeneration after loss of two or three lobes was prolonged in comparison with lesser injuries.

To determine the cytological basis of these responses, it is necessary to examine the pattern of cell division in livers subjected to different degrees of ablation. This was attempted by Glinos (1958a) who removed 10 per cent (caudate lobes) or 30 per cent (median lobes) of rat livers and found mitotic indices of 0·03 and 1·63 per cent, respectively. However, the comprehensive investigations of MacDonald, et al. (1962) on the number of mitoses and the extents of tritiated thymidine uptake into DNA 21 and 23 hours after the extirpation of varying amounts of rat livers, have yielded especially interesting and valuable information. These studies showed that the number of mitotic figures and labelled nuclei increased commensurate with the amount of liver removed, at least above a threshold of 9·4 to 12·3 per cent hepatectomy. Below this level, the differences between experimental and sham operated livers were not statistically significant, even in animals injected with tritiated thymidine 21, 23, or 27 hours after removal of 3 to 5 per cent of their livers. In another series, rats were similarly examined after only 8 and 16 hours. At this time there was no enhanced uptake of the label no matter how much liver had been removed. Thus, it would appear that the onset of DNA synthesis is neither accelerated after extensive hepatectomies nor retarded by lesser operations. However, the conclusion that hepatectomies of less than 9 to 12 per cent do not give rise to regeneration may not be warranted in view of the high degree of proliferative variability normally characteristic of both intact and operated livers. Such a situation would render it impossible to detect a statistically significant difference between control and experimental livers following minor hepatectomies unless prohibitively large numbers of animals were used. Hence, a small response in these circumstances would be expected to be obscured by the individual variations of the material.

Along similar lines, Bucher and Swaffield (1962) and Bucher (1963) have investigated the rate of uptake of labelled thymidine into regenerating rat livers at frequent intervals after varying extents of partial hepatectomy. They found that when 40 or 68 per cent of the liver was removed the maximal rates of DNA synthesis were 17 and 50 times that of controls, respectively. The peaks occurred at approximately 25 hours after operation in both instances. When only 30 per cent of the liver was removed, however, the resultant response was only several times greater than normal, and 10 per cent hepatectomy yielded an insignificant increase in thymidine incorporation. These interesting results raise some provocative questions concerning the problem of tissue redundancy and its relation to growth control.

There is a dearth of knowledge about comparable phenomena in other tissues and organs. With reference to the replacement of blood, however, Fowler and Barer (1942) have reported some interesting facts relating to the regeneration of haemoglobin in humans following blood donations. The average amount of blood removed was 555 ml. which caused an 18 per cent average drop in haemoglobin concentration from an initial level of 12·8 gm. per 100 ml. to 10·5 gm. per 100 ml. in 24 hours. Subsequent determinations of the recovery of normal haemoglobin values in these individuals revealed wide variations from a minimum of 18 days to a maximum of 98 days. The average recovery period was 49·6 days and the average rate of haemoglobin synthesis during this interval was 49 mg. per 100 ml. per day in males and 40 mg. per 100 ml. per day in females. When the cases were grouped according to the amount of haemoglobin removed, regardless of the actual volume of blood depletion, it was found that the recovery period was proportional to the original drop in haemoglobin levels. An average decline of 3·2 gm. per 100 ml. required an average of 61·2 days to replace. Loss of 1·6 gm. per 100 ml. took 43·1 days to recover and 1·2 gm. per 100 ml. was regenerated in an average of 33·3 days. These data raise the important question of whether or not the rate of erythropoiesis varies in proportion to the amount of blood lost. The complete answer to this is not known, but from the above results it can be concluded that such a graded response, if it occurs, is not sufficient to bring about the regeneration of different amounts of blood in equal periods of time.

In addition to the foregoing studies of liver and blood regeneration, the kidney has yielded pertinent information concerning the relationship between the amount of tissue removed and the pattern of compensatory response. McCreight and Sulkin (1962a) studied this problem by removing one-half, three-quarters, or seven-eighths of the total complement of rat kidney tissue and studying the incidence of cell division in proximal tubule cells 50 hours post-operatively. They found that after 50 per cent nephrectomy there was a sixfold increase in the mitotic index in comparison with controls. Loss of 75 per cent of the renal tissue, however, caused 18 times the normal amount of mitotic activity in the residual part of the kidney, whereas seven-eighths nephrectomy (87·5 per cent ablation) increased the proliferative rate by a factor of 25. These data show that the magnitude of the compensatory response in the kidney varies directly with the amount of renal mass excised.

The above results could be accounted for by two possible alternatives. Either the magnitudes of the mitotic maxima differ according to the extent of nephrectomy, or the time interval from operation to mitotic peak may vary. To resolve this question, Goss (unpublished) designed experiments to determine mitotic indices in the remaining portions of kidneys at various intervals after different degrees of partial nephrectomy. Groups of 24 rats were subjected to the excision of approximately 25, 50, or 75 per cent of the total renal mass and sacrificed in groups of six at 24-hour intervals during the subsequent four days. Sham operated animals revealed that the basal rate of mitosis in intact kidneys remained relatively constant. Each of the experimental groups, however, exhibited a characteristic mitotic climax 48 hours after operation (figure 37).

There was no indication of a precocious reaction in any of the groups, indicating that the onset of the response is not affected by the severity of the injury, at least within the limits of the time intervals studied. However, the magnitudes of the two-day mitotic peaks increased with each increment in the amount of kidney removed. Moreover, in the groups from which half of one kidney had been excised, separate mitotic counts in the bisected and uninjured organs revealed a slightly higher proliferative rate in the former, probably attributable to some direct effects of local injury. Following the maximal response, the mitotic indices returned towards normal levels on the third and fourth days, the higher curves being slower to decline than the lower ones.

As in the case of the liver, therefore, the remaining kidney reacts to varying degrees of ablation not by modifying the onset of its response, but by adjusting the magnitude and, to a lesser extent, the duration of its compensatory hyperplasia in proportion to the amount to which its substance has been reduced. Although these experiments were not designed to explore the lower limits of compensatory growth responses, they do indicate the possibility that even very small losses of renal tissue may be able to elicit a mitotic reaction, as is indicated in figure 38 by extrapolation from the maximal levels of proliferation in the two-day series of residual kidneys.

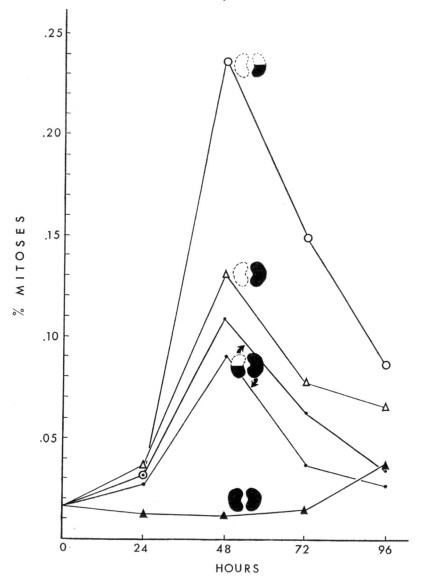

If one takes into account the variability normally encountered under these experimental conditions with groups of six rats, the difference between control and partially ablated kidneys 48 hours after operation loses its statistical significance (i.e. $P > 0.05$) when the amount of tissue removed is in the general vicinity of 10 per cent. This, of course, does not mean that the effect is lacking, but that with only six animals per group the confidence in one's results is below the 95 per cent level. This could be rectified only by using progressively larger numbers of rats as less and less tissue is excised. Thus, despite the statistical difficulties of proving that compensations for minor ablations do occur, an affirmative assumption is more consistent with established facts than is a negative one.

Clearly, the loss of tissue in many organs triggers a proliferative reaction which is responsible for their restoration. The magnitude of the response is proportional to that of the stimulus. Presumably, the population of the reacting cells is heterogeneous to the extent that varying thresholds of sensitivity to the stimulating influences (either positive or negative) are represented. Thus, the greater the reduction in tissue mass, the greater will be the resultant physiological deficiency to which the remaining cells are exposed. Those whose thresholds are exceeded will thereby follow a course leading to mitosis. Since their daughter cells will mitigate the emergency, the probability of subsequent mitogenic stimulation becomes progressively reduced. This would explain the abrupt preclimactic increase in compensatory hyperplasia in contrast to the more gradual denouement to normal mitotic levels (figure 37). Of fundamental concern, therefore, is the nature of these hypothetical variations in the responsiveness of the cells in a given population to mitotic stimulation. Such individual differences probably represent the basis for the random distribution of cell divisions in time and space.

Figure 37. Graphic representation of how the amount of kidney removed affects compensatory renal hyperplasia during the subsequent four post-operative days. Amount of kidney left intact is represented in black. In sham operated controls (▲) the mitotic counts remained low. 25 per cent ablation (●) caused moderate hyperplasia on second day, the operated kidney showing the greater response. Unilateral nephrectomy (△) elicited an even greater proliferative reaction, and 75 per cent nephrectomy (○) was followed by the highest percentage of mitoses. Thus, the magnitude and duration of hyperplasia, rather than its time of onset, are affected by the extent of nephrectomy.

M

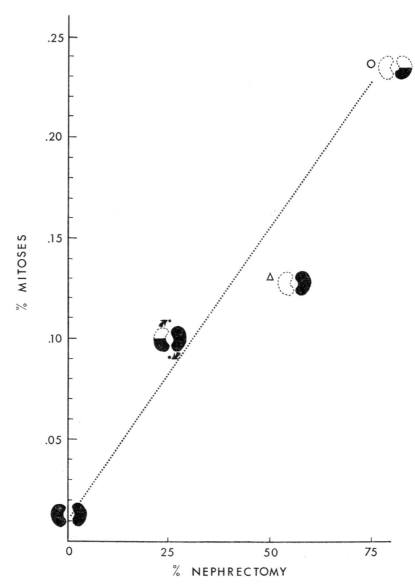

Figure 38. Relationship between amount of kidney removed and magnitudes of 48-hour mitotic peaks (cf. figure 37).

XI

Molecular Aspects of Compensatory Growth

THE physiological equilibrium of an organ is normally maintained through a variety of homoeostatic mechanisms by which functional activity is adjusted to systemic demands. Naturally, the work performed by a functional unit in a compound organ is inversely proportional to the total number of such units sharing the load. Reduction of the latter presumably results in a temporary deficiency in functional output followed by a compensatory physiological response on the part of the residual units. This added burden ultimately leads to the visible manifestations of compensatory growth. How this is achieved will be understood only when the cytological attributes of hypertrophy and hyperplasia have been interpreted in biochemical terms. Thus, the consequences of such physiological upheavals must eventually be traced to their origins in the metabolic modulations brought about by the loss of part of an organ.

Next to organ enlargement, the most conspicuous criterion of compensatory growth is hyperplasia. What causes mitosis under these conditions is not known, but the obvious way to look for a solution to this problem is to examine the immediately preceding events. As the principal antecedent to mitosis, DNA synthesis is an especially important process occurring slightly earlier in the division cycle of a cell. Even this, however, is more in the nature of an effect than a cause and must itself be stimulated by prior events. Ultimately the quest may lead to enzyme kinetics, for in this realm are the controlling mechanisms of biochemical synthetic reactions upon which the rates of molecular turnover and cell growth depend.

DNA Synthesis

The mammalian liver has constituted an especially convenient system in which to analyse the biochemistry of growth. The rate of DNA synthesis in normal growing livers climbs rapidly at about the age of weaning in rats (Kennedy, *et al.*, 1958). Bucher, *et al.* (1961) report that the maximum incorporation of labelled thymidine or orotic acid into rat liver takes place at 24 to 27 days of age, representing about twice the rate of DNA synthesis that occurred at 21 days. This nearly coincides with Doljanski's (1960) observations that at weaning the nucleo-cytoplasmic ratio decreases, the rate of mitosis is maximal, and the number of polyploid cells increases. Indeed, it was estimated that by 31 days of age, approximately half of the rat's liver cells are polyploid. Wilson and Leduc (1948) have called attention to the abundance of binucleate liver cells in 3 to 4-week-old mice, again emphasizing the profound changes occurring in the liver at the critical time of weaning when hepatic physiology is most seriously affected.

The adult liver, in contrast, is well known for its very low mitotic rate and its minimal level of DNA synthesis. This has been substantiated by various studies indicating very low turnover rates in resting livers of DNA phosphorus (Brues, et al., 1944) and DNA adenine (Furst, et al., 1950). Orotic acid-6-C^{14} administered to growing rats by Takagi, et al. (1956) was incorporated into the pyrimidines of the DNA being synthesized during the next 24 hours and was retained there for at least the next seven weeks. During this period the growing labelled livers underwent a threefold weight increase without losing their radioactivity. Even regeneration induced by partial hepatectomy of such livers after 40 to 46 days did not cause a turnover of the labelled DNA when analysed 5 or 21 days postoperatively. Thus, DNA in the liver is extremely stable under conditions of normal or regenerative growth. The liver, therefore, normally loses negligible amounts of DNA once it is formed, but can augment its DNA by adding more cells, producing binucleate cells, or forming polyploid nuclei. This is the basis for Doljanski's (1960) calculation that the adult rat liver contains 30 per cent more DNA than do normally diploid tissues.

In many respects, the process of liver regeneration recapitulates normal hepatic development. This is particularly evident with reference to the rate of DNA synthesis which rises to a peak after a lag period and them gradually subsides to pre-operative levels as the final size of the liver is approached. Following the observations of Furst, et al. (1950) that the adenine turnover in the DNA of regenerating livers is considerably faster than in resting livers, many investigators have analysed in detail the course of DNA synthesis after partial hepatectomy. Whereas Nygaard and Rusch (1955) found very little uptake of P^{32} into DNA during the first 12 hours, Price and Laird (1950) noted that between 12 and 24 hours the amount of DNA per hepatic nucleus doubled, but soon returned to normal as mitotic activity commenced. This increase represented the temporary tetraploid condition of a proportion of the nuclei after DNA synthesis and before mitosis. The earliest rise in DNA may occur as soon as 12 to 15 hours after partial hepatectomy (Holmes and Mee, 1954). By 15 hours the initiation of DNA synthesis in the rat liver was detected by Hecht and Potter (1958), while Swift (1953) and Bollum and Potter (1959) reported an increase after 18 hours.

Maximum rates of DNA production in regenerating livers occur relatively soon after the onset of its synthesis. As measured by P^{32} incorporation, DNA is most rapidly produced between 20 and 24 hours (Nygaard and Rusch, 1955). In agreement with this, Cater, et al. (1956) reported a maximum rate of DNA synthesis that was nine times the normal rate after 22 to 24 hours. Hecht and Potter (1958), however, believed the highest rate occurred between 24 and 30 hours, while Hammersten (1951) noted a peak at 30 hours. It was at this interval that Eliasson, et al. (1951) measured maximal rates of N^{15} uptake in the polynucleotides of regenerating rat liver. In the mouse, however, Barnum, et al. (1957) stated that DNA synthesis rises to a maximum as late as 36 hours after operation. Variations in liver regeneration with age were detected by Bucher, et al. (1961), who found maximum rates of DNA formation at 22 hours in rats 24 to 27 days old, at 25 hours in 200 to 250 gramme rats, and at 32 hours in 1-year-old rats weighing between 350 and 400 grammes. In another investigation, a secondary peak was reported to occur in the rat liver at 35 hours, some 12 hours after a primary one (Cater, et al., 1956).

In general, therefore, the rate of DNA synthesis reaches a climax between 24 and 30 hours after partial hepatectomy and then begins to decline (Bollum and Potter, 1959), reaching minimal levels characteristic of the resting liver after 6 to 9 days (Hecht and Potter, 1958). From figure 39, it is evident that the pattern of DNA synthesis in the regenerating liver mimics that of mitotic activity which it foreshadows by approximately 6 hours, although Barnum, et al. (1957) observed a 12-hour lag between the DNA and mitotic maxima in regenerating mouse livers.

A similar relationship may be seen in rat livers regenerating after carbon tetrachloride injury. Leevy, et al. (1959) found the onset of DNA synthesis, as measured by tritiated thymidine uptake, to occur about 24 hours after treatment, before mitoses were encountered. This reached maximum levels between 36 and 72 hours, and declined after 96 to 120 hours. This paralleled the observed rates of proliferation. In comparison with surgical removal of parts of the liver, therefore, hepatic regeneration after injury with carbon tetrachloride is slower to begin and lasts longer.

The kidney resembles the liver in many respects, but differs from it in others. Unlike the liver, for example, the amount of DNA per nucleus is constant throughout the normal rat kidney regardless of age (Kurnick, 1951, 1955). Therefore, polyploid cells are extremely rare (Pisi and Cavalli, 1955). Following unilateral nephrectomy, however, the amount of DNA per nucleus rises, indicating that synthesis is occurring in preparation for mitosis (Pisi and Cavalli, 1955). Mandel, et al. (1950) found a 42 per cent increase in DNA in the remaining kidneys of rats 30 hours after uninephrectomy. According to Franck (1958), there is a two- to six-fold increase in transient tetraploid nuclei two days after operation. Becker and Ogawa (1959) noted an increase in the DNA content of renal nuclei on the third day after partial nephrectomy, which was when Reiter and McCreight (1963) found the maximum uptake of tritiated thymidine to occur. Still later increases in DNA have been reported one week after uninephrectomy (Fautrez, et al., 1955), but such modifications later disappear (Becker and Ogawa, 1959).

Measurements of the total DNA per kidney have been used to estimate the role of hyperplasia versus hypertrophy in compensatory renal enlargement. Variations with age have been described by Kennedy (1958), who found a rapid rise in DNA phosphate in young rats after uninephrectomy, but noted a reduced response in older animals. Indeed, in six-month-old rats, no increase in DNA was detected in the remaining kidney. Other authors likewise failed to demonstrate any increase in the DNA contents of compensating mouse kidneys even five to six days after partial ablation (Straube and Patt, 1961). This is difficult to understand in view of the abundance of evidence proving the occurrence of hyperplasia after uninephrectomy. Different results were obtained by Rossi and Compagnari (1959) and Miyada and Kurnick (1960), who were unable to detect changes in renal DNA before the fourth post-operative day, but who noted increases thereafter through the second week. From these data, it was concluded that the early increases in kidney weight are attributable to cellular hypertrophy, which is eventually followed by hyperplasia. Nevertheless, it is not easy to reconcile the above results with the previously described facts pertaining to the renal mitotic activity

(Chapter X) which reaches a maximum at least by 48 hours after contralateral extirpation. It can only be concluded that these discrepancies may be accounted for by technical limitations in methods of measuring DNA. No such difficulties have been encountered in the case of liver regeneration, perhaps because the greater magnitude of its hyperplastic response, which is about 25 times that in the kidney, may have permitted an earlier detection of DNA synthesis.

Clearly, the preferred method of studying DNA synthesis in compensating organs is to inject tritiated thymidine at different intervals after operation. Subsequent calculations of the radioactive index will then reveal with considerable accuracy the incidence of cells synthesizing DNA within rather narrow time limits. This would yield information concerning the onset, climax, and decline of DNA synthetic activity in relation to similar data relevant to the mitotic index. Such methods have been very successful in the liver. Although they have hardly been attempted in the kidney and other organs, there is every reason to believe they should be equally fruitful.

RNA Synthesis

Whereas DNA synthesis is a prerequisite to mitosis, RNA synthesis is essential for the formation of proteins, a process so fundamental that growth and differentiation cannot occur in its absence. Thus, the rapid growth of the liver that occurs after weaning or during regeneration is characteristically accompanied by increases in the RNA content (Doljanski, 1960). This substantiates the observation of Nygaard and Rusch (1955) that more P^{32} was incorporated into the RNA of regenerating liver than into normal ones. Following a lag phase of 12 to 14 hours after partial hepatectomy, Von Der Decken and Hultin (1958) found an increase in the microsomal RNA of liver cells that probably accounts for the 62 per cent rise in the RNA content of regenerating livers between 12 and 24 hours as reported by Price and Laird (1950).

Increases such as these are the outcome of still earlier modifications in the rates of RNA synthesis. Within a few hours after partial hepatectomy (Glinos, 1958a) or CCl_4 treatment (Leduc and Wilson, 1958), there is a depletion of the cytoplasmic basophilia of hepatic cells, indicating some kind of effect on ribonucleic acid and protein metabolism. First evident in the liver cells of the periportal region, this process spreads to the centrilobular cells by the eighth hour. Restoration takes place in the reverse direction and is completed at the end of the first post-operative day. Perhaps this is analogous to the chromatolysis that takes place in the nerve cell bodies of traumatized neurons.

The earliest indications of increased RNA synthesis in the regenerating liver have been reported by McArdle and Creaser (1963), who detected a rise in P^{32} incorporation into RNA as early as one to two hours after partial hepatectomy in the rat. These observations may be correlated with the changes in cytoplasmic basophilia reported above. Cater, et al. (1956) have shown that the rate of RNA synthesis is doubled a few hours post-operatively in such livers, and Hecht and Potter (1958) reported that RNA synthesis is accelerated by the sixth hour after partial hepatectomy. Novikoff and Potter (1948), however, had found no change until 24 hours. All of these reports, however, indicate a continued rise during the first two days. According to Eliasson, et al. (1951) and Hammersten (1951), the maximum rate of RNA turnover is at 30 hours, whereas Johnson and Albert (1952) reported a maximum uptake of P^{32} into RNA after three to five days. These elevated levels of RNA synthesis are said to return to normal on the fourth post-operative day in mice (Tsuboi, et al., 1954). In rats, Nygaard and Rusch (1955) found that RNA levels were restored to normal after approximately the same period of time. Hecht and Potter (1958), however, reported that the rate of RNA synthesis does not decrease to pre-operative levels until the sixth to ninth days. Thus, it is evident that enhancement of RNA synthesis is initiated very soon after partial hepatectomy, well before DNA replication and mitosis are under way (figure 39). It rises to a maximum simultaneously with these latter events and does not completely subside to normal levels until full restoration of the liver has been achieved.

Comparable changes apparently occur in connection with compensatory renal hyperplasia, although the available information is less detailed than in the case of liver regeneration. Mandel, et al. (1950) found a 42 per cent increase in the RNA content of remaining rat kidneys within 30 hours of unilateral nephrectomy, and Sulkin (1950) measured a continued rise up to 72 hours after operation, followed by a gradual decline. Also reflecting at least in part the process of RNA synthesis was Simpson's (1960) observation that the uptake of P^{32} in rat kidneys was 1·8 to 4·0 times normal after 36 to 48 hours. An even later increase was reported by Kurnick (1955) who found that the ratio of RNA to DNA in remaining kidneys was maximal between three and four days after operation. From these observations, it may

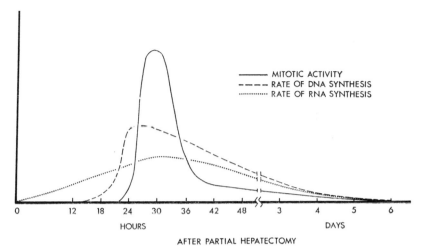

Figure 39. Graphic relationship between mitotic activity, and rates of DNA and RNA synthesis in the regenerating liver. Curves are schematic, and their amplitudes are arbitrary. Although times of onset and maximal activity differ from one process to another, they all gradually return to pre-operative levels together.

be concluded that the rate of RNA synthesis, being proportional to changing organ weight (Nygaard and Rusch, 1955), is a sensitive indicator of the degree to which anabolic activity is stimulated in the cells of the kidney and the liver and presumably in other tissues as well.

Protein Synthesis

The nucleic acid synthesis that accompanies compensatory growth finds expression in the enhanced production of proteins. This is especially true in the liver which is normally engaged in the synthesis of many of the plasma proteins. As determined by the rate of C^{14}-L-leucine uptake into liver microscomes, Von Der Decken and Hultin (1958) and Hultin and Von Der Decken (1958) detected the earliest increase in amino acid incorporation following a 12 to 14-hour lag period after partial hepatectomy in rats. This continued until approximately the twentieth hour and then gradually decreased to the normal range by 5 to 6 days. In agreement with this, Braun, *et al.* (1962) found that by 14 hours the concentration of free amino acids in regenerating liver was maximal, and declined thereafter. This increase in availability of amino acids is further augmented by a decrease in the rate of amino acid catabolism during the first post-operative day, as has been determined by the perfusion of amino acids through regenerating livers (Burke, 1962). Thus, protein synthesis is made possible by the prior mobilization of RNA and amino acids.

As early as 18 hours after partial hepatectomy in the mouse, Tsuboi, *et al.* (1954) found an increase in the total amount of protein in the liver, and by the end of the first day there was a 17 per cent rise in protein nitrogen in regenerating rat liver (Price and Laird, 1950). The maximum rate of protein synthesis in the rat occurs one day after operation, according to Johnson and Albert (1952) and Braun, *et al.* (1962), while Gurd, *et al.* (1948) report the highest levels of protein on the first and second days. An even later period of maximal protein synthesis has been noted by Hammersten (1951) to occur between 48 and 56 hours, at which time the cytological changes associated with liver regeneration are decreasing. After 60 hours the rate of amino acid turnover diminishes (Hammersten, 1951; Eliasson, *et al.*, 1951), and protein synthesis returns nearly to normal on the sixth day (Braun, *et al.*, 1962). Indeed, the amount of protein nitrogen in the liver may decrease from 17 per cent above control levels one day after operation to 32 per cent below normal on the fourth day.

It has been shown that in liver regeneration increased RNA synthesis commences 12 to 14 hours after operation, concomitant with heightened rates of amino acid incorporation. These processes are followed by the initiation of DNA synthesis on the fifteenth hour, and detectable increases in liver protein after 18 to 24 hours. What happens during the first 12-hour lag period, however, is of considerable importance in understanding how the above processes are stimulated. As mentioned earlier, one change that occurs soon after partial hepatectomy is the depletion of ribonucleoprotein from liver cells (Glinos, 1958a). Within 30 minutes following operation, this effect has been detected in periportal cells. Subsequently, the more centrally located cells of the liver lobules become similarly affected. After about eight hours, however, the cytoplasmic basophilia begins to return and may be completely restored centrally at the end of 24 hours. Noting that partial hepatectomy activates the synthesis of proteins in residual portions of the liver, Glinos (1958a) explored the possibility that the early depletions of plasma proteins might stimulate the loss of cytoplasmic basophilia described above. It had been shown that the periportal cells, which are in an environment relatively poor in proteins, are affected before the more centrally situated cells, which are presumably exposed to less severe modifications in plasma composition. However, since the loss of plasma proteins apparently does not precede the decrease in cytoplasmic basophilia in the periportal cells of the liver, it is possible that the latter might cause the changes in the composition of the blood, rather than vice versa. Unhappily, this would still leave unanswered the question of what initiates the early depletions in ribonucleoprotein.

Even earlier alterations in liver cytology relate to the appearance of cytoplasmic inclusion bodies following partial hepatectomy. First discovered by Price and Laird (1950), these structures appear on the first day of regeneration and disappear by the second day. Doniach and Weinbren (1952) observed that they first appeared in the periportal cells only ten to 30 minutes after operation, as cytoplasmic vacuoles measuring three to five micra in diameter. Later they occurred in other hepatic cells as well, and enlarged to diameters of about 15μ. By 48 hours, they had generally disappeared. Histochemical evidence revealed their predominantly proteinaceous composition. Aterman (1952a,b, 1961) found apparently identical structures only five minutes after partial hepatectomy, which he believed were the result of the transient hypoxia following operation. Also appearing in livers after ligation of the bile duct, injections of CCl_4, or anoxia, it was shown that they contained neither glycogen nor fat, but that they did not occur in starved rats. Confirming the latter observation, Doniach and Weinbren (1952) believed they may be causally related to subsequent liver growth by storing excess proteins. They suggest that they may form in the remnant of the reduced liver which either retains or acquires the extra material from the relative superabundance of protein in the plasma.

In general, the pattern of protein formation in the regenerating liver parallels the growth curve. Actually, however, the regenerating liver must produce more proteins than are needed for its own growth. In addition to making new liver, it must compensate for the depletion of plasma proteins that follows partial hepatectomy. Confronted with this dilemma, the residual liver cells give preference to the synthesis of cellular proteins during the early stages of regeneration, and only after substantial amounts of tissue have been replaced do they manufacture plasma proteins predominantly. On the basis of this, Braun, et al. (1962) conclude that the kinds of proteins synthesized are controlled by the bodily demands, although the *modus operandi* remains unknown.

Plasma Protein Synthesis

With the exception of the γ-globulins, all of the major protein components of the plasma are produced by the liver cells. Following partial hepatectomy, therefore, their synthesis is temporarily interrupted with the result that their concentrations decrease (figure 40). This is accompanied, on the first two days, by a decrease in plasma

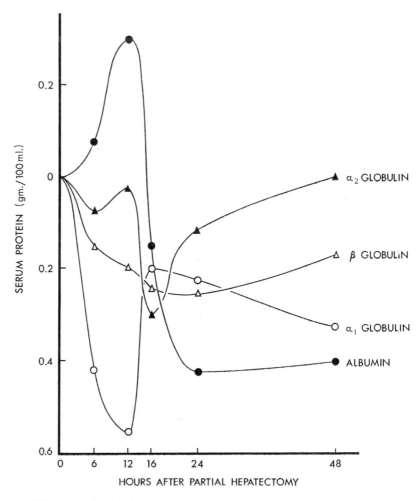

Figure 40. Deviations from the norm occurring in concentrations of serum proteins in rats during the first 48 hours following partial hepatectomy. (After Roberts and White, 1949.)

and red blood-cell volume (Lowrance and Chanutin, 1942). In view of the normally rapid plasma protein replacement rate, especially in small mammals, (McFarlane, 1957), the depletion of plasma proteins promptly becomes evident. It is curious, however, that albumin, which is the most abundant plasma protein, first exhibits a rise in concentration 6 to 12 hours after partial hepatectomy (Roberts and White, 1949) and then drops to subnormal levels between 12 and 24 hours (Chanutin, *et al.*, 1938; Roberts and White, 1949; Lamirande and Cantero, 1952). There then occurs, after the second day, a very gradual return to pre-operative levels during the next few weeks. Thus, there appears to be a considerable delay in the total regeneration of the albumin fraction of the plasma proteins after the original mass of the liver has been fully restored.

The globulins, however, return to normal levels more quickly after their initial depression (Chanutin, et al., 1938). According to Roberts and White (1949) the α-globulins are more severely depleted after partial hepatectomy than any other component, reaching minimum levels after 12 hours but rising thereafter. The early decrease in α_2-globulin concentration lasts for 16 hours before it returns to normal levels after two days. Possibly this may be related to the appearance of an α_2-globulin in the blood of rats after partial hepatectomy or carbon tetrachloride administration (Heim and Kerrigan, 1962). First appearing after 12 hours, this component increases up to the third day and then declines. Since it is also present in pregnant and lactating animals, and in cases of neoplastic growths, its presence may be significantly correlated with increased rates of protein synthesis. With reference to β-globulins, Roberts and White (1949) found a steady decline in concentration for 24 hours after partial hepatectomy, followed by an incipient rise on the second day.

In contrast to the foregoing data, however, Lamirande and Cantero (1952) reported that α- and β-globulins double their concentrations by 24 hours after partial hepatectomy in rats. They also found that the concentration of fibrinogen was reduced after 24 hours, which again is in disagreement with other investigators. Chanutin, et al (1938) had shown that the amount of fibrin in the blood of partially hepatectomized rats increased above normal levels after 24 hours and remained elevated for approximately three weeks. But despite the lack of harmony in the results of various investigations, the consensus appears to favour the occurrence of a general decrease in albumin and globulins following partial hepatectomy, and a gradual return to

normal levels for some time afterwards, the globulins being regenerated sooner than albumin.

Storage and Secretion in Regenerating Livers

Next to protein synthesis, one of the most conspicuous functions
of the liver is to store glycogen, which it does maximally during the
assimilatory phase after feeding (Forsgren, 1929; Higgins, et al.,
1932). Following partial hepatectomy (Doljanski, 1960) or injections
of CCl_4 (Leduc and Wilson, 1958), the glycogen content of the liver
is decreased. This effect has been observed as early as three to six
hours after operation by Aterman (1952a) and after ten hours by
Harkness (1952). According to Novikoff and Potter (1948), the glycogen has almost completely disappeared from regenerating livers by
twelve hours. Following this early decline, however, glycogen deposition again begins a day or two after operation (Gurd, et al., 1948;
Harkness, 1952), but remains at subnormal levels at least until the
fifth day (Novikoff and Potter, 1948). It would be hazardous to
attempt to give a specific explanation of the post-operative decrease
in liver glycogen deposition. It may represent in part just another
facet of the general suspension of hepatic activities following injury.
Alternatively, the tendency of animals not to eat following an operation is perhaps not too pedestrian an explanation of the so-called lag
phase in liver regeneration.

Another feature of liver cytology is the conspicuous presence of
lipid in the cytoplasm. In contrast to the early drop in liver glycogen
after partial hepatectomy, however, fat deposition is consistently
resumed during the first day (Ludewig, et al., 1939; Gurd, et al.,
1948; Rosenthal, et al., 1951; Tsuboi, et al., 1954). This has been
confirmed by Johnson and Albert (1952) who studied the rates of P^{32}
uptake in the phospholipids of regenerating rat livers. By similar
techniques, Jardetzky, et al. (1956) noted enhanced uptake after
eighteen hours. Others, however, have reported increases in the concentration of fat in regenerating livers as early as ten hours (Harkness,
1952), or even within six hours (Stowell, 1948). According to Jardetzky, et al. (1956), the maximum incorporation of P^{32} into phospholipids occurs at about 24 hours. After about three days in the mouse
(Tsuboi, et al., 1954), or a week in the rat (Ludewig, et al., 1939;
Rosenthal, et al., 1951), the lipid content of the regenerated liver
returns to normal. In contrast to the foregoing, Tsuboi, et al. (1951)
found a decrease in the lipid contents of mouse livers injured by

exposure to CCl_4. This, however, may only reflect the destruction of many cells that might otherwise have accumulated fat, for Leduc and Wilson (1958) reported histochemical evidence for lipid deposition in similarly treated livers.

In view of the embryonic derivation of the liver, perhaps its original function was to secrete bile. Forsgren (1929) has described the occurrence of a secretory phase in the physiology of the liver that is normally preprandial in alternation with the assimilatory phase. Accompanied by an overall reduction in size of organ and cell, the secretory phase is characterized by depleted glycogen reserves and increased amounts of bile precursors. In the regenerating liver, Bollman and Mann (1936) reported that the process of bile secretion was relatively unaffected. Weinbren and Billing (1956), however, found that during the first 24 hours after partial hepatectomy the amount of bilirubin produced as a function of liver weight was below normal but increased thereafter. Judging hepatic function by serum bilirubin concentrations 42 hours after CCl_4 poisoning in the rat, Leevy, et al. (1959) measured an increase from control levels of 0·12 mg. to 0·52 mg. per cent. Either this results from the inordinate release of bilirubin into the blood from necrotic liver cells, or it represents the inability of the injured liver to excrete these compounds at normal rates.

Of incidental interest is the water content of livers. According to Higgins, et al. (1932), the increase in normal liver weight after feeding is largely accounted for by increases in the amount of hepatic water. Although Novikoff and Potter (1948) claimed that the water content of regenerating livers remained unchanged, Zaki (1954) reported an increase to maximum levels by 36 hours, followed by a gradual decrease. Similarly, Tsuboi, et al. (1951) found greater amounts of water in CCl_4-treated mouse livers than in normal controls.

Enzyme Activity in Regenerating Livers

The physiological activity of an organ may be estimated from the quantitative measure of its end products. Thus, in the liver the amounts of nucleic acids, proteins, glycogen, fat, etc. may be taken as indications of the metabolic state of the organ. Variations between normal and regenerating livers may, therefore, yield information concerning the effects of partial ablation on hepatic physiology. More exact determinations of functional activity may be obtained by measuring the rates at which the various products of an organ's metabolism are synthesized. This can be achieved by isotopic uptake techniques, or by enzymatic analyses. Inasmuch as the rates of biochemical reactions are controlled by enzymes, knowledge of enzyme concentrations and activities provides a basis for judging the rates of the reactions they catalyze. Changes in enzyme activities in regenerating organs may in part be the effects of prior disturbances, and as such would represent compensatory responses to functional demands. To the extent that enzyme concentrations are elevated in this way, they may in turn initiate mitotic activity thereby restoring cellular components to their original states of equilibrium (Rosenthal, et al., 1951). There is ample reason to suspect that the demand for increased physiological activity may be translated into cellular proliferation via alterations in enzyme activities. A first approximation towards determining the validity of this notion must involve an inventory of the current status of our knowledge about enzymatic responses to partial hepatectomy. Information along these lines pertaining to organs other than the liver is virtually nil.

Many of the enzymes associated with cellular respiration are depressed in their activities following partial hepatectomy (figure 41A). The investigations of Novikoff and Potter (1948) on rats revealed decreased activity during the first two days of such enzymes as succinoxidase, malic dehydrogenase, oxaloacetic oxidase, and cytochrome reductase. In the regenerating mouse liver, Tsuboi, et al. (1954) reported that succinoxidase levels had returned to normal after ten days. Glucose-6-phosphatase, according to Von Der Decken and Hultin (1958), is also less active after half a day. Other phosphatases react differently, however. In the regenerating mouse liver, acid phosphomonoesterase is little changed from normal levels (de Burgh, 1957). ATP-ase showed a rise from 30 per cent of the normal total liver activity after 70 per cent hepatectomy to 38 per cent of original levels after one day, and to 55 per cent on the second day (Rosenthal, et al., 1951). Alkaline phosphatase in the plasma and liver is also increased during liver regeneration. Oppenheimer and Flock (1947) detected increased concentrations of this enzyme on the first two days, and an eventual return to normal after 15 days, indicating that alkaline phosphatase in the blood is largely produced in the liver.

Of particular interest in relation to tissue growth and cell division is the occurrence of DPN (coenzyme I, or nicotinamide adenine dinucleotide) and the enzyme (DPN-pyrophosphorylase) which catalyses its synthesis from ATP and nicotinamide mononucleotide.

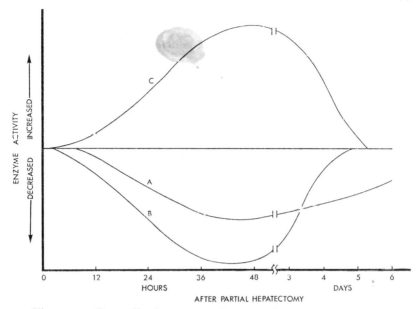

Figure 41. Generalized patterns of enzymatic activity in the regenerating liver. Horizontal line arbitrarily designates normal levels. There is a general tendency for respiratory enzymes (A) to be depressed during regeneration. Enzymes associated with uracil catabolism (B) also exhibit decreased activities. In contrast, the activities of enzymes that catalyse nucleic acid synthesis (C) are enhanced after partial hepatectomy. Further details in text.

DPN-pyrophosphorylase is confined to the nucleus where DPN is synthesized (Hogeboom and Schneider, 1952; Branster and Morton, 1956a). The concentration of the enzyme and the amount of DPN produced are inversely proportional to growth rate. In tumours of the mouse mammary gland, for example, the rate of DPN synthesis is about one-third that found in non-lactating mice, and about one-fifth the rate in lactating mammary glands (Branster and Morton, 1956b). The same authors have also demonstrated a twentyfold increase of DPN-pyrophosphorylase in adult mouse liver as compared with foetal livers.

In view of this apparent relationship to growth activity, extensive studies have been carried out on livers under varying physiological conditions. Glock and McLean (1957) have shown that hepatomas contain about half the normal amounts of DPN, and even less (13 per

N

cent) TPN. When artificially induced to grow by infection with ectromelia virus or by partial hepatectomy, mouse livers exhibited depressed rates of DPN synthesis following administration of nicotinamide (de Burgh, 1957). In regenerating livers, DPN production was only 65 per cent of normal after 24 hours, and had dropped to 39 per cent by 48 hours. The activity of DPN-pyrophosphorylase in catalysing DPN synthesis is apparently not related to mitotic activity *per se*, for ectromelia infection, which inhibits proliferation in regenerating livers (de Burgh and Miller, 1955), nevertheless depresses DPN levels in otherwise intact livers (de Burgh, 1957). Both regeneration and infection, however, cause cell enlargement during the first day, suggesting the possibility that the altered nucleo-cytoplasmic ratio may be causally related to the lower rates of DPN synthesis in foetal, cancerous, regenerating, or infected livers.

Morton (1958) has proposed a theory to explain this inverse relationship between the occurrence of DPN-pyrophosphorylase and the rate of growth. Originally synthesized in the nucleus, DPN is transferred to the cytoplasm where it takes part in various catalytic dehydrogenations. It is constantly degraded by nucleosidases and pyrophosphatases in the cytoplasm. When the growth of cells is stimulated, either as a consequence of cell division or following ectromelia infection in mouse liver, the cytoplasmic concentration of DPN is diminished. When a certain critical low level of cytoplasmic DPN is reached, by some unexplained mechanism cell division is again stimulated. There then occurs a net increase in DPN-pyrophosphorylase in the nucleus. This in turn enhances the production of DPN, and as its concentration rises the amount of cytoplasm is allowed to increase, again leading to more mitoses. The controlling mechanism may involve ATP, the cytoplasmic synthesis of which requires DPN from the nucleus. Synthesis of DPN, however, depends upon ATP supplied from the cytoplasm. The balance between these two factors may be related in some way to growth and cell division.

The liver exhibits an especially active amino acid metabolism, some of the enzymes for which have been investigated following partial hepatectomy. DOPA-decarboxylase activity is unchanged for the first two days, after which its concentration in the regenerating liver gradually rises to about 80 per cent of original levels after three weeks (Hawkins and Walker, 1952). Amine oxidase follows a similar pattern. Tryptophan peroxidase remains normal for one day, but then decreases to one-half its usual value on the second day and returns to pre-operative levels after a week or ten days (Thompson and Moss, 1955). Glutamic dehydrogenase, which catalyses the deamination of L-glutamic acid to α-ketoglutaric acid, is somewhat depressed after partial hepatectomy inasmuch as its regeneration occurs at a slower pace than does that of the liver as a whole (Greenbaum, et al., 1954). Between the third and seventh days, however, its concentration is commensurate with the restored liver weight. In contrast, the transaminase that promotes the transfer of the amino group from glutamic acid to oxaloacetic acid to yield aspartic acid was found to increase after partial hepatectomy by virtue of its faster rate of regeneration compared with that of the compensating liver (Greenbaum, et al. 1954). Cohen and Hekhuis (1941), however, had noted a different pattern of transaminase recovery, involving a decrease between the fifth and ninth post-operative days, followed by a return to normal.

In view of the marked increases in the synthesis of RNA and DNA during the premitotic phase of liver regeneration, the enzyme activities associated with the production of nucleic acids are correspondingly altered. Fritzon (1962) has pointed out that nucleic acid precursors accumulate in the liver soon after partial hepatectomy and thus act as repressors of uracil catabolism and inducers of anabolic enzymes. Accordingly, he showed that three enzymes catalysing the degradation of uracil in the liver undergo striking decreases in activity after partial hepatectomy (figure 41B). Dihydrouracil dehydrogenase and β-ureido propionic acid decarboxylase, which promote the breakdown of uracil to β-alanine and CO_2, decline to levels approximately 60 per cent of normal after 24 to 48 hours in the regenerating rat liver. By the fourth day, however, when mitotic activity has subsided, they were found to have returned nearly to normal levels. Dihydrouracil hydrase decreased 25 per cent by the first day, remained low for a week and rose again on the eighth day. The net effect of these changes is to increase the pool of uracil derivatives available for nucleotide synthesis.

In contrast, anabolic enzymes become increasingly abundant and active throughout the period of most rapid proliferation during liver regeneration (figure 41C). In the synthesis of DNA, two- and three-carbon sources are utilized in the elaboration of deoxyribose in a reaction catalysed by deoxyribose phosphate aldolase. Investigating this enzyme in the rat liver, Boxer and Shonk (1958) found increased activities during regeneration and even greater amounts in hepatomas.

Three days after partial hepatectomy, it doubled or tripled control levels and returned to normal after a week. Thus, the activity of deoxyribose phosphate aldolase is correlated with the pattern of DNA synthesis in the liver.

Calva and Cohen (1959) have discovered a similar situation with respect to the catalytic activity of carbamyl phosphate-aspartate transcarbamylase. This enzyme promotes the transfer of the carbamyl group from carbamyl phosphate to L-aspartate. It is from the latter compound that pyrimidine nucleotides are synthesized. Increased activity was encountered as early as 6 hours after partial hepatectomy, reaching a maximum after 50 hours. Activity remained elevated for five days and then gradually approached the normal condition.

The sequence of reactions leading from uracil to the formation of thymidine, without which DNA cannot by synthesized, involves the operation of a series of enzymes some of which have been analysed in regenerating rat livers. Sköld (1960) reported that uridine phosphorylase, which converts uracil to uridine, increases threefold between 36 and 73 hours in the regenerating rat liver, whereas deoxyuridine phosphorylase was shown to increase by a factor of four after 48 hours. The production of uridine monophosphate from uridine, catalysed by uridine kinase, is accelerated fivefold between 24 and 36 hours. Deoxyuridine kinase, which catalyses the formation of deoxyuridine monophosphate, becomes ten times as active after 36 to 48 hours. In all of these cases, enzyme activities reverted to normal after 6 days. Deoxyuridine monophosphate production is also promoted by deoxycytidylic acid deaminase. Absent from normal livers, this enzyme appears after only 12 hours in regenerating livers, reaches a maximum in 48 hours, and falls to normal between 3 and 6 days (Maley and Maley, 1960).

The conversion of deoxyuridine monophosphate to thymidine monophosphate is catalyzed by thymidylate synthetase, another enzyme lacking in the normal liver. According to Maley and Maley (1960), this enzyme first reaches detectable levels about 18 hours after operation, attains a maximum by 30 hours and then decreases. Its end product serves as a substrate for thymidylate kinase, which converts thymidine monophosphate to the triphosphate. Hiatt and Bojarski (1960) recorded high levels of this enzyme in foetal and new-born livers, in contrast to very low concentrations in adult livers. During regeneration, however, the activity of this enzyme begins to increase by 18 (Hiatt and Bojarski, 1960) or 23 (Bollum and Potter,

1959) hours. The former authors reported a peak from 36 to 48 hours and a return to normal by the fifth day. Again, the parallel with the rise and fall of mitotic activity is evident.

One of the final steps in the production of DNA involves the polymerization of the nucleotides into the helical configuration of the molecule. This reaction is catalysed by DNA polymerase, an enzyme that is present in greater concentration in regenerating livers than in intact ones. As in the previous cases discussed above, Bollum and Potter (1959) have found that it also increases in activity by 23 hours after partial hepatectomy, thus coinciding with the onset of mitotic proliferation.

The duality of the biochemical reactions ensuing partial ablation is emphasized by the increases in some cellular constituents and the decreases in others. This testifies to the importance of metabolic alterations in influencing growth rates, and may be reflected in three general categories of molecules. The first may be classified as end products, and includes those compounds which are synthesized by the cells of an organ either for export or for domestic consumption. A second, and obviously important, group of molecules affected by partial ablation are the many enzymes which catalyze the reactions, both anabolic and catabolic, by which the end products are elaborated. The fact that some enzyme systems are activated while others are inhibited in growing organs indicates the selective precision with which they are capable of mediating the syntheses of some compounds to the exclusion of others (figure 41). But this still leaves unexplained how the various enzymes themselves are regulated. Perhaps the answer to this is to be found in a third category of substances, namely, the substrates upon which the enzymes react. To the extent that all chemical reactions are reversible, these are in a sense identical with the first category of molecules, namely, cellular end products. Yet the direction in which a reaction goes is largely determined by mass action, with the result that the accumulation of precursor molecules will favour the synthesis of their respective end products, provided other conditions are conducive to such reactions. Should substrates be capable of inducing the formation or activation of their respective enzymes in metazoan systems, the role of substrate mobilization in regulating growth would be all the more important. Aside from this possibility, however, a relative increase in substrate could be achieved by depletion of end products. The latter would thus create a physiological demand to be satisfied by enhanced enzymatic activity and eventually by compensatory growth.

Much remains to be learned about the molecular changes attending compensatory hyperplasia. Notwithstanding the relative abundance of information about liver regeneration, data of a more comparative nature relating to other organs would unquestionably reveal many similarities and perhaps a number of interesting differences. Only by this approach will it be possible to identify the mechanisms shared in common by all systems, and thereby to formulate a unifying hypothesis of growth regulation. Already, however, it is becoming clear that physiological overload is the principal reaction of an organ remnant to reduction in its mass. What remains to be determined is whether it is the overwork *per se* which stimulates compensatory growth reactions, or whether increased function and accelerated growth are different (but complementary) effects of a common cause. In the latter event, the *demand* for greater functional output might initiate physiological reactions leading to growth as well as to function. Such physiological demands resulting from partial organ ablation may well take the form of depletions in the concentrations of functional end products, which in turn might lead to increased availability of precursor molecules. Inasmuch as the latter are substrates for enzyme action, they would be expected to induce greater enzymatic activities in order to catalyse their conversion into end products. Such a scheme of physiological compensation applies to the formation of functional products as well as to the synthesis of additional systems to perform these functions.

XII
Tissue Augmentation

ON the theory that growth regulation is largely a matter of self-inhibition, numerous experiments have been designed to preclude or reverse, by a form of replacement therapy, the compensatory growth responses following partial ablation (see review by Paschkis, 1958). If reduction in mass stimulates growth in the remaining portion of an organ, then replacement of the removed tissues should prevent growth. The trouble is that it is seldom possible to replace the missing parts without doing at least some violence to their organized structure. Devised with the intention of isolating tissue-specific growth regulating substances, much of the research along these lines has, unhappily, led to conflicting results.

Rationale and Techniques

The experimental replacement of tissues removed from an animal constitutes a rather effective test of the possible roles of mass and function in the control of growth. In line with the theory of Weiss (1955) and Weiss and Kavanau (1957) concerning the hypothetical existence of intracellular growth-promoting materials (templates) and extracellular growth inhibitors (antitemplates), experiments involving the replacement or addition of tissues would be expected to arrest or stimulate growth in homologous tissues depending on whether or not the supplementary cells remained viable and intact. If so, they ought to continue producing antitemplates which would then exert inhibitory influences on the growth of homologous cells. Otherwise, the normally intracellular templates would be released into the extracellular pool. Here they could find their way to the residual tissues of their own kind and stimulate growth. Alternatively, they might achieve the same result by inactivating some of the circulating antitemplates. It is perhaps an unavoidable weakness of this aspect of the theory that either inhibition or stimulation can be accounted for *ex post facto* according to the above rationale because unless cells are intentionally disrupted prior to injection it is difficult to measure their degree of viability after administration. It is important, therefore, to avoid defining the condition of the added cells according to the experimental outcome.

What is done to tissues in the process of preparing them for administration is especially pertinent. In certain cases it is possible to graft part or all of an organ relatively intact. If blood vessels are sutured to those in the host site, or if the transplant is not so large that revascularization can occur in time to prevent necrosis, normal functional relationships (with the exception of innervation) may be re-established. In such instances, both mass and function are restored. In most experiments, however, the histological integrity of the tissue is disrupted, as when tissues are dissociated mechanically or chemically in order to prepare cell suspensions. This treatment is sufficient to abolish functional capacity when it is dependent upon the existence of histological entities such as nephrons, acini, follicles, etc. Thus, in some instances isolated cells may remain alive after implantation, but unable to carry on the functions for which they were originally differentiated. This represents one way of restoring the missing portions of organs without making up for their functional deficiencies.

More drastic measures result in the destruction of cells, as in the production of homogenates or extracts of tissues. This renders a large number of tissues functionless but nevertheless yields preparations that are the equivalent in mass of the parts removed. When the cell is the chief functional unit of an organ or tissue, its replacement in non-viable form cannot compensate for the physiological loss except in so far as its subcellular constituents might be reincorporated by homologous cells. Yet if there exist molecules whose function is to regulate growth (to the exclusion of other possible physiological roles), they should remain intact and active under the above conditions.

There are some cases in which the functional competence of an organ may reside in specific molecules capable of operating outside the confines of their cells of origin. Hormones, and perhaps certain other cell products, may be included in this category. Thus, the administration of homogenates of endocrine glands may be tantamount to replacing both mass and function, at least temporarily. Moreover, by the use of extracts it is possible to compensate for secretory deficiencies following partial extirpation of endocrine glands without restoring the original mass of tissue. Hence by judiciously matching the experimental method to the organ to be investigated, it is possible to study the effects of alteration in mass and function either separately or in combination.

Not only do methods of preparation vary, but there is also some choice in selecting the route of administration. Grafts can be made to any well-vascularized site, one of the best being the chorioallantoic membrane of the chick embryo. Cell suspensions, homogenates, or extracts may be administered intraperitoneally, subcutaneously, or intravenously, and the effect achieved may vary accordingly. Unless they are considerably diluted, suspensions and homogenates cannot be injected intravenously without seriously jeopardizing the host's life. It is best, therefore, to give these by intraperitoneal injection, whereas extracts or supernatant solutions which are relatively free of particulate material can usually be successfully administered directly into the circulatory system. In addition to these factors, the timing of injections with respect to partial ablation or sacrifice may affect the reaction of the host. Other variables may include the condition of the material injected (heated, frozen or autolysed), the dose administered, and the species and ages of donors and recipients.

Liver

The most straightforward approach is to inject homogenates of adult organs into otherwise normal animals in order to determine what the effect will be on the intact homologous organs of the host. In the liver, variable results have been obtained by several different investigators. According to the theory proposed by Weiss and Kavanau (1957), one would expect to find enhanced growth in the host liver, presumably stimulated by the added templates. This was the case in experiments performed by Teir and Ravanti (1953) on rats in which saline suspensions of liver were injected intraperitoneally. Greater mitotic responses in host livers were noted following injections of liver derived from young rats than from older ones. They also found slight increases in mitotic rates of rat livers after intraperitoneal injections of orbital gland homogenates. Kelly and Jones (1953) injected saline homogenates of liver (as well as of embryos, tumours, and spleens) into mice and detected enhanced incorporation of radioactive phosphate into the DNA of recipient livers. Experiments carried out by Paschkis, *et al.* (1957) involved the subcutaneous injection of liver suspensions into rats, whose livers exhibited increased mitotic activity after ten days. A single intraperitoneal injection of alcohol extracts of regenerating rat liver was found by Kuru, *et al.* (1960) to stimulate hepatic mitosis in the rat within 24 hours. Semenova (1961) has reported that daily intraperitoneal injections of saline liver extracts into mice stimulated mitosis by the third day. Mitotic rates in the liver can also be increased by tumour grafts (Annau, *et al.*, 1951; Malmgren, 1956; Trotter, 1961) or by injections of tumour homogenates (Malmgren, 1956). Alov and Zhirnova (1957) believed that such results represented non-specific responses of the liver to protein breakdown products in general, since administration of horse serum and liver extracts both stimulated hepatic proliferation in mice.

Other investigators, however, have failed to detect any effects of liver homogenates on hepatic mitosis. Although Blomqvist (1957) noted increased proliferation in host livers or regenerating adult livers, he also reported that homogenates derived from intact three or nine-month-old rats were ineffectual. Administration of liver homogenates to infant rats, however, had no influence on proliferation in host livers (Stich, 1960), nor was mitotic activity stimulated in the livers of mice injected subcutaneously with normal liver homogenate (Malmgren, 1956). The RNA and DNA contents of host livers was also uninfluenced by homogenates of orbital glands (Teir, *et al.*, 1957). Decreased mitotic activity was reported by Saetren (1956) in the intact livers of young rats within two days after intraperitoneal injections of liver macerates. Depressed proliferation in normal mouse livers was also observed by Wilson and Leduc (1947) for three days after intraperitoneal injections of homogenized liver, but this was followed by a stimulation of mitosis reaching a peak on the fifth day. The same results were also produced by injections of fresh guinea pig liver, boiled or autolysed mouse liver, homogenized kidney, or boiled egg yolk. The only conclusion to be drawn from the foregoing investigations is that the effects of homogenate injections on normal liver mitosis are both variable and non-specific.

Comparable treatments of animals with regenerating livers have also yielded a spectrum of results. McJunkin and Breuhaus (1931) claimed that injections of liver macerates into partially hepatectomized rats promoted the regeneration of host livers. More recently, Lahtiharju (1961) has reported enhanced mitotic activity in regenerating livers of rats with pieces of liver left in the coelom. Injections of autolysed liver homogenates was also effective, even after boiling. No species specificity was noted, although a degree of tissue specificity was indicated by reduced responses to kidney homogenates. Mitotic stimulation of regenerating livers was also observed by Marshak and Walker (1945) when preparations of hepatic chromatin were injected intravenously. A number of studies, however, have yielded results inconsistent with the above. Saetren (1956), for example, injected macerated liver into rats 30 hours after partial hepatectomy and noted mitotic inhibition in the regenerating livers 18 hours later. Stich and Florian (1958) obtained similar results when homogenized normal liver was administered to rats possessing livers that had been regenerating for 24 hours. This influence lasted only one day, however, indicating that the effective agent is relatively labile. In contrast, the same authors found no inhibition of mitosis in regenerating livers when homogenates of regenerating, instead of intact, livers were injected. Other materials, such as kidney (Saetren, 1956) or brain (Stich and Florian, 1958) were also without effect when injected as homogenates into rats with regenerating livers, nor did hepatoma grafts (Trotter, 1961) affect hepatic hyperplasia.

Kidney

Replacement of kidney mass to the exclusion of function is easily achieved, as in the case of liver, by administration of homogenates. Accordingly, the following experiments have provided data relevant to the possible role played by the mass of renal tissue in governing kidney growth. Intraperitoneal injection of homogenized kidney by Breuhaus and McJunkin (1932) resulted in increased renal mitosis in the rat after two weeks. Daily intraperitoneal injections of kidney extracts in the mouse stimulated a threefold increase in mitoses on the third day (Semenova, 1961) in contrast to the lack of efficacy exhibited by extracts of liver or pancreas in the same system. Saetren (1956) also noted no influence on renal mitosis in young rats injected with liver macerates. Other investigations have demonstrated the capacity of injected tissue preparations to reduce renal mitosis. Kidney homogenates, for example, cause a temporary decline in mitotic rate in the homologous organs of young rats 24 hours after injection (Saetren, 1956). Similarly, Stich (1960) has reported reduced proliferative activity in the kidneys of infantile rats as a result of the injection of homogenates of liver or parotid glands. Along somewhat different lines, Weiss (1952) cultured embryonic metanephros *in vitro* in the presence of whole chick embryo extract, or in extracts made from embryos lacking kidneys, and noted that more new tubules differentiated in the latter medium. He concluded that homologous organs inhibit each other's differentiation.

Animals in the process of compensatory renal hyperplasia afford a better opportunity to detect mitotic inhibition than do intact hosts because of the higher rate of cell division in controls with which to compare the experimental results. Nevertheless, Breuhaus and McJunkin (1932) reported three times the control rate of mitotic activity in compensating kidneys of rats injected with adult kidney macerates, despite the fact that animals were not sacrificed until two weeks after injection. More short-term experiments, however, are preferable for studies of mitotic responses. Accordingly, Saetren (1956) found that in rats from which one and a half kidneys had been removed, intraperitoneal or subcutaneous injections of homogenized kidneys depressed the magnitude of the 48-hour mitotic peak. Liver homogenates, however, had no effect nor did preparations made from kidneys rendered non-functional by ligation of the ureter for ten days prior to use. It was further noted that the active agent in kidney tissue is relatively unstable, since the longer the interval from injection to sacrifice the more homogenate must be administered to achieve the same effect. Moreover, Saetren (1956) contended that the mitosis-inhibiting substance is not inactivated by desiccation, freezing, thawing, or storage at 1° C. for ten days. The effect of the substance was lost, however, by heating to 60° C., but not by dialysis.

Other experiments along these lines have been carried out by Steuart (1958), who administered kidney and liver homogenates to rats subjected to 75 per cent nephrectomy. When treated 18 to 30 hours before sacrifice at 48 hours, it was found that kidney homogenates caused an 80 per cent reduction in mitotic activity in the compensating kidneys, whereas liver decreased renal mitosis only 50 per cent.

Williams (1962b) detected an antimitotic effect of kidney macerate injected intraperitoneally into uninephrectomized rats (but spleen and liver macerates were ineffectual). Subsequent studies showed, however, that the depression of compensatory renal hyperplasia in this way was attributable to the reduced feeding of animals subjected to such injections. These results indicate that the effects of tissue injections are non-specific, and cannot be interpreted in favour of tissue-specific growth-controlling factors derived from the affected organ.

In an attempt to re-examine the possible influence of the replacement of renal mass on compensatory hyperplasia of the kidney, Goss

(1963b) has recently tested the effects of a variety of materials when injected into rats 30 hours after uninephrectomy and 18 hours before sacrifice. It had been shown that proliferation is at its highest approximately 48 hours after uninephrectomy. In these experiments it was found that the mitotic index of compensating kidneys was reduced about one-half when rats were injected intraperitoneally with fresh kidney homogenates or trypsin-dissociated suspensions of kidney cells. Ultracentrifugation of renal homogenates yielded a supernate that was also effective when administered intravenously. However, the effect was not tissue-specific, for administration of either homogenized liver, testis, spleen, or whole blood was equally effective in inhibiting renal mitosis. Kidneys that had been previously frozen or heated (100° C. for three hours) were likewise capable of depressing the 48-hour mitotic peak, although homogenates of frozen kidney injected subcutaneously instead of intraperitoneally were ineffectual. Presumably the route and rate of uptake of the active agent(s) is of importance. Whereas whole homogenized blood lowered the mitotic peak of compensating kidneys, normal plasma failed to exert an effect. Finally, intraperitoneal administration of fresh egg albumin proved to be effective, but similar injections of egg yolk were not.

Collectively considered, these results lead to the conclusion that the agents responsible for decreasing the hyperplastic reaction in remaining kidneys are highly non-specific, and that the antimitotic effect may be attributable solely to overloading the system with proteins or their breakdown products. In view of the failure of these results to confirm Saetren's (1956) contention that the antimitotic substance in kidneys is heat labile and tissue-specific, and since there is very little general agreement as to what effect, if any, the injection of homogenates has on the growth of homologous organs, it would be extremely hazardous to accept any results unequivocally, even if one knew which ones to believe.

Orbital Glands

The possibility that injections of tissue homogenates might influence homologous organ growth has also been explored by Teir and his associates with special reference to the orbital gland in the rat. Although the results were often disturbingly variable, the general contention was that homogenates of the outer orbital gland injected intraperitoneally stimulate mitotic activity in outer (Teir, 1950; Teir and Isotalo, 1954) or inner (Teir, 1952a) orbital glands. This treatment, however, did not affect mitosis in the epidermis (Teir and Isotalo, 1954) but had a slight stimulatory action on liver (Teir and Ravanti, 1953). Conversely, thymus suspensions injected intraperitoneally caused the rate of cell division in the thymus to rise but did not increase orbital gland mitosis (Telkkä and Teir, 1955). Homogenates of new-born rat liver, however, stimulated a rise in the DNA content of outer orbital glands (Teir, *et al.*, 1957). Therefore, there is reason to question the tissue specificity of this phenomenon. Nevertheless, it has been noted that the age of the donor and recipient rats (Teir, 1952a) and the dose of homogenate administered (Teir, 1950) are important factors in determining the response. Furthermore, the active agent is apparently thermostable (Teir, 1950, 1952b; Kuusi and Teir, 1953), resistant to desiccation (Teir, 1952b), not inactivated by freezing or x-irradiation (Voutilainen, *et al.*, 1959), soluble in chloroform, and insoluble in ether (Teir, 1952b). Unfortunately, however, the validity of these data is subject to the same objections previously noted in the cases of liver and kidney, namely, that the repeatability of experimental results is plagued by serious inconsistencies.

Very limited information is available concerning other organs. Stich (1960) has investigated the responses of the parotid salivary gland in young rats and has noted decreased proliferative activity following injections of parotid or liver homogenates. However, these same preparations also suppressed mitosis in the kidneys but not in the livers of recipient animals. In contrast, Alov and Semenova (1958) claimed that the injection of salivary gland extracts caused increased mitotic activity in mouse salivary glands, but that extracts of intestines had no such effect. As in the cases of other organs, it is difficult to attach any great significance to such conflicting results as these.

Red Blood-Cells

Because erythropoiesis is such an advantageous process to study, the results of investigations on the influence of red blood-cell replacement on the rate of erythropoiesis have been more consistent than comparable studies in other tissues. This is especially true of the transfusion of intact blood-cells, which leads to the condition of polycythaemia. When rabbits were rendered plethoric in this way, Robertson (1917) and Boycott (1934) observed that the number of reticulocytes in the blood diminished, indicating reduced red blood-cell production. In the human, Smith, et al. (1955) have noted that the transfusion of blood into anaemic individuals suppressed the rate of haematopoiesis. Experiments on mice by Fried, et al. (1957) and Jacobson, et al. (1957a) have demonstrated that repeated intraperitoneal injections of red blood-cells abolished erythropoiesis within six days. As Robertson (1917) and Boycott (1934) showed, when the transfused blood eventually disappears erythropoiesis again increases. Robertson (1917) also found that when rabbits which had been made polycythaemic were later bled to normal haemoglobin levels, erythropoiesis was accelerated as indicated by reticulocytosis. This interesting effect was interpreted as a regenerative response to a *relative* loss of blood, perhaps indicating that the animals had become adapted in some way to what was originally a superabundance of red blood-cells.

When a rabbit is given a second transfusion after recovering from the first one, Boycott (1934) noted that the excess red blood-cells were more rapidly destroyed than the first time and that the reticulocyte count rose to normal sooner. Thus, he was led to write that "it is difficult to maintain a high degree of polycythaemia by this method since most rabbits soon learn to destroy the excess of red cells with an inconvenient efficiency" (probably attributable to secondary immunological responses). He also observed that it was impossible to abolish the production of reticulocytes altogether by massive transfusions. This he regarded as an adaptation for survival, since "The danger of haemorrhage is always present" (Boycott, 1934).

It is to be expected that owing to a kind of replacement therapy, the augmentation of red blood-cells should inhibit erythropoiesis. Whether or not this is to be attributed to the functional capacity of the added cells can only be determined by injecting erythrocytes that have been disrupted in various ways. Theoretically, such treatment should not stimulate erythropoiesis if that process is governed by the oxygen-carrying function of red blood-cells. Moreover, growth-promoting templates (cf. Weiss and Kavanau, 1957) should not exist in red blood-cells inasmuch as they are no longer capable of growth. In view of these considerations, it is especially interesting that various derivatives of red blood-cell breakdown are apparently capable of stimulating the rate of erythropoiesis. Although Itami (1910) and Robertson (1917) found no change in the blood or in the activity of marrow in normal rabbits injected intraperitoneally or intravenously with laked red blood-cells, Ono (1926) reported that haemolysed blood caused the production of increased numbers of red blood-cells when injected in small doses, but exerted inhibitory influences in large doses. In the dog and human, Naswitis (1922) obtained increased red blood-cell production following the injection of defibrinated blood that had been frozen and thawed. Such procedures are evidently more effective when the experimental animals are bled prior to the administration of the test material. Hess and Saxl (1912) noted that control rabbits normally made good the loss of 30 millilitres of blood in twelve to fourteen days. This regenerative interval, however, was reduced to eight or nine days by the subcutaneous administration of whole defibrinated blood or haematin, and to seven days by the injection of haemin or washed red cells. Haematoporphyrin, a compound lacking iron, did not accelerate erythropoiesis. Oka (1932) performed some similar experiments by injecting red cell stromas or whole haemolysed blood intraperitoneally into bled rabbits, and thus obtained increased rates of erythropoiesis.

Intact red blood-cells understandably depress erythropoiesis because of their functional competence. The acceleration of red blood-cell production by the injection of destroyed erythrocytes, however, is more difficult to fathom. Probably the most logical explanation is the simplest, namely, that the replacement of iron permits the more rapid synthesis of haemoglobin in the differentiating red cell precursors of the marrow. In point of fact, Fowler and Barer (1942) reported that in human subjects the daily administration of iron after loss of blood caused an average 49 per cent increase in the rate of haemoglobin replacement and a 29 per cent decline in recovery time.

Endocrine Glands

The difficulties previously noted with reference to the influences of tissue homogenates on liver, kidney, and orbital glands do not apply to many of the endocrine glands, perhaps because of the nature of their functional units. In the foregoing tissues, physiological efficiency depended upon the existence of intact functional structures (e.g. renal nephrons, exocrine acini, liver cells, red blood-corpuscles) which were vulnerable to destruction by homogenization. Such is not the case with the endocrine glands in which intact cells are necessary for synthesizing hormones but not for their subsequent activities. Thus, homogenates or extracts of glands are well known for their efficacy in mimicking the actions of normal glands when administered to experimental animals. Isolation and purification of hormones has made it possible to achieve the same effects under more precisely controlled conditions. In general, an excess of a given hormone suppresses the secretion of more of the same, causes atrophy of the homologous gland under chronic conditions, and specifically inhibits compensatory growth following partial ablation. In these cases, therefore, the molecule substitutes for the mass of an organ, and the function that is performed acts as the principal regulator of growth.

This principle is illustrated by the relationship between the adrenal cortex and its hormones. Ingle and Kendall (1937) demonstrated that adrenal cortical extracts caused the involution of the adrenal gland, a result that was later duplicated by the administration of desoxycorticosterone acetate (Selye, 1940; Hall and Hall, 1952). When one adrenal is removed from the rat, MacKay and MacKay (1938) showed that the compensatory hypertrophy normally manifested in an enlargement of the remaining gland to 65 to 73 per cent of the original combined weight in the next eight to ten days, is reduced to zero to 16 per cent if cortical extract is administered. Bernstein and Biskind (1957) also inhibited compensatory hypertrophy following unilateral adrenalectomy by administering five milligrams of cortisone per week to rats. Using hydrocortisone on dogs, Ganong and Hume (1955) demonstrated that the degree to which compensatory growth of the remaining adrenal is suppressed is proportional to the dose of hormone injected. Indeed, atrophy instead of hypertrophy will occur if large doses of hydrocortisone are given. Desoxycorticosterone acetate will also suppress compensatory adrenal hypertrophy, as Brody (1963, unpublished) has discovered in rats.

The role of ACTH in stimulating cortisone secretion and cortical growth has recently been investigated by Davidson and Feldman (1962) by implanting small crystals of hydrocortisone (too minute to exert a systemic effect) into the hypothalamus of rats. When one adrenal gland was removed from such animals, compensatory hypertrophy of the remaining gland was suppressed. Similar implantations of hydrocortisone crystals directly into the pituitary failed to inhibit compensatory cortical enlargement. These results may be taken to indicate, therefore, that the secretion of ACTH by the pituitary is stimulated by the hypothalamus, the cells of which are in turn directly sensitive to the concentration of hydrocortisone in their microenvironments. It is interesting that the regulation of adrenal cortical growth (and function) is mediated directly via the concentration of hormone produced and apparently not by the efficiency with which

o

the hormone performs its other functions in the body, although the latter may have a modulating influence.

A similar hypothalamo-pituitary relationship has been demonstrated in the case of the gonads. Ovarian or testicular atrophy ensues the infliction of hypothalamic lesions (Lisk, 1960) or the implantation of oestrogen or testosterone into the hypothalamus (Lisk, 1960; Davidson and Sawyer, 1961). Apparently either sex hormone will suffice to cause atrophy of either gonad via inhibition of pituitary gonadotrophin secretion.

As expected, systemic administration of these hormones also affects growth and function of the gonads. Progesterone, for example, has been shown capable of inhibiting oestrous cycles and causing ovarian atrophy (Selye, et al., 1936). Not only does oestrogen promote ovarian atrophy in intact rats (d'Amour, 1931), but it also completely prevents compensatory hypertrophy in unilaterally spayed animals (Heller, et al., 1942). Peterson, et al. (1962) have obtained similar results in rats with a variety of steroid preparations, including testosterone and progesterone.

In the case of the fowl, in which left ovariectomy normally results in the development of the rudimentary right gonad into predominantly testicular organs, the administration of oestrogen tends to suppress this compensatory response of the right gonad (Kornfeld and Nalbandov, 1954; Kornfeld, 1958). Inasmuch as rudimentary right gonads often possess varying amounts of cortical tissue, in addition to the constant occurrence of medullary tissue, these gonads are capable of giving rise to ovarian and testicular structures, respectively (Taber, et al., 1955, 1956). Treatment of young poulards with oestrogen, however, selectively suppresses the development of the medullary components of the right gonads without adversely affecting the cortical tissue (Taber, et al., 1958a). Therefore, only those gonads that would have developed in part as ovarian organs are allowed to grow under conditions of oestrogen administration (Taber and Salley, 1954). Testosterone treatment likewise suppresses development in the rudimentary right gonad after left ovariectomy (Kornfeld and Nalbandov, 1954), an effect that completely inhibits medullary differentiation and reduces the incidence of cortical development from 21·3 to 12·4 per cent (Taber, et al., 1958a).

Since hypophysectomy inhibits hypertrophy of the right gonad following left ovariectomy in the fowl (Kornfeld and Nalbandov, 1954), there is reason to believe that the effects of exogenous sex hormones are mediated via the suppression of pituitary gonado-trophins. However, the differential responses of medulla and cortex to sex hormones would indicate that the male (medullary) component of the gonads is more highly susceptible to pituitary stimulation (or inhibition) than are the female (cortical) portions. Indeed, the latter appear to be relatively independent of such influences, a possibility that might be tested on intact female birds by studying the effects of hypophysectomy, and of oestrogen and gonadotrophin treatment, on normal ovarian growth. Since oestrogen does not prevent compen-satory development of the right gonadal cortex in the ovarian direction, it might also fail to promote atrophy of the left ovary, a result which, if true, would be interestingly different from the situation in mammals (cf. d'Amour, 1931; Heller, et al., 1942). Conceivably, such a difference might also account for the unilateral occur-rence of ovaries in certain species of birds, and the unexpected pro-pensity of the right rudimentary gonads of females to develop into testes instead of ovaries. Assuming that gonadotrophins are respon-sible for stimulating compensatory growth of the right gonad rudi-ment, it remains to be determined why it failed to do so during embryonic development, despite the fact that anterior pituitary preparations stimulate follicular development when injected into immature female chickens (Taber, et al., 1958b). As one of the most puzzling and exceptional examples of compensatory hypertrophy, this general phenomenon poses a number of important questions that have remained unanswered not because of technical limitations but for lack of sufficiently serious attention by endocrinologists.

The influence of the ovary on its own growth is illustrated by its reactions to transplantation. Ovarian grafts into the eyes of rabbits do not develop until the host ovaries are removed (Lane and Markee, 1941). Similarly, Lipschütz and Adamberg (1925) found that if extra ovaries are grafted to otherwise intact guinea pigs, no functional activity is manifested in the transplants. However, ovarian grafts made to previously castrated females underwent normal growth and development, including the formation of corpora lutea. It has been claimed that homografts of ovaries are enabled to survive longer if their functional activity is stimulated. Thus, injections of pregnant mare's serum into mice (Ferguson and Kirschbaum, 1954) or rats (Ingram and Krohn, 1956) prolonged the survival of ovarian homo-grafts. Stevens (1955) has shown that in mice in which one ovary was replaced by one from another strain, subsequent offspring were seldom derived from the graft. Removal of the host's other ovary, however, resulted in the production of litters from the transplant.

The responses of the mammalian testis are not unlike those of the ovary. Atrophy is caused by treatment with excessive testosterone (Korenchevsky, et al., 1933; Schoeller and Gehrke, 1933) or implantation of crystalline testosterone (Davidson and Sawyer, 1961) or oestrogen (Lisk, 1960) into the hypothalamus to prevent pituitary secretion of gonadotrophin. Chorionic gonadotrophin administered to rats exerts a trophic influence on the interstitial cells, and when given to mice as pregnant mare's serum may induce tumour formation after about a year (Gardner, 1943). Prolonged oestrogen injections in the mouse have been reported to do likewise (Bonser and Robson, 1940), although the mechanism remains obscure.

It is clear that each of the steroid-secreting endocrine glands is regulated in its growth by the secretion of the appropriate pituitary hormones in response to hypothalamic stimulation. Control of the latter resides in a sensitivity to the level of the steroid hormones in the system. These hormones are normally broken down in the liver, as has been repeatedly demonstrated by the effects of transplanting adrenals or gonads to sites drained by the hepatic portal circulation. If adrenal glands are transplanted to the spleen, for example, they will grow only if there is no other cortical tissue left *in situ* (Bernstein, 1950). Under these conditions relatively few steroid hormone molecules escape degradation in the liver, with the result that the hypothalamus is exposed to a chronic deficit of hormones and therefore stimulates the secretion of extra amounts of ACTH from the pituitary. Without this ACTH, the secretion of which would have been suppressed had a normal adrenal cortex been left in place, the intrasplenic adrenal graft can neither grow nor regenerate.

A comparable situation obtains with reference to the gonads. Ovarian autografts to the spleen or mesentery undergo no hypertrophy. Indeed, they may become atrophic so long as the other ovary remains intact and capable of secreting oestrogen that can act on the hypothalamus (Golden, et al., 1938; Biskind and Biskind, 1948; Biskind, et al., 1950). In the absence of any other ovarian tissue outside the portal circulation, however, such grafts usually undergo enlargement (Biskind and Biskind, 1944) that may reach dimensions three times normal after a month or two (Heller and Jungck, 1947). If grafts are allowed to become extremely atrophic for a couple of months before the remaining ovary is removed, reversal of the atrophy can still occur (Biskind and Biskind, 1948). If both ovaries are grafted to the spleen and oestrogen is administered, the transplanted ovaries decrease considerably in weight (Heller and Jungck, 1947). In rats with one intrasplenic ovary and one functional ovary, pregnancy causes active growth of follicles in previously atrophic grafts, but the postpartum changes are again atrophic (Biskind and Kordon, 1949; Biskind, et al., 1950). Intrasplenic ovarian grafts in castrated animals generally give rise to follicles which become luteinized, and after a number of months develop into luteomata (Biskind and Biskind, 1949; Biskind, et al., 1950; Iglesias, et al., 1953). Granulosa cell tumours may form after more prolonged residence in the portal circulation (Peckham and Green, 1952; Gurthrie, 1954). Klein (1952) has noted that intrasplenic grafts of young ovaries give rise to more tumours than do older ovaries, but Li and Gardner (1952) could detect no effect of graft age on the incidence of tumour production.

The foregoing data indicate that oestrogens are normally inactivated by the liver and that chronic exposure to pituitary gonadotrophins causes hypertrophy and tumourigenesis in intrasplenic ovarian grafts in laboratory rodents. This is not a universal phenomenon, however, for Van Wagenen and Gardner (1950) noted the persistence of normal function in monkey ovaries grafted to the portal circulation. Moreover, Bernstorf (1951) concluded that not all of the ovarian oestrogen is inactivated by the liver since the weights of the vagina and uterus in castrated mice bearing intrasplenic ovarian grafts were intermediate between those of castrated and normal controls. A similar situation may explain the results of Gardner and Taber (1963) who compared the degree of compensatory growth of right rudimentary gonads in fowl in which the left ovary had been transplanted either to the portal circulation, the systemic circulation, or discarded altogether. It was noted that ovarian grafts to the portal circulation of the gizzard permitted some growth of the right gonadal rudiment, but not as much as that occurring in normal poulards. Subcutaneous ovarian grafts, however, usually prevented hypertrophy of the right rudimentary gonad. Although birds with ovarian grafts in the portal circulation failed to develop female-type plumage as did those with subcutaneous ovarian transplants, it is possible that their livers inactivated enough oestrogen to cause the development of neutral plumage but not enough to inhibit completely the growth of the right gonads in some cases. Such a differential response to varying concentrations of oestrogen seems to be a more logical explanation of these phenomena than is the suggestion of Gardner and Taber (1963) that the ovary produces a non-steroid substance capable of inhibiting development of the right gonad. Were this to be the case, the marked difference in response of the right gonads to ovarian grafts in the portal as opposed to the systemic circulation should not have occurred.

The testis behaves in an analogous manner when grafted to the spleen. When hosts are not completely castrated, Sundell (1957) found that only one out of 30 transplants grew. But when the hosts were completely castrated except for the intrasplenic testicular grafts, 20 out of 50 cases gave rise to tumours. This confirms the previous observations of Biskind and Biskind (1945) that nodular tumours develop in testes after 11 months of residence in the spleens of castrated rats, and of Twombly, et al. (1949) that Leydig cell tumours were produced in 6·5 and 8 per cent of the 1-day-old testes grafted to the spleens of castrated male and female hosts, respectively. In non-castrated male hosts slight testicular hyperplasia was observed in a few cases of intrasplenic grafts, but none developed into tumours.

The effect of thyroxine, or its equivalent, on growth of the thyroid gland can be predicted from what is known of other endocrine glands. Administration of various thyroid preparations to intact animals results in decreased weight and diminished secretion by the host's thyroid (Herring, 1917; Loeb, et al., 1930). Blumenthal and Loeb (1942) noted that mitotic activity in the normal guinea pig thyroid was depressed by treatment with thyroid substance. In guinea pigs subjected to partial thyroidectomy, the compensatory growth response can be counteracted by feeding thyroid preparations or injecting thyroxine (Loeb, 1920, 1928a; Gray, 1929).

The influence of iodine administration on thyroid growth is more equivocal. Loeb (1920, 1926, 1928b) fed or injected doses of potassium iodide ranging from 10 to 100 milligrams per day to partially thyroidectomized guinea pigs. In most cases there was no effect on the ensuing compensatory hypertrophy, although with the highest doses the extent of hypertrophy was diminished. In normal guinea pigs, however, Blumenthal and Loeb (1942) enhanced thyroid proliferation by feeding potassium iodide. Marine (1926) injected even smaller doses (25 milligrams of potassium iodide semi-weekly) into partially thyroidectomized animals and noted that the thyroid remnants were less hypertrophic than in uninjected controls. Unfortunately, these discrepancies do not appear to have been resolved. To the extent that thyroid growth is stimulated by TSH from the pituitary, iodine would be expected to play only a secondary role by facilitating the synthesis of thyroxine, which in turn has a reciprocal relationship with TSH via the hypothalamus. Thus, iodine deficiency leads to thyroid enlargement owing to excessive secretion of TSH. The goiterogenic compound, thiouracil, exerts a similar effect because of its blocking action on thyroxine synthesis. The hyperplasia induced in rat thyroids by thiouracil (Thomas, 1945; Rupp, 1952; Santler, 1957), can thus be abolished by hypophysectomy or by administering thyroid powder, but not by supplementary iodine (Astwood, et al., 1943).

Unlike the steroid hormones, thyroxine is able to traverse the hepatic circulation without significant inactivation. Rupp (1952) found that when all of an animal's thyroid tissue was transplanted to the spleen, the graft was able to function normally. It remained histologically indistinguishable from normal thyroid tissue for at least a year, yet retained the capacity to become hyperplastic following thiouracil treatment.

Replacement therapy likewise prevents growth of the parathyroid glands. Treatment of dogs with parathyroid hormone caused a reduction of the glands to about one-half the normal size which Jaffe and Bodansky (1930) referred to as "functional involutional atrophy due to substitution therapy". According to McJunkin, et al. (1932) the number of cell divisions in the rat parathyroid was reduced to 7·4 per cent of normal after 3 to 15 days of treatment with parathyroid hormone. Burrows (1938) attributed the 25 to 45 per cent reduction in parathyroid size after a month of hormone treatment in the rat to a decrease in the numbers rather than the sizes of parathyroid cells.

The β-cells of the islets of Langerhans are especially sensitive to excesses of their secretory product, insulin. Animals treated chronically with insulin exhibit decreased mitoses in their islet tissues (McJunkin and Roberts, 1932) which eventually leads to regression as a result of β-cell atrophy (Latta and Harvey, 1942). Administration of α-cell extracts to guinea pigs caused an inhibition of secretory activity in the α-cells of the islets of Langerhans (Bensley and Woerner, 1938).

Embryonic Organs

Thus far, attempts to substitute for the missing portions of organs by the administration of various homologous preparations have failed to demonstrate convincingly the existence of any growth regulating factors that are not directly related to the physiological activities of the organ. Indeed, the results of experiments along these lines have been most inconsistent with reference to organs (e.g. liver, kidney) whose functions depend upon structures most likely to be destroyed in the preparation of homogenates for injection. However, more definitive data relevant to comparable experiments on the various endocrine glands reflect the fact that their growth is regulated by their functional products which, because of their molecular natures, are stable to the usual methods of tissue homogenization and extraction. In general, therefore, many experiments that were originally designed to prove whether or not organ growth is controlled by specific factors related to tissue mass *per se*, when considered collectively, have lent considerable support to the theory of growth regulation by functional demand. Although such an explanation is reasonable as applied to organs sufficiently mature to be functional, there are obvious difficulties in adapting it to prefunctional systems such as are encountered in embryos. Special attention, therefore, is warranted for the consideration of the effects of tissue augmentation on the growth rates of homologous embryonic organs.

Growth of the four-day embryonic chick liver under the influence of six-day-old embryonic livers grafted to the chorioallantoic membrane has been investigated by Weiss and Wang (1941). It was found that the host livers grew 31 per cent more than controls. Simonsen (1957) noted that embryonic livers were not enlarged following transplantation of adult liver tissue to the chrioallentoic membrane, but Van Alten and Fennell (1959) reported hepatic hypertrophy in embryos with chorioallantoic grafts of adult liver, spleen, or duodenum, an effect which may be the result of immunological relationships. Most experiments on this problem, however, have involved the injection of liver suspensions or extracts into chick embryos of various ages. Alov and Semenova (1958) injected liver extracts into the vascular fields of seven-day chick embryos. Two or three days later they observed hypertrophy and hyperplasia of hepatic cells, together with increases in the relative weights of the recipients' livers. Extracts injected intravenously into three to five-day-old embryos also stimulated extra growth of the host liver after seven to thirteen days, according to studies of Croisille (1958). In embryos six to thirteen days of age, Tumanishvili, *et al.* (1956) noted increases in the relative weights of host livers within 24 hours of injection of liver extracts. This treatment was less effective in fifteen-day-old embryos. Using suspensions of fresh or frozen liver from six-day-old chick embryos, Andres (1955) noted a slight stimulation of hepatic mitosis in six-day-old hosts injected intravenously. There is doubt as to the specificity of this effect, for he showed that similar injections of mesonephros suspensions also stimulated host liver mitoses. Not evident during the first 12 hours, the effect of injected embryonic mesonephros suspensions on host livers amounted to a 32 per cent increase by 24 hours, and a 41 per cent increase after 48 hours. Mensonephric suspensions also increased mitotic activity in the mesonephros of injected hosts (Weiss, 1952) but liver suspensions did not (Andres, 1955). Simonsen (1957), moreover, failed to obtain enlargement of host kidneys by the administration of adult chicken kidney. Thus, in the cases of hepatic and renal embryonic tissues, perhaps it is encouraging that treatment with various tissue preparations, if effective at all, tends to cause growth stimulation, though the specificity of this effect leaves something to be desired. But if these results in embryonic systems seem less inconsistent than those in adults, it may only be correlated with the lesser volume of research thus far reported. More extensive investigations along these lines are clearly in order.

Embryonic or foetal endocrine glands respond in fashions similar to those in adults when subjected to excess tissue or hormones. Grafts of adult chicken thyroid to the chorioallantoic membrane resulted in reduced homologous organs in host embryos (Willier, 1924). In the case of the foetal rat adrenal cortex, compensatory hypertrophy failed to occur after unilateral adrenalectomy when one milligram pellets of cortisone were implanted subcutaneously two days before term (Kitchell and Wells, 1952). Although the same authors were unable to observe size changes in the normal foetal adrenal following subcutaneous implantation of various steroid hormones (cortisone, desoxycorticosterone, testosterone, progesterone, oestrogen), Yakaitis and Wells (1956) later succeeded in inhibiting the growth of adrenal glands in rat foetuses given cortisone or hydrocortisone subcutaneously on the fourteenth day of gestation. In these animals, sacrificed just before parturition, the width of the cortex was decreased owing to reduction of the inner zone. Similar implantations of desoxycorticosterone acetate were less effective, causing only a decrease in the width of the outer zone.

The embryonic circulatory system has yielded some interesting results under the influence of specific tissue extracts. With reference to the blood, Lenique (1959) found that in 18 to 20-hour-old chick embryos injected with extracts of blood, erythropoiesis was inhibited in 31 per cent of the cases as measured by decreased haemoglobin formation. Similar injections of heart extracts likewise partially suppressed blood formation, in addition to delaying heart differentiation. Other investigators, however, have reported the stimulation of heart growth by treatment with heart extracts (Tumanishvili, *et al.*, 1956), and Van Alten and Fennell (1959) noted cardiac enlargement in chick embryos with adult spleen, liver, or duodenum grafts on their chorioallantoic membranes. In tissue culture experiments, Weiss (1952) observed enhanced differentiation of embryonic chick heart (using pulsatile activity as a criterion) in media containing extracts of embryos deprived of their hearts, as compared with cultures grown in whole embryo extract. If differentiation is interpreted as being antagonistic to proliferative growth, then these results indicate an homologous inhibition of growth by tissue extracts.

One of the most remarkable examples of organ enlargement in embryonic systems relates to the stimulation of splenomegaly in the chick embryo following the transplantation of immunologically competent tissues to the chorioallantoic membrane. The histological changes attending splenic enlargement in the host, reviewed by DeLanney and Ebert (1962), include changes that are both degenerative (necrosis) and constructive (granulopoiesis). These alterations are most effectively initiated by chorioallantoic grafts of adult chicken spleen (reviewed by Ebert, 1958), but can also be stimulated to lesser degrees by adult bone marrow, liver, kidney (Murphy, 1916), duodenum, brain, skin (Van Alten and Fennell, 1959), and blood (Cock and Simonsen, 1958; Biggs and Payne, 1959). Terasaki (1959) concluded that the responsible cell type, shared in common by all of these tissues, was the lymphocyte. Mun, *et al.* (1959a) noted that adult turkey and pheasant spleens were effective, but to lesser extents than chicken spleens, whereas guinea pig and rat spleens were ineffectual. They also demonstrated that devitalized or heavily X-rayed spleens were incapable of stimulating splenomegaly in hosts. Spleens from immature donors were also without effect (Solomon, 1961) as were those from adults of the same inbred strains (Mun, *et al.*, 1962). Various lines of evidence derived from experiments using donor cells identified by their sex chromosomes (Biggs and Payne, 1959) or labelled with tritiated thymidine (Mun, *et al.*, 1962) indicate that donor cells actually colonize host spleens and participate in the subsequent proliferative processes (although host cells multiply too).

The foregoing body of information clearly implicates the operation of immunological processes in this graft-versus-host reaction which leads to splenic enlargement. Mun, *et al.* (1962) concluded that it is this aspect of the phenomenon that is responsible for the destructive changes occurring in host spleens, i.e. necrosis, vascular damage, and accumulation of mucopolysaccharides. To explain the proliferative responses, however, they proposed that this destruction of tissue as a result of the primary immunological reaction leads to a secondary proliferative response on the part of host cells. This, together with the multiplying population of donor cells, contributes significantly to the resulting splenomegaly. If the enhanced granulopoiesis of host spleens is stimulated by the release of materials from the degenerating tissues, as Mun, *et al.* (1962) believe it is, then such a reaction must be a very local one since the presence of necrotic spleen grafts on the chorioallantoic membrane does not exert the same influence (Mun, *et al.*, 1959b). In view of the general confusion regarding the possible role of degenerating tissues in regulating growth, as reviewed in the present chapter, any interpretation of experimental results along these lines must be accepted with caution. In the cases of splenomegaly reported above, different explanations may eventually prove to be more valid.

Other approaches to the general problem of growth regulation by tissue preparations have included investigations of the selectivity with which tissue components are incorporated in various growing organs. Ebert (1953) was one of the first to recognize the value of this method in elucidating tissue-specific growth reactions. Accordingly, he labelled adult chicken spleens and kidneys with S^{35}-methionine and subsequently grafted samples to the chorioallantoic membranes of nine-day-old chick embryos. Sacrificed three to five days later, the homologous host organs proved to be as much as $2 \cdot 4$ times as radioactive as other organs. Similar experiments using S^{35}-labelled adult liver homogenates injected into nine-day embryos resulted in maximal uptake in host livers 24 hours later (Walter, *et al.*, 1956). Horn and House (1955) attempted comparable studies on six-week-old mice in which preparations of adult organs (liver, kidney, spleen, thymus) labelled with C^{14} were injected intraperitoneally. They were able to detect no selective uptake of the label by homologous host organs, but noted that the spleen incorporated more label than any other organ, probably owing to its phagocytic activity. It is possible, therefore, that selective uptake of tissue components may be more prevalent in rapidly growing systems. If so, the significance of this phenomenon may lie in its possible role in cellular differentiation and induction (cf. Ebert, 1959). Alternatively, it may represent a form of intercellular communication (at the systemic level) by which growth rates in homologous tissues are co-ordinated. On the strength of existing evidence, however, it will be prudent to reserve judgment until these very interesting avenues of investigation have been more extensively explored.

In conclusion, it must be admitted that the arguments in favour of the occurrence of tissue-specific growth-regulating compounds do not inspire confidence. Neither are they completely without foundation. Most experiments, however, probably represent oversimplified approaches to theoretical possibilities, and unfortunately have not fulfilled the hope of isolating specific growth inhibiting or stimulating substances. This failure is not attributed to a lack of effect, but to serious inconsistencies in the influences of tissue preparations on growth. The current, task, therefore, is to reduce some of the chaos by using increasingly standardized approaches. Until the systems for assaying experimental results yield repeatable data, it will be useless to seek information on a subject that is apparently going to demand the proficient application of many technical skills. Most important of all will be the methods by which tissues to be tested are prepared. Having demonstrated that crude homogenates and extracts are of little value in yielding consistent results, the only alternative is to test extracts of increasing purity. And this must be done with no more assurance of success than only a theoretical possibility that the material being sought may actually exist.

XIII

Humoral Growth Regulation

THE occurrence of compensatory hypertrophy, especially in paired organs, demands the existence of a communication system by which the effects of partial ablation may be transmitted to residual homologous tissues. Thus, the search for tissue-specific growth-regulating compounds has naturally prompted many investigators to conduct experiments designed to detect such hypothetical substances in the body fluids. Most studies have concentrated on the serum, although some interesting results have been obtained with urine. Experiments testing the effects of aqueous humor on lens regeneration have already been described in Chapter VI. Methods of approaching the problem have usually involved the exchange of serum between various combinations of donor and recipient animals, either intact or subjected to partial organ ablation. This may be achieved by direct injection or by joining animals together parabiotically. In some studies, the effects of removing quantities of blood fluid (plasmapheresis) have yielded pertinent results, and in others it has been possible to measure the growth of tissues cultured in sera obtained from animals with or without the organ under investigation. These several approaches have been applied largely to the specific problems of liver regeneration, compensatory renal hyperplasia, and erythropoiesis, each of which is discussed below.

Effect of Serum on Liver Regeneration
    The most direct approach to identifying serum factors capable of altering the growth of the liver is to transfer serum between various combinations of intact and partially hepatectomized rats. Normal serum injected into normal animals is the simplest experimental combination. Friedrich-Freksa and Zaki (1954), for example, injected 1 to 3 millilitres of normal serum derived from 2 to 3-month-old rats into normal recipients of the same age, and noted no change in hepatic mitosis after 24 to 72 hours. MacDonald and Rogers (1961) likewise failed to obtain any effects on liver mitosis or DNA synthesis 12 to 20 hours following intravenous administration of 3 to 5

millilitres of normal plasma to male rats weighing 220 to 367 grams. Recent experiments by Leong, et al. (1963) and Moya (1963) have revealed no significant effects of normal serum on normal hepatic mitoses of the recipients. Smythe and Moore (1958) conducted similar experiments by giving repeated intravenous injections of 1 millilitre of normal serum every 8 hours and sacrificing five injections and 48 hours later. This treatment resulted in a slight increase in hepatic cell division to 0·14 per cent from control levels of 0·019 per cent. The results of Fisher, et al. (1963) are in agreement with this. The positive results thus obtained in such experiments may be attributable to the more prolonged exposure to serum. However, if any general conclusion can be drawn from the above combination of slightly positive and noncommittal results, it is that serum may normally contain either growth stimulants or a mixture of stimulating and inhibiting factors. Indeed, Alston and Thomson (1963) have recently found that liver mitoses are depressed by injections of normal serum.

Another method of testing normal serum for its possible growth-controlling capacity is to inject it into partially hepatectomized rats. According to the technique of repeated serum injections of Smythe and Moore (1958), this resulted in a one-third decrease in the rate of liver regeneration, as determined by liver weight after 48 hours. However, hepatic mitosis was slightly increased by this treatment. Other investigators failed to influence liver regeneration by injecting normal serum. Partially hepatectomized rats, for example, were given normal serum intravenously at four-hour intervals by Bucher (1958). Over a period of 30 hours this amounted to a threefold turnover of blood fluid. Nevertheless, this treatment had no more effect on liver regeneration (measured by weight increase or mitotic index) than did saline similarly injected into controls. MacDonald and Rogers (1961) likewise failed to affect mitotic activity in livers of rats partially hepatectomized 8 hours before the injection of normal serum and sacrificed 12 to 20 hours afterwards. Alston and Thomson (1963) also found no significant effect of normal serum on compensatory liver hyperplasia. Repeated intraperitoneal injections of normal serum at 12-hour intervals were given by Kohn (1958) to partially hepatectomized rats that were sacrificed at 72 hours. When doses of 1 millilitre were administered on this schedule no increase in the relative weight of the regenerating liver was observed in comparison with saline-injected controls. However, injections of 1·2 or 2·0 millilitres every 8 hours succeeded in decreasing the rate of liver regeneration as determined by weight, a result in reasonable agreement with those of Smythe and Moore (1958) described above. Using mitotic activity 48 hours after partial hepatectomy as a criterion of response, Stich and Florian (1958) were able to inhibit liver regeneration in rats treated with 1·5 millilitres of normal serum per 100 grams body weight 18 hours before sacrifice. Weinbren (1959) injected normal scrum into rats ten hours after partial hepatectomy and found a 50 per cent reduction in mitotic activity 29 hours post-operatively, but noted an increase in proliferation after 48 hours, perhaps in response to the earlier depression. Jackson and Bohnel (1962) and Survis, et al. (1962) have recently reported that liver regeneration was reduced in rats receiving injections of normal scrum. Thus, there appears to be no consensus as to the influence of normal serum on liver regeneration. Indeed, the experiments involving the greatest number of injections (Smythe and Moore, 1958; Kohn, 1958) have yielded diametrically opposite results.

The reciprocal experiment, namely, the injection of serum from partially hepatectomized rats into normal ones, has been carried out by many investigators with reasonably consistent results. Although Smythe and Moore (1958) found no significant increase in liver weight after five injections (at eight-hour intervals) of serum removed from rats 24 hours after partial hepatectomy, they did notice a slight increase in the number of liver mitoses. Varying degrees of mitotic stimulation in normal liver of animals administered serum from partially hepatectomized donors have also been reported by Friedrich-Freksa and Zaki (1954), Hughes (1960), Laquerrière and Laumonier (1960), Zimmerman and Celozzi (1960), Van Lancker and Borison (1961), Survis, et al. (1962) and Fisher, et al. (1963). It has also been demonstrated that the stimulating factor is nondialysable (Friedrich-Freksa and Zaki, 1954), is associated with the α-globulin and albumin fractions of the serum (Hughes, 1960), is not species specific (Survis, et al., 1962), is precipitated by 75 per cent saturated ammonium sulphate and is stable to lyophilization (Zimmerman and Celozzi, 1960). Nevertheless, MacDonald and Rogers (1961) were unable to detect mitotic responses or DNA synthesis in normal livers 12 to 20 hours after administering 3 to 5 millilitres of plasma taken from donor rats 24 hours after partial hepatectomy. Peters (1962), Leong, et al. (1963) and Moya (1963) likewise failed to affect liver mitoses by serum from partially hepatectomized donors, whereas Alston and

Thomson (1963) reduced the mitotic rate by this kind of treatment. Using plasma from donor rats with livers induced to regenerate by CCl$_4$ treatment, Leevy, *et al.* (1959) also found no effect on mitosis or DNA synthesis in the livers of normal recipients 16 to 20 hours after injection. With the exception of these latter investigations, however, it is generally agreed that serum from rats in the process of regenerating livers will stimulate cell division in the livers of normal recipients. If true, this would indicate the existence of a mitotic stimulant in the blood of compensating animals.

The last possible combination of donor and recipient by which serum can be tested involves injections from partially hepatectomized rats into others similarly operated. Though unanimity is lacking, most experiments of this kind tend to indicate the presence of a stimulating material in serum from rats compensating for the removal of parts of their livers. For example, increased proliferation in regenerating livers was observed by Stich and Florian (1958) and Smythe and Moore (1958) following injection of serum from partially hepatectomized donors. The former authors found that serum from donors that had been partially hepatectomized for 72 hours brought about a 100 per cent increase in liver mitosis of recipients, whereas that obtained 24 hours after operation stimulated a 40 per cent increase in cell division. The latter authors, while noting no difference in the weight increase in comparison with normal regeneration, reported a 71 per cent rise in mitotic index after 48 hours. In a similar experimental system, Adibi, *et al.* (1959) compared the effects of serum derived from the general circulation with that obtained directly from the hepatic veins of rats partially hepatectomized 24 hours earlier. Injected intraperitoneally in quantities of 1·5 millilitres into 200 gram recipient rats 24 hours after partial hepatectomy, these sera stimulated hepatic mitotic activity by factors of 15 and 30, respectively. From these results, the authors concluded that during regeneration the liver manufactures growth-stimulating substances which are released into the circulation where they outbalance the normal complement of inhibitory factors. In contrast to the above results, however, MacDonald and Rogers (1961) failed to increase hepatic hyperplasia by injecting plasma from partially hepatectomized donors. Except for a very transient depression of liver hyperplasia, Moya (1963) also reported no effects of post-hepatectomy serum on the regenerating livers of recipients. Kohn (1958) likewise reported no effect of such treatment on liver regeneration (as judged by weight after 72 hours) when low doses of serum were injected every 12 hours, but found that higher doses at more frequent intervals retarded the rate of liver regeneration.

It is obviously difficult to compare in a meaningful way the results of many different investigations, each with its varying approaches to the same problem. But if they make little sense when considered collectively, it is perhaps significant that in the two investigations which tested all four possible combinations of serum injection experiments the results were consistent among themselves. Smythe and Moore (1958) detected increases in mitotic activity in all cases, regardless of whether the donor or recipient was intact or partially hepatectomized. In contrast, MacDonald and Rogers (1961) noted no effect in any of the combinations. Possibly this could be taken as an argument against the existence of any real growth-regulating factors in the serum. Yet other authors have reported differing effects according to dose, injection schedule, or duration of liver regeneration in donor animals prior to recovering serum from them for injection. In view of such discrepancies, if any sense is to be made out of these studies it may emerge only by constructing some alternative hypothetical models to determine which one, if any, is least inconsistent with the known facts.

Let it be assumed that the body fluids contain either stimulators or inhibitors of growth, the normal concentration of which permits an organ such as the liver to maintain a *status quo*. Regeneration may then result either from an inordinate increase in stimulating factor or a decrease in inhibitor. Now, if the concentrations of these hypothetical agents are increased by the addition of a fixed amount of serum (e.g. 20 per cent by volume) from other animals, various combinations of donors and recipients would be expected to promote or retard liver growth to varying degrees according to whether stimulating or inhibiting substances are assumed to be present. To simplify matters, it is probably safe to disregard the dilution effect that the addition of excess serum would have on the recipient animal's blood, for the body is normally very efficient at adjusting for changes in fluid volume. If it is also assumed that partial hepatectomy doubles the concentration of stimulating factors or reduces the number of inhibitors by one-half, then the relative effects of serum injections between normal and partially hepatectomized rats can be predicted according to the schematic outlines in figures 42 to 44.

P

THEORETICAL EXPECTATIONS OF NET EFFECT OF SERUM INJECTION (20% BY VOLUME),
ASSUMING EXISTENCE OF HUMORAL GROWTH STIMULATORS

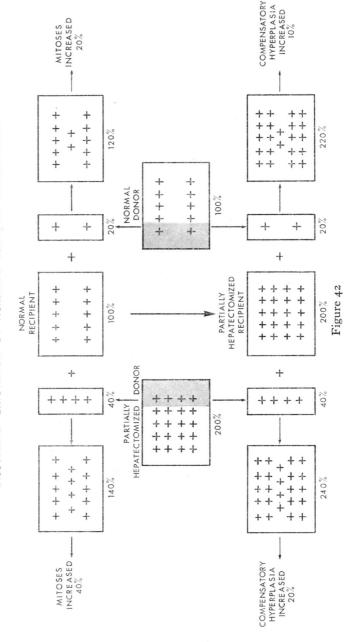

Figure 42

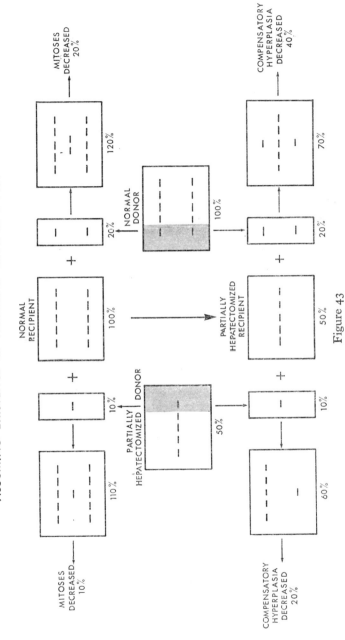

THEORETICAL EXPECTATIONS OF NET EFFECTS OF SERUM INJECTIONS (20% BY VOLUME), ASSUMING EXISTENCE OF HUMORAL GROWTH INHIBITORS

Figure 43

This line of reasoning reveals that if one calculates the effects of serum injections on systems assumed to contain mitotic stimulants, no matter what combinations of serum exchange are tested the result must be a net increase in the concentration of stimulating molecules in the recipient. As indicated in figure 42, any serum that is added must perforce augment the concentration of those already present. Accordingly, the addition of 20 per cent by volume of normal serum to intact rats will raise the stimulator concentration to 120 per cent of normal and thus promote proliferative activity in the liver. Partial hepatectomy, however, is assumed to double the number of stimulating molecules in the body. Addition of 20 per cent of serum from such rats would increase the stimulant concentration in unoperated animals by 40 per cent and thereby cause a pronounced increase in hepatic proliferation. By the same token, similar injections into rats in the process of liver regeneration would act synergistically to heighten the proliferative responses. Regardless of the nature of the donor and recipient, therefore, the occurrence of mitotic stimulators in the serum would be expected to enhance to varying degrees the proliferative activity in the livers of injected animals.

On the other hand, if inhibitors are assumed to be the effective agent in promoting liver regeneration (by a reduction in their concentrations after partial hepatectomy), then the opposite results are obtained (figure 43). Serum supplements would bring about a rise in the concentration of inhibitors in the recipient blood causing a decline in mitotic activity compared with uninjected controls. This would manifest itself as a decrease in proliferative activity in unoperated livers, or a depression of compensatory hyperplasia in regenerating livers. In view of the variations in the data available in the literature, as outlined below, it is obvious that neither of the above schemes fits the facts.

A third alternative, however, is that the blood might contain both inhibitors and stimulators, such that an imbalance in one direction or the other would either arrest or promote mitotic activity. This theoretical possibility can be explored by adding together the two previous proposals (figures 42 and 43), to arrive at the outline shown in figure 44.

When these hypothetical results are compared with the actual ones outlined below, fairly reasonable agreement is obtained.

I—*Normal recipients*
  A. Normal donors:

1. Mitoses increased
   (a) Smythe and Moore (1958)
   (b) Fisher, Fisher, and Saffer (1963)

2. No effect on mitoses
   (a) Friedrich-Freksa and Zaki (1954)
   (b) MacDonald and Rogers (1961)
   (c) Leong, Grisham, and Hole (1963)
   (d) Moya (1963)

3. Mitoses decreased
   (a) Alston and Thomson (1963)

B. Partially hepatectomized donors

1. Mitoses increased
   (a) Friedrich-Freksa and Zaki (1954)
   (b) Smythe and Moore (1958)
   (c) Hughes (1960)
   (d) Laquerriére and Laumonier (1960)
   (e) Zimmerman and Celozzi (1960)
   (f) Van Lancker and Borison (1961)
   (g) Survis, Kennedy, and Hass (1962)
   (h) Fisher, Fisher, and Saffer (1963)

2. No effect on mitoses
   (a) MacDonald and Rogers (1961)
   (b) Peters (1962)
   (c) Leong, Grisham, and Hole (1963)
   (d) Moya (1963)

3. Mitoses decreased
   (a) Alston and Thomson (1963)

II—*Partially hepatectomized recipients*
A. Normal donors:

1. Compensatory hyperplasia increased
   (a) Smythe and Moore (1958)

2. No effect on compensatory hyperplasia
   (a) Bucher (1958)
   (b) MacDonald and Rogers (1961)
   (c) Alston and Thomson (1963)

3. Compensatory hyperplasia decreased
   (a) Stich and Florian (1958)
   (b) Weinbren (1959)

(c) Survis, Kennedy, and Hass (1962)
(d) Leong, Grisham, and Hole (1963)

B. Partially hepatectomized donors

1. Compensatory hyperplasia increased
   (a) Smythe and Moore (1958)
   (b) Stich and Florian (1958)
   (c) Adibi, Paschkis, and Cantarow (1959)

2. No effect on compensatory hyperplasia
   (a) MacDonald and Rogers (1961)
   (b) Leong, Grisham, and Hole (1963)
   (c) Moya (1963)

According to the predictions shown in figure 44, the addition of normal serum to a normal animal should have no net effect inasmuch as the stimulators and inhibitors would cancel each other out. The observed facts more or less average out to this expectation. Although Smythe and Moore (1958) and Fisher, *et al.* (1963) reported increases in mitotic rates under these conditions, neither Friedrich-Freksa and Zaki (1954), MacDonald and Rogers (1961), Leong, *et al.* (1963), nor Moya (1963) detected an effect of such treatment, and Alston and Thomson (1963) noted an inhibitory influence on liver mitoses.

When serum from regenerating rats is injected into normal animals, however, theory would predict a net increase in mitotic activity. Again, the consensus of observations agrees with this interpretation. MacDonald and Rogers (1961), Peters (1961), Leong, *et al.* (1963), and Moya (1963) found no effect, and Alston and Thomson (1963) observed diminished proliferation, but positive results have been reported by Friedrich-Freksa and Zaki (1954), Smythe and Moore (1958), Hughes (1960), Laquerriére and Laumonier (1960), Zimmerman and Celozzi (1960), Van Lancken and Borison (1961), Survis, *et al.* (1962), and Fisher, *et al.* (1963).

In partially hepatectomized recipients, the injection of normal serum should theoretically cause a 30 per cent depression in the amount of compensatory hepatic hyperplasia. Actual data from such experiments are not consistent, for Smythe and Moore (1958) reported an increase in mitotic activity whereas Bucher (1958), MacDonald and Rogers (1961), and Alston and Thomson (1963) noted no effect. However, Stich and Florian (1958), Weinbren (1959), Survis, *et al.* (1962), and Leong, *et al.* (1963) all observed decreased levels of

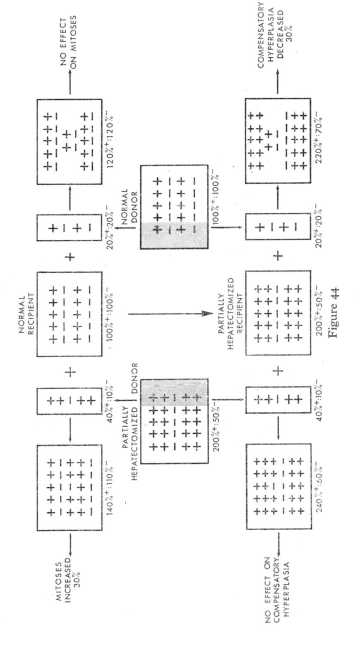

Figure 44

proliferation. Nevertheless, if these investigations are assumed to be equally valid, the net result does not favour an increase in mitotic activity. Indeed, the majority of available reports suggests that normal serum inhibits liver hyperplasia. The plausibility of this is strengthened by noting that the only cases of decreased mitotic activity in regenerating livers, either actual or predicted, occur with this combination of donor and recipient.

Less agreement is encountered when the theoretical and actual effects of injecting serum from regenerating rats into regenerating recipients are compared. Theoretically this treatment should have no influence on the course of liver regeneration because the ratio of stimulators to inhibitors remains unchanged at 3:1. Both MacDonald and Rogers (1961) and Leong, et al. (1963) report findings in agreement with this prediction. Moya (1963), too, found no effect of post-hepatectomy serum on hepatic hyperplasia, except for a very transient depression of proliferation 18 to 26 hours after injection. The mitotic stimulation observed by Smythe and Moore (1958), Stich and Florian (1958), and Adibi, et al. (1959) is difficult to reconcile with the theoretical expectations and must therefore remain unexplained. Perhaps it is significant, however, that of the four possible combinations of donors and recipients, this remains the only group in which no one has reported a definite decrease in liver proliferation following serum administration.

Notwithstanding such discrepancies, the overall factual observations most closely approximate the results predicted by a concept based upon the assumed existence of both stimulating and inhibiting substances. Therefore, unless the validity of the known facts is discredited by their inconsistencies, they must be interpreted as supporting the existence of a counterbalanced system of growth stimulators and inhibitors in the blood. At best, however, the cumulative evidence is far from convincing, and judgment should be reserved pending the examination of other experimental approaches to the problem.

In seeking to understand a general mechanism of humoral growth regulation applicable to all growing parts of the body, it is unwise to draw conclusions from data relevant to only one organ, especially if that organ is the source of most plasma proteins. Miller and Bale (1954) demonstrated that by perfusing labelled amino acids through rat liver it was possible to recover labelled albumin, α- and β-globulins, and fibrinogen (but not γ-globulins). When the totally hepatectomized carcass was similarly perfused, none of these labelled proteins was produced. The high rate of synthetic activity in the liver is emphasized by the data of Madden and Zeldis (1958), who calculated the following half-lives of serum proteins;

albumin	5 days
α_1-globulin	3 days
α_2-globulin	2 days
β-globulin	3 days
γ-globulin	3·2 days

In view of the role of the liver in producing plasma proteins, it is probable that the rate of protein synthesis in the liver is adjusted to the rate of their loss from the plasma. It is conceivable that the rate of liver growth, especially as exemplified by liver regeneration, might be correlated with the demand for plasma protein synthesis. As mentioned in Chapter XI, partial hepatectomy is followed in 24 hours by a general depletion of those serum proteins manufactured by the liver (Chanutin, et al., 1938; Roberts and White, 1949; Lamirande and Cantero, 1952) after which their concentrations are gradually restored to normal levels (figure 40). Electrophoretic analyses of serum proteins by Glinos (1956a) revealed decreased concentrations of serum albumin during hepatic hyperplasia. By artificially lowering the serum protein concentrations by plasmapheresis (and replacing equal amounts of saline), Glinos (1958a,b) and Glinos and Gey (1952a) reported that normal rat livers could be stimulated to proliferate in direct proportion to the per cent of plasma removed. He concluded that serum depletion stimulates liver cells to accelerate synthesis of more proteins and that this activates DNA synthesis and mitosis. In reciprocal experiments, Glinos (1956b, 1958a) succeeded in raising the concentration of serum proteins 30 per cent by restricting the fluid intake of rats. In partially hepatectomized animals this treatment had the effect of inhibiting hyperplasia, again supporting the conclusion that liver regeneration, or its normal absence, may be causally related to the levels of plasma proteins. However, there is less reason to expect similar results with reference to other organs.

Compensatory Renal Hyperplasia

Only a few investigations along these lines have been carried out in conjunction with compensatory renal hyperplasia. Sacerdotti (1896) injected serum from bilaterally nephrectomized dogs twice a day for six days into normal animals and reported that the recipient's kidneys became enlarged. More recently, Goss and Rankin (1960) removed substantial amounts of blood from rats and detected no influence on normal kidney mitosis but did observe a decrease in compensatory renal hyperplasia in such animals 48 hours after unilateral nephrectomy. Injections of serum from either normal or nephrectomized donors had no detectable influence on the 48-hour mitotic peak in uninephrectomized recipients (Goss, 1963b). This confirms the observations of Williams (1962b), to the effect that injections of plasma from uninephrectomized rats into recipients at intervals after unilateral nephrectomy exerted no significant effect on the resulting compensatory renal hyperplasia. Nevertheless, Lowenstein and Stern (1963) have reported that the kidneys of rats had twice the normal number of nuclei labelled with tritiated thymidine four days after the injection of serum from uninephrectomized rats, while their livers remained unaffected.

Erythropoietin

In 1906, Carnot and Deflandre reported that when the serum of previously bled rabbits was injected into normal rabbits, a remarkable increase in red blood corpuscle production occurred in one to three days, accompanied by hyperplastic bone marrow. The agent responsible was called "haemopoïétine". Several decades were to elapse, however, before this provocative observation was confirmed and amplified. The consistency with which this effect can be repeated has in recent years fostered such a proliferation of productive research that our knowledge of the control of red blood-cell production far surpasses that of any other tissue or organ. Leukocyte production may be subject to a similar controlling mechanism (Gordon, *et al.*, 1960).

It is thoroughly established that plasma from anaemic animals, when injected into normal ones, is capable of stimulating erythropoiesis. This effect is not species-specific, at least among mammals. How the donor animal is rendered anaemic is of little consequence, for the efficacy of such plasma has been demonstrated after repeated loss of blood (Erslev, 1953; Erslev and Lavietes, 1954), or following phenylhydrazine induced haemolysis of erythrocytes (Gordon, *et al.*, 1954, 1956). Goldwasser, *et al.* (1957) observed 2·8 to 3·1 per cent uptake of Fe^{59} into the haemoglobin of rats injected with normal serum, whereas serum from rats previously made anaemic with phenylhydrazine caused 15·1 per cent Fe^{59} incorporation under the same conditions. Treatment with plasma from such animals, according to Gordon, et al. (1954), increased the peripheral red blood-cell count, the haemoglobin concentration, reticulocyte percentage, haematocrit, and the concentration of nucleated erythrocytes in the marrow. Serum obtained from human patients with Cooley's anaemia will also enhance erythropoiesis when injected into rats (Piliero, et al., 1956). Even urine from anaemic patients (but not from normal humans) is effective (Van Dyke, et al., 1957a; Winkert, et al., 1958). Urine obtained from rabbits rendered anaemic by bleeding also increases the rate of haemoglobin synthesis (Hodgson and Tohá, 1954).

Similar results can be produced by using plasma from certain other non-anaemic conditions. A relative anaemia, for example, caused by hypoxia or exposure to high altitudes, will also suffice to accelerate erythropoiesis (Dill, 1938; Huff, et al., 1951). Erythropoiesis can be stimulated by injections of plasma from foetuses (Rambach, et al., 1957) or from pregnant rats (Contopoulos, et al., 1956), and activity can be detected in normal plasma provided it is sufficiently concentrated.

The opposite of anaemia is polycythaemia. Serum from humans with polycythaemia vera will increase the rate of erythropoiesis when injected into rats (Contopoulos, et al., 1957) as will that from individuals with secondary polycythaemia caused by hypoxia in association with abnormal heart conditions (Linman and Bethell, 1957). Polycythaemia can be artificially produced by the administration of cobalt (in the form of $CoCl_2$) to rats. Not only does this stimulate erythropoiesis but it elevates the concentration of the erythropoietic stimulating factor in the plasma. Accordingly, Goldwasser, et al. (1957) were able to increase the rate of Fe^{59} uptake in rats injected with plasma from rats with cobalt-induced polycythaemia. The active ingredient produced in the plasma by these manifold conditions is referred to as erythropoietin. It is present in the plasma (and urine) of animals in which there has been created a demand for oxygen in excess of that which the red blood corpuscles can deliver to the tissues.

Erythropoietin is not present, at least in easily detectable amounts, in normal plasma (or urine). Its production cannot be stimulated by adding 6 per cent dextran to the blood to give rise to a condition of dilution anaemia (Erslev, 1955), for apparently the resulting reduction in oxygen content of the blood is compensated by increased cardiac output. In rabbits rendered anaemic by loss of blood, the normal occurrence of erythropoiesis can be precluded by exposure to 100 per cent oxygen, as indicated by the absence of a reticulocyte response in normal rabbits injected with plasma from such animals (Hodgson and Tohá, 1954). Although certain kinds of polycythaemic plasma have been shown to contain erythropoietin, plasma from transfusion-induced conditions of polycythaemia is devoid of erythropoietin. Erythropoietin cannot be demonstrated in extracts of the intestine, liver, kidney, adrenal cortex, spleen, thymus, lung, brain, skeletal muscle, bone marrow, or packed red blood-cells of anaemic animals (Carnot and Deflandre, 1906b; Gordon, et al., 1956).

In view of these results, many experiments have been designed to identify the source of erythropoietin. Since hypophysectomy causes anaemia, and partially inhibits the erythropoietic response that is normally stimulated by hypoxia, Van Dyke, et al. (1954) proposed that the pituitary might be the site of erythropoietin production. Indeed, the normal rate of erythropoiesis in animals used for assaying erythropoietin is routinely reduced by such measures as hypophysectomy (or starvation) in order to exaggerate their response to anaemic plasma (Fried, et al., 1957). The stimulation of erythropoiesis in normal as well as hypophysectomized rats by the oral administration of anterior lobe extracts has also suggested that the pituitary may be one source of an erythropoietic factor (Van Dyke, et al., 1954, 1957b). But since there is still an erythropoietic response to bleeding, hypoxia (Van Dyke, et al., 1957b), and cobalt administration (Crafts and Meineke, 1957) in hypophysectomized rats, Van Dyke, et al. (1957b) have also concluded that there has to be still another source of erythropoietin. There is ample reason to believe that this may be in the kidney.

Bilateral nephrectomy seriously interferes with erythropoiesis (figure 45). Naets (1958a,b,c) kept arenal dogs alive for 10 to 15 days by means of two or three daily peritoneal lavages, during which time the rate of incorporation of Fe^{59} was significantly decreased. As early as one day after loss of the kidneys there occurred a sharp drop in the concentration of erythroblasts in the bone marrow. Erslev (1960) confirmed these results, noting that erythropoiesis is considerably reduced but not altogether abolished by bilateral nephrectomy. Possibly the residual red blood-cell production may be attributable to the pituitary factor, although this has not been put to the test. If both kidneys are left in situ with their ureters ligated, Naets (1958b) reported that erythropoiesis was undisturbed, but Erslev (1960) claimed

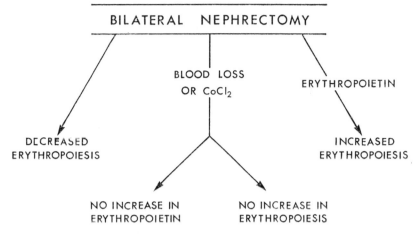

Figure 45　Outline of the experimental evidence in favour of the kidneys as a source of erythropoietin.

that red blood-cell production was suppressed. The latter author concluded that inhibition of erythropoiesis under these conditions was the result of azotaemia rather than the lack of erythropoietin production. He also showed (Erslev, 1958) that in uraemic rabbits the injection of erythropoietin did not cause the usual reticulocytosis. Thus it was suggested that anaemia resulting from the loss or incapacitation of the kidneys is caused by the metabolic conditions associated with uraemia.

An important facet of this problem, then, is to determine if erythropoietin can be produced by animals without kidneys or with their ureters occluded. Jacobson, *et al.* (1957b) and Erslev (1958) demonstrated that loss of blood from bilaterally nephrectomized rats and rabbits was not followed by an increase in the rate of erythropoiesis, nor did the serum of these animals exhibit erythropoietic activity when injected into test animals (figure 45). Thus, the decline in the rate of erythropoiesis following bilateral nephrectomy appears to be associated with the failure of the animal to elaborate erythropoietin rather than an inability to utilize it. Indeed, Fisher, *et al.* (1962) showed that red blood-cell production was stimulated in bilaterally nephrectomized animals injected with erythropoietin (figure 45). When both ureters were ligated, bleeding still stimulated the production of erythropoietin (Jacobson, *et al.*, 1957b). Erslev

(1958), however, removed one kidney from rabbits and ligated the ureter of the contralateral one, with the result that erythropoietin production failed to occur after bleeding, nor was erythropoiesis accelerated in the operated animals. The discrepancy between these various results concerning whether or not erythropoiesis or erythropoietin production can occur in bled animals with ligated ureters is not as yet resolved. The weight of many indirect lines of evidence, however, favours the kidney as a source of erythropoietin, rather than the agent by which uraemia is prevented and erythropoiesis normally permitted.

Administration of cobalt, which in normal animals stimulates both polycythaemia and erythropoietin production, is not effective in bilaterally nephrectomized animals (figure 45). Fisher, *et al.* (1962) found no increase in Fe^{59} uptake under these conditions, nor could Jacobson, *et al.* (1957b) detect increased levels of erythropoietin in cobalt-treated animals lacking kidneys. In rats with both ureters ligated, however, injection of $CoCl_2$ was followed by a rise in erythropoietin concentration in the plasma (Jacobson, *et al.*, 1957b). Presumably cobalt also stimulates erythropoiesis in animals with ureters ligated. It is evident, therefore, that the polycythaemia caused by cobalt is the ultimate consequence of enhanced erythropoietin production, but exactly how cobalt stimulates the latter is not known. It is probable that its site of action is where erythropoietin is produced, and this appears to be in the kidneys. The physiological rationale for such an arrangement still eludes us, but the answer, when it is found, should be an interesting one.

Investigations of erythropoiesis have been particularly rewarding for what they have revealed concerning the physical and chemical properties of erythropoietin. Aside from more commonly recognized hormones, erythropoietin is the only proven example of a growth-regulating compound normally occurring in the serum. As such, its chemical characterization is of considerable significance. In view of the numerous ways in which erythropoietin production can be experimentally or pathologically induced, it is possible that the discrepancies encountered in the literature concerning its chemical nature may indicate the existence of more than one compound. It is generally accepted that the factor is thermostable (Tohá, *et al.*, 1955; Gordon, *et al.*, 1956; Linman and Bethell, 1956; Piliero, *et al.*, 1956), but this may depend upon the pH at which it is boiled. Slaunwhite, *et al.* (1957) found it to be heat labile at pH 1 or 13, whereas they and

Rambach, *et al.* (1957) reported that it was stable to boiling at pH 5·5 or 9·0. Hodgson and Tohá (1954), however, destroyed its activity by boiling for five minutes at pH 9·0, but not at pH 5·5. Stohlman and Brecher (1956) and Gurney and Pan (1960) have also inactivated erythropoietin by heating. In view of such lack of agreement, it is only safe to conclude that the factor is stable to boiling at pH 5·5, and may or may not be destroyed under other conditions. However, Rambach, *et al.* (1957) have shown that it can be lyophilized and stored at room temperature without loss of activity.

There is also little concurrence as to whether or not erythropoietin is dialysable and the extent to which this property may be correlated with its thermostability. Some investigators have claimed that it is dialysable (Hodgson and Tohá 1954; Tohá, *et al.*, 1955; Goldwasser, *et al.*, 1957) but many others have shown that it is not (Stohlman and Brecher, 1956; Rambach, *et al.*, 1957; Slaunwhite, *et al.*, 1957; Hodgson, *et al.*, 1958; Borsook, 1959). The latter conclusion is probably the more reliable.

Other procedures designed to determine whether or not a compound is proteinaceous indicate that erythropoietin is probably only partly so. Many treatments that denature most proteins do not inactivate erythropoietin. Thus, it is not precipitated by perchloric acid (Linman and Bethell, 1956; Goldwasser, *et al.*, 1957; Rambach, *et al.*, 1957) nor is it denatured by ether (Goldwasser, *et al.*, 1957). However, it is precipitated by 75 per cent saturated ammonium sulphate (Rambach, *et al.*, 1957). According to electrophoretic analysis, Rambach, *et al.* (1957) found that it migrates with the a_2-globulins. That it is at least in part a polypeptide is indicated by the fact that its activity is abolished by digestion with pepsin, trypsin, or chymotrypsin (Slaunwhite, *et al.*, 1957; Gordon, *et al.*, 1959). The analyses of Gordon, *et al.* (1959) have indicated that erythropoietin has an ultraviolet absorption peak at 280μ, that it stains metachromatically with toluidine blue, and is approximately 23 per cent carbohydrate. The extensive analyses of Rambach, *et al.* (1957) have demonstrated that erythropoietin contains nitrogen, and stains for carbohydrate but not for fat. Mild hydrolysis in 0·005N sulphuric acid destroys its activity by removing neuraminic acid, while by stronger hydrolysis (0·01N to 0·04N H_2SO_4) glucosamine, fucose, galactose and mannose are removed (Rambach, *et al.*, 1958b). Rambach, *et al.* (1958a) have concluded from purification studies using a DEAE-cellulose ion-exchange column that the active factor has a relatively low molecular weight. Thus, most evidence indicates rather convincingly that ery-thropoietin may be classified as a mucoprotein.

Parabiosis

Although the demonstration of growth-regulating substances in the serum may be easily achieved by means of serum injections in the case of erythropoiesis, such methods have yielded considerably less consistent results with reference to the regeneration of other organs, such as the liver. The most obvious objection to his method of ap-proach is that if the active agent has a short half-life, repeated injections of sufficiently high doses are required. Even then, negative results could mean that the dose was too low. In a logical endeavour to obviate this objection, a number of investigators have attempted to demonstrate vicarious regenerative responses in the intact partners of parabiosed animals following partial organ ablation in the contra-lateral member. This technique has been most extensively applied to the problem of liver regeneration.

This was first attempted by Christensen and Jacobsen (1949), who noted that in three parabiotic pairs of rats subjected to unilateral partial hepatectomy the livers of the intact partners underwent increased mitotic activity. The operated livers, however, exhibited no reciprocal decrease in hyperplasia. These results were confirmed and extended by Bucher, et al. (1951) and Allegri, et al. (1954). The former group found that partial hepatectomy of one member of para-biotically paired rats, or of two members of parabiotic triplets, resulted in six- to fiftyfold increases in mitotic activity in the livers of intact partners after 48 to 72 hours, respectively. No rise in mitotic rate was noted after only 24 hours, however. Hurowitz and Studer (1960) have found that 62 per cent of the intact rats in parabiosis with partially hepatectomized partners exhibited increased rates of liver mitosis. In similar experiments, Wenneker and Sussman (1951) recorded sympathetic regenerative responses in unoperated para-biotic partners as measured in terms of increases in wet weight and number of liver cells. By other criteria, comparable reactions have likewise been reported. Van Lancker and Sempoux (1959) measured the uptake of orotic acid-C^{14} in parabiotic rats after partial hepatec-tomy of one partner, and found six times the normal incorporation into the DNA of the unoperated liver after 36 to 72 hours. Neverthe-less, the two livers did not grow at equivalent rates, for the specific activity in the DNA of the partially hepatectomized one was 30 per cent greater than its intact partner. Kim and Cohen (unpublished, quoted by Calva and Cohen, 1959) demonstrated a twofold rise in the activity of carbamyl phosphate-aspartate transcarbamylase, which is involved in pyrimidine synthesis, in normal rats parabiosed to partially hepatectomized ones.

In contrast to the foregoing data, which have been taken to indicate the existence of blood-borne factors affecting growth and regeneration of the liver, other investigations have not yielded such encouraging results. Islami, et al. (1959), for example, found no increase in mitotic index in the intact livers of parabiotic rats 48 to 72 hours after one partner had been partially hepatectomized. However, it was claimed that the rate of weight increase in the operated livers was retarded in comparison with non-parabiotic rats with regenerating livers, presumably owing to influences from the contralateral intact livers. Yet this study, together with some of the earlier ones by other investigators, cited above, involved inadequate numbers of animals. In view of the disconcerting individual variations normally encountered in research of this kind, substantial numbers of animals must be used to yield statistically reliable results. Recognizing the seriousness of this, Rogers, et al. (1961) repeated these experiments on greater numbers of rats. They found extreme variations in the results, as measured by mitotic activity and tritiated thymidine uptake, and accordingly failed to detect statistically significant responses in normal livers 48, 72, or 96 hours after partial hepatectomy of the parabiotic partners. Nor was regeneration of the latter any different from that observed in individually operated rats. Similarly, Fisher, et al. (1963) have been unable to detect vicarious proliferation in the livers of intact rats grafted parabiotically to partially hepatectomized ones. Even when rats were joined by reciprocal carotid artery-jugular vein cannulation (Alston and Thomson, 1963), regeneration of one liver did not stimulate mitosis in the other during periods of up to 48 hours, despite exchanges of one-quarter of the blood volumes per minute. In view of the care with which these last three investigations were carried out, a note of caution must be introduced into the interpretation of experiments along these lines.

It is with these reservations, therefore, that the interesting experiments of Steuart (1958) should be evaluated. Designed to determine if compensatory renal hyperplasia in the rat depends upon vascular communication, parabiotic pairs and triplets were partially nephrectomized. When three kidneys of paired rats were excised the

Q

remaining one became hyperplastic after 48 and 72 hours, as did residual renal tissue following 75 per cent nephrectomy in single rats. In parabiotic triplets, the four kidneys were removed from the outside rats. This gave rise to a mitotic response in the middle rat after 72 hours.

In a sense, it would appear superfluous to perform such experiments on parabiotic animals to learn if compensatory hypertrophy in paired organs following unilateral ablation is mediated via humoral agents. Removal of two organs from one partner of a parabiotic pair is equivalent to unilateral ablation in a single animal only if it is assumed that the humoral agents responsible for such effects are distributed equally in both instances.

Theoretically, the response of an intact parabiotic animal to partial or total organ ablation in its partner should depend upon how extensive their circulatory exchange may be. On the basis of studies using Fe^{59} tagged red blood-cells, Van Dyke, et al. (1948) showed that only 0·64 per cent of the total erythrocyte population crosses the parabiotic junction per minute, a rate of exchange that results in complete mixing of the blood within several hours. Recognizing the occasional ineffectiveness of hormonal transfer in some instances of parabiosis, Finerty (1952) attempted to explain the apparent existence of such a parabiotic barrier as follows: "It seems reasonable to postulate that when passing from one partner to another in small amounts, those substances which are readily inactivated never reach a minimally effective level in the recipient, and those materials which are more resistant are readily equilibrated in both partners."

In accordance with this, the endocrine glands of parabiotic animals react differently to partial ablation depending upon how rapidly their hormones are broken down. Steroid-secreting glands in intact parabiotic animals regularly undergo hypertrophy following ablation of the homologous organs from their partners. Total adrenalectomy of one parabiotic rat, for example, results in the enlargement of the adrenals of the intact partner after three to six weeks (Li and P'An, 1940), but unilateral adrenalectomy of one partner was without effect on the intact parabiont. Similarly, removal of both ovaries (Kallas, 1929) or testes (DeMello, 1940) from one partner causes gonadal hypertrophy in the opposite intact animal. To the extent that the steroid hormones of the remaining organs are inactivated by the liver, the pituitary of the adrenalectomized or gonadectomized animal secretes excessive ACTH or gonadotrophins which readily cross to the intact partner where they stimulate adrenal or gonadal hypertrophy. In contrast, Zeckwer (1940) has shown that thyroidectomy of one parabiotic partner is not followed by hypertrophy of the thyroid of the intact rat, presumably because thyroxin is not inactivated as fast as are steroid hormones. Consequently, thyroxin becomes equilibrated between both parabionts thereby inhibiting either pituitary from secreting excessive amounts of thyrotrophic hormone.

It is hardly surprising, in view of the efficacy of anaemic serum injections in stimulating erythropoiesis, that parabiosis should reveal a vicarious response in the untreated member to stimulation of its partner. Accordingly, Reissmann (1950) has shown that when parabiotic rats are maintained in separate atmospheres, one with low oxygen tension and the other normal, each partner responds by an increase in the concentration of nucleated red cells in the marrow after several weeks. In a study of leukocyte production, Gordon, et al. (1960) selectively removed leukocytes from one member of parabiotically paired rats. Leukocytopheresis was achieved by repeated intraperitoneal injections of saline solutions which permits the withdrawal of many leukocytes, primarily neutrophils and monocytes. This procedure, known to stimulate leukocytopoiesis in the treated animal, was observed also to increase the leukocyte counts in the intact partners. As expected, therefore, the production rates of various kinds of blood-cells is clearly regulated by blood-borne factors.

Tissue Culture Studies

A theoretically ideal, though little exploited, method of assaying serum for the presence of growth-regulating agents is to test its effects on the growth of cells *in vitro*. Using plasma from normal or partially hepatectomized rabbits in the culture medium, Akamatsu (1923) noted that rabbit liver cells grew better when cultured with the latter serum. Similar results have been reported by Glinos and Gey (1952b) for the growth of rat liver explants. More recently, Wrba, *et al.* (1960) have reported that twice the normal amount of labelled phosphate becomes incorporated into embryonic rat liver *in vitro* when maintained for 24 or 72 hours in the presence of serum derived from golden hamsters partially hepatectomized 48 hours before. Moreover, serum from similar donors in which liver regeneration was inhibited by the administration of N-mustard was also effective in enhancing phosphate uptake in culture. The active factor was found to be thermostable, organ-specific, but not species-specific (Wrba, *et al.*,

1962). Therefore, all of these studies favour the existence of humoral factors that promote the growth of liver cells in partially hepatectomized animals. Indeed, Moya (1963) has found that although post-hepatectomy rat serum does not alter the normal growth rate of rat ascites hepatoma cells in culture, normal serum exerts an inhibitory effect. Therefore, there may be growth-inhibitors instead of, or in addition to, growth-stimulants.

Comparable results have been obtained in the case of kidney growth. Ogawa and Nowinski (1958) explanted fragments of rat renal medulla to plasma clots which were cultured for several days in Eagle's medium. The explants that grew best were selected for testing the effects of serum, from uninephrectomized rats, which was added to the medium. After three days, mitotic activity was determined by counting the number of dividing cells derived from each kidney fragment. The results, though admittedly variable, indicated that serum taken from rats two days after uninephrectomy promoted more proliferation *in vitro* than did normal serum, but that the effect was lost 15 days post-operatively. The factor was found to be thermo-labile at 100° C. (but stable at 56° C.), non-dialysable, organ specific, but not species specific. Interesting as these results are, however, they emphasize the importance of using an *in vitro* system that has been standardized accurately enough to provide a reliable reference with which to compare the effects of experimental sera. Until such precision shall have been achieved in tissue culture techniques, the results of the foregoing experiments should be cautiously interpreted.

With reference to erythropoiesis, a number of investigations have attempted to demonstrate the efficacy of erythropoietin in *in vitro* systems. Thomas (1955) noted that haemin synthesis, as measured by the rate of labelled glycine uptake, was stimulated by the addition of normal rabbit serum. Erslev and Hughes (1960) described the gradual decline in growth of rabbit bone marrow cells maintained in culture. Normal development continued for 4 to 8 hours, after which it decreased to minimal levels by 24 to 48 hours, reflecting the fact that maturing red cell precursors continue to differentiate. Presumably, no new stem cells are fed into the system as normally occurs *in vivo*. The addition of serum from anaemic rabbits did not promote stem cell differentiation. Others, however, have succeeded in demon-strating erythropoietic stimulation in bone marrow tissue cultures. Having observed the normal decrease in the population of differenti-rating erythroblasts, Rosse and Gurney (1959) were able to prolong erythropoiesis by incubation with serum from bled rats or from animals treated with $CoCl_2$. The effectiveness of anaemic serum in stimulating mitosis in rabbit bone marrow suspensions has also been demonstrated by Matoth and Ben-Porath (1959). Conversely, serum from polycythaemic rats depressed erythropoiesis *in vitro* (Rosse and Gurney, 1959).

The capacity to detect humoral growth-regulating substances appears to depend largely upon devising the proper *in vitro* assay system. If methods can be sufficiently perfected, this approach appears to be the most promising one by which growth stimulating or inhibiting factors can be demonstrated, analysed, and isolated.

XIV

Maternal-Foetal Relationships

PURSUANT to the possible existence of growth controlling factors in the blood plasma, it is conceivable that inhibitory or stimulatory effects might be transmitted reciprocally between mother and foetus. Representing a special case of parabiosis, the viviparous condition provides certain circumstances not realized in grafted animals with confluent circulations. By virtue of what is known about the permeability of the placenta, something can be deduced concerning the nature of influences by which the growth of organs is governed, especially in foetal tissues capable of compensating for maternal deficiencies.

Placental Permeability

First and foremost, the placenta acts as a filter through which some things can readily pass, and by which other substances are held back. This selective action protects the integrity of the foetal system against intrusing by foreign specific molecules from the mother, and also prevents transfers in the opposite direction. To what extent the selective permeability is affected by the anatomical variations represented by the placentae of various mammalian types is not yet understood. That imperfections in the placenta may sometimes occur, however, is attested by the passage of rubella viruses from mother to foetus, or the escape of foetal red blood corpuscles into the maternal circulation, occasionally leading to Rh incompatibilities.

Under normal circumstances, according to Hagerman and Villee (1960), the placenta is permeable to most small molecules, including vitamins and the various non-specific nutrient compounds essential for embryonic growth. In addition, most drugs can cross into the foetal circulation, provided they are relatively small and soluble molecules. Some hormones, including thyroxin and the steroids, also penetrate the placental barrier. Protein hormones, however, are generally believed to be held back, although the status of some of the very small polypeptides remains questionable. Compounds involved in maternal blood clotting (e.g. prothrombin) do not pass through the placenta, nor are other plasma proteins generally believed to enter the foetal circulation via the placenta in appreciable quantities. The latter point, however, may depend on methods of detection. Hormones, for example, can be assayed by their effects on target organs, whereas plasma proteins (with the exception of antibodies) must be traced by means of radioactive labels. Although Kulangara and Schjeide (1962) noted the transfer of labelled maternal proteins into the foetal blood of rabbits, Kelleher, et al. (1963) obtained no convincing evidence in rats that plasma proteins produced by the maternal liver are taken into the foetus. Both groups have demonstrated, however, that 24-day rabbit embryos and 20-day rat foetuses are capable of manufacturing their own plasma proteins. Any contributions from the mother are apparently more incidental than essential.

Antibodies, curiously enough, do enter the foetal circulation from the mother, but according to the extensive studies of Brambell (1958) they are incapable of crossing the placenta. Instead, when the mother's immunological endowment is transferred prenatally to her offspring, the route is via the uterine lumen and yolk sac vasculature. Indeed, maternal antibodies may even be absorbed from the amniotic fluid by the foetal alimentary canal. Exactly how such large molecules can be selectively transmitted across tissue membranes remains to be explained. Calman and Murray (1950) have suggested that the maternal antibodies may be broken down on one side and reassembled in the foetal circulation, but this would require the exact replication of their tertiary structure (in which antibody specificity presumably resides), a possibility with little or no basis in proven fact.

Current interest in teratology has led to numerous experiments on the effects of various drugs, administered to pregnant animals, on embryonic development. The efficacy of many of these compounds has made it abundantly obvious that many antimetabolites readily cross placental barriers to exert effects on developing embryos. It does not necessarily follow, however, that because a substance may produce an influence on the embryo that it actually has invaded the latter's circulation. Trypan blue, for example, has long been known to have teratogenic effects on mammalian embryos, yet it fails to pass through the placenta. Therefore, certain agents may owe their teratogenic influence to indirect efficacy, the latter being alterations in maternal physiology to which the offspring might be sensitive. Nevertheless, such effects ultimately must involve quantitative variations in the transfer of chemical factors between maternal and foetal systems.

In view of these considerations, it is of interest to seek relationships between what substances can cross the placenta, and which foetal organs are capable of exhibiting vicarious compensatory responses to partial or total extirpations of homologous maternal organs. Such data should yield valuable information concerning the humoral factors by which growth may be controlled.

Endocrine Glands

As might be expected, these principles are best illustrated by some of the endocrine glands, the growth of which is regulated by hormones which can themselves pass back and forth between the maternal and foetal circulations, or which can affect the concentration of other molecules that may cross the placenta. The adrenal cortex has been most extensively investigated from this point of view. It has long been known, for example, that totally adrenalectomized pregnant animals survive longer than do non-pregnant ones. This has been demonstrated with respect to pregnant dogs by Rogoff and Stewart (1927) and Billman and Engel (1939), the latter authors noting that the mothers died in a state of adrenal insufficiency soon after delivery. In the rat, Firor and Grollmann (1933) found that pregnant females survived an average of 15·4 days after bilateral adrenalectomy, compared with normal controls which lived only 7 to 9 days without their adrenals. Animals operated on early in gestation survived longer than those adrenalectomized late in pregnancy, and in no case did any such animal die before term.

That this effect is attributable to increased secretory activity by the foetal adrenals is indicated by the compensatory enlargements of the latter. Ingle and Fisher (1938) adrenalectomized pregnant rats on the seventh or fourteenth day of gestation and noted an average increase of 50 per cent in the relative weights of the foetal adrenal glands at term (Table 5), an effect which was due in part to the reduced size of offspring born to adrenalectomized mothers. Although the absolute weights of male adrenals were consistently greater than in females, this discrepancy disappeared when relative weights were calculated. Confirmatory results have since been reported by Walaas and Walaas (1944), Davis and Plotz (1954), Knobil and Briggs (1955), Christianson and Jones (1957), and Angervall (1962) who bilaterally adrenalectomized pregnant rats during the latter half of the gestation

Maternal adrenalectomy (gestational age)	No. of litters	Foetal body weight		Foetal adrenal weight			
		♂	♀	♂		♀	
		gm.	gm.	gm.	%	gm.	%
Unoperated	18	5·34	5·03	0·90	(0·0169)	0·82	(0·0163)
7th day	10	4·70	4·51	1·17	(0·0249)	1·13	(0·0251)
14th day	15	4·96	4·78	1·23	(0 024/)	1·18	(0·0246)

TABLE 5. Compensatory growth response of foetal adrenals to maternal adrenalectomy in the rat (Ingle and Fisher, 1938). Relative weights of foetal adrenals at term (in parentheses) are considerably greater in experimental animals, but are not affected by the time of maternal adrenalectomy.

period and observed hypertrophy of the foetal glands (accompanied by hyperaemia), a threefold increase in mitotic activity, and enlargement of the zona fasciculata and zona reticularis. In mice, Eguchi (1960) has shown that adrenal enlargement is not apparent until the eighteenth day of gestation in the foetuses of mothers adrenalectomized four days prior to sacrifice. Unilateral adrenalectomy of the pregnant rats on the fourteenth day of gestation does not affect the growth of foetal adrenals when examined at term, although the residual maternal gland undergoes hypertrophy (Lombardo, 1964).

In two investigations, the response of the remaining adrenal to the loss of one adrenal gland in the foetus itself has been studied. Cauterization of one foetal adrenal between 16 and 20 days of gestation in the rat results in 15 to 20 per cent enlargement of the remaining foetal adrenal (Tobin, 1939). According to Kitchell (1954), a 43 per cent increase in foetal rat adrenal weight occurs during the last two days of gestation after unilateral adrenalectomy on the nineteenth day. Tobin (1939) claimed that foetal adrenal hypertrophy involved an increase in the width of the zona glomerulosa, but Kitchell (1954) reported that this zone was thinner than normal and that the zona fasciculata was wider, whereas the zona reticularis remained unchanged. In all zones, however, the individual cells were found to have enlarged, but there was no change in mitotic activity. Perhaps the above differences may be correlated with the varying durations between operation and sacrifice in these different experiments. Nevertheless, the foregoing results in general indicate a definite capacity of the foetal adrenal cortex to respond functionally as well as developmentally to hormonal deficits.

Changes in the concentration of cortisone appear to be the major factor in affecting the growth of foetal adrenals. Injected into pregnant rats, cortisone retards the growth of the foetal adrenals (Courrier, et al., 1951). Walaas and Walaas (1944) and Davis and Plotz (1954) showed that the increased proliferation and hypertrophy in foetal adrenals that is normally caused by maternal adrenalectomy, can be diminished by administering cortical hormones to the mother. Kitchell and Wells (1952) implanted one milligram pellets of cortisone subcutaneously into unilaterally adrenalectomized foetal rats *in utero* and thereby prevented compensatory hypertrophy in the residual foetal adrenal glands. Similar treatment of intact foetuses, however, had no effect on their adrenals (Kitchell and Wells, 1952), although Yakaitis and Wells (1956) were subsequently able to inhibit the growth of the intact foetal adrenal cortex by subcutaneous *in utero* implantations of cortisone and hydrocortisone on the fourteenth day of gestation. Comparable administration of desoxycorticosterone *in utero* failed to prevent compensatory foetal adrenal hypertrophy (Kitchell and Wells, 1952), but did cause a slight reduction in the width of the zona glomerulosa of unoperated foetal adrenals (Yakaitis and Wells, 1956). Other steroid hormones (progesterone, oestrogen, testosterone) administered subcutaneously to rat foetuses, were generally without effects on adrenal size (Kitchell, 1950; Kitchell and Wells, 1952).

In view of the predominant influence of cortisone on the regulation of foetal adrenal size, it becomes important to determine if the growth (and secretory activity) of the foetal adrenal cortex is mediated by ACTH from the foetal or maternal pituitaries. Hypophysectomy of pregnant rats has no effect on the growth of foetal adrenals, but if the foetus is also hypophysectomized growth of its adrenals is retarded (Yakaitis and Wells, 1956). Indeed, foetal hypophysectomy alone also prevents growth of the adrenals (Wells, 1947, 1948, 1949; Raynaud and Frilley, 1947; Jost, 1948), indicating that the adrenal-pituitary axis is operating prenatally. In fact, atrophy of the foetal anterior pituitary has been produced by subcutaneous administration of hydrocortisone, whereas pituitary enlargement is caused by bilateral adrenalectomy in the foetus (Coetzee and Wells, 1957). Moreover, ACTH injected into the foetus stimulates growth of the foetal adrenal glands (Wells, 1948). Nevertheless, there is some evidence that maternal ACTH may directly affect the foetal adrenals, for Knobil and Briggs (1955) found that in pregnant rats subjected to both hypophysectomy and adrenalectomy, there was no compensatory growth of the foetal adrenals. Moreover, the atrophy of the adrenal cortex that normally occurs after hypophysectomy does not take place in pregnant rats (Knobil and Briggs, 1955) and monkeys (Smith, 1955). This is evidence, therefore, that ACTH may be produced by the placenta or that foetal ACTH may enter the maternal system. Both possibilities obviously require confirmation.

In a somewhat different approach to the problem, Schmidt and Hoffman (1954) injected ACTH into pregnant monkeys. This caused hypertrophy of the zona fasciculata of the maternal adrenals, but resulted in a concomitant atrophy of the foetal zona fasciculata (without affecting the foetal zona glomerulosa). Similar results have been obtained in pregnant rats when subjected to cold stress or treated with exogenous ACTH (Jones, et al., 1953). It was suggested that the stimulated maternal adrenals secreted extra amounts of cortisone which crossed the placenta, inhibited foetal ACTH secretion, and thus retarded growth of the foetal adrenals.

Sex steroids, like adrenocortical hormones, are likewise capable of crossing the placenta. Embryos of both sexes are thus exposed to the female hormones of the mother, but these apparently do not seriously influence the development of the foetal gonads or accessory structures under normal conditions. In sufficient concentrations, however, Greene, et al. (1941) have shown that sex hormones exert mutually antagonistic effects on embryonic gonads. Normally, of course, the foetus is never exposed to exogenous testosterone, but according to Wells (1946c), when testosterone is administered to pregnant rats during the last week of gestation, or when one milligram pellets are implanted subcutaneously into castrated foetuses, there occurs an enlargement of the seminal vesicles and bulbo-urethral glands. Foetal castration alone had opposite effects. Therefore, the foetal rat testes are normally engaged in secretory activity during the last third of gestation, and presumably are stimulated by the pituitary. If gonadotrophins are injected subcutaneously into rat foetuses twice a day for the terminal three days of pregnancy (Wells, 1946a), the interstitial cells become larger and more numerous. The foetal ovaries, however, are unaffected by this treatment.

Inasmuch as thyroxine is a relatively small molecule, there is reason to expect that foetal thyroids might compensate for maternal hypothyroidism. This was first investigated by Marine (1908) who removed three-quarters of a dog's thyroid at the time of conception. The thyroids of the resultant litter were enlarged in comparison with those of a previous normal litter. In a later pregnancy the same mother was given supplemental iodine, which prevented compensatory thyroid hypertrophy of her contemporary offspring. Although Loeb (1919) was unable to confirm these observations in the guinea pig, more recent investigations have clearly shown that thyroxine does indeed cross the placenta at least in rats. Vyasov, et. al. (1962) removed a thyroid lobe from rats which were nine days pregnant and detected a twofold increase in 16-day foetal thyroids as compared with controls. Horn and LoMonaco (1958) showed that foetal as well as maternal thyroid hyperplasia can be induced by feeding thiourea to pregnant rats during the last week of gestation. Using this technique, Hamburgh, et al. (1962) fed propylthiouracil to pregnant rats and were able to preclude subsequent foetal and maternal goitre development by also feeding L-thyroxine. Since maternal hypophysectomy prevents neither normal foetal thyroid development nor hypertrophy following administration of propylthiouracil, the above results indicate that thyroxine can pass from the maternal to the foetal circulation, but that maternal thyrotrophic hormone probably does not. Foetal thyroid growth is apparently mediated by foetal thyrotrophic hormone. The latter apparently cannot enter the maternal circulation, for in hypophysectomized pregnant monkeys the maternal thyroid glands are not prevented from undergoing atrophy by the presence of the foetus. Thus, it is again evident that small hormone molecules can pass through the placenta, but that proteins cannot.

Apropos of this, an especially interesting situation is exemplified by the relationship between the maternal and foetal islets of Langerhans and the problem of whether or not insulin (containing only 51 amino acids) can cross the placenta. Numerous clinical reports have indicated that the offspring of diabetic mothers often have enlarged islets of Langerhans (Gordon, 1936; Helwig, 1940; Potter, et al., 1941). Cardell (1953) found an average threefold increase in the amount of islet tissue in human infants born of diabetic mothers, as compared with normal ones. In most of these cases, the enlargement could be accounted for by the presence of excessive numbers of β-cells. Gordon (1936) was able to produce similar effects by experimental pancreatectomy in dogs. Hultquist (1950) found that pancreatectomy of pregnant rats between the eighth and twelfth days of gestation, while causing a high percentage of foetal death, also resulted in the enlargement of the islets of Langerhans in the offspring. Angervall (1959) has recently obtained the same results in rats made diabetic by the administration of alloxan on the tenth to twelfth days of gestation. Despite the fact that insulin is not a large protein, there is little reason to attribute the above results to its passage across the placenta in either direction. Gordon's (1936) explanation, involving the transfer of glucose from mother to foetus, is still adequate to account for the principal effects. He contended that maternal hyperglycaemia as a result of diabetes mellitus results in the transfer of excessive amounts of glucose to the foetal blood. The foetus, developing in a hyperglycaemic environment, must secrete abnormally large quantities in insulin in order to convert its blood sugar to glycogen. Consequently, the foetal islets of Langerhans become enlarged and during pregnancy the mother's diabetic condition is partially alleviated by foetal compensation. Moreover, such foetuses are usually larger than normal, partly because of the excess carbohydrates available to them. At parturition, however, the "diabetic" foetus is suddenly deprived of its exogenous source of glucose, yet it still secretes large amounts of insulin. Thus, the prenatal equilibrium is followed by a state of severe hypoglycaemia which is usually lethal. Hence to explain hypertrophy of foetal islets of Langerhans, it need only be postulated that glucose, not insulin, be transferred across the placenta in excessive quantities.

Other endocrine organs have not as yet been investigated for their capacities to respond to transplacental influences. On the basis of what is already known, it might be predicted that such glands as the pituitary and parathyroid would not be directly affected in the foetus by the maternal hormones because the latter are proteinaceous and probably incapable of passing through the placenta. Yet in view of some tentative evidence that ACTH might be transmitted between mother and foetus (see above) the possibility that the placenta might be permeable to some of the smaller protein hormones (e.g. the octopeptides of the posterior lobe of the pituitary) cannot be categorically denied. In the case of the parathyroid glands, it is conceivable that an effect might be produced not by the parathyroid hormone itself but by alterations in the Ca^{++} concentration in the maternal and foetal circulatory systems. Further investigations on such endocrinological problems, as they relate to maternal-foetal relationships, should prove as rewarding as they are important.

It is speculatively interesting to note that those hormones which cross the placenta are not only non-proteinaceous, but are also (with the apparent exception of desoxycorticosterone) all dependent upon trophic hormones of pituitary origin. If the trophic hormones, all of which are proteins, are unable to intrude directly on the foetal system, then the foetal endocrine organs must develop under the influences of their own pituitaries. Possibly the secretory activities of the latter have adapted to the normal presence of maternal steroids. Although the phylogenetic advent of trophic hormones evidently antedated the evolution of vertebrate viviparity, such hormones may still constitute a convenient mechanism by which the autonomous growth of foetal glands is safeguarded against excessive maternal influences.

Liver

Considerably less is known about how non-endocrinological organs in the foetus might be affected by removal of the homologous maternal organs. In view of the obvious importance of obtaining such information, it is surprising that so little is known about the liver in this respect. Judging from the reports of Fels and DeEandi (1943) and Paschkis and Cantarow (1958), one difficulty in successfully studying the effects of maternal partial hepatectomy on foetal livers would be the high incidence of abortion attending such operations. However, in the author's laboratory, Ballantine (unpublished) has found that when pregnant rats are partially hepatectomized on the thirteenth day of gestation, the foetal livers one week later (twentieth day) were significantly larger than were those of sham operated mothers, as measured in terms of fresh weight. Although the average body weights of the experimental foetuses were somewhat less than normal, both the absolute and relative weights of their livers were greater than in controls.

It is known that the foetal and maternal plasma proteins of hepatic origin are generally segregated to the extent that the mother contributes little if anything to their accumulation in the foetal blood (Kulangara and Schjeide, 1962; Kelleher, et al., 1963). Thus, the compensatory response of foetal livers to maternal hepatectomy would appear to be stimulated by mechanisms other than alterations in the serum concentrations of albumin or globulins. Whatever may be the nature of the mediating influences in this case, a major problem to emerge will relate to the mechanisms by which development can proceed normally despite the intrusion of maternal influences on the foetal system.

Kidneys

If organ growth, even in the foetus, is stimulated by functional demands, then one would expect that renal insufficiency in pregnant animals should accelerate the function and growth of foetal kidneys. Such a response, of course, would not alleviate the maternal distress because foetal excretory products must ultimately be returned to the mother. Attempts to test the compensatory capacities of foetal kidneys, however, have yielded little data indicating that they can grow in response to maternal nephrectomy. Rollason (1961) studied the effects of bilateral nephrectomy of mothers pregnant for eighteen and a half days on foetal rat kidneys. One day later the relative weights of the foetal kidneys had declined, but returned to normal afterwards despite the general reduction in foetal body weight in comparison with controls. Renal mitotic activity at nineteen and a half days of gestation (one day after operation) was above normal, but was unaltered during the following two days. It was suggested that this increase in proliferation, coincident with the reduction in relative weight of foetal kidneys one day post-operatively, may account for the restoration of normal renal proportions thereafter. Correlative histochemical studies indicated that the experimental foetal kidneys differentiated more precociously than did controls, perhaps due to the greater concentrations of urea in the system. Another investigation along these lines (Goss, 1963a), in which only one maternal kidney was removed on the nineteenth day of gestation, revealed no evidence of compensatory renal hyperplasia in foetal kidneys two days later despite the increase in mitotic activity of the remaining maternal kidneys. If it is assumed that renal growth is regulated by factors directly connected with excretion, this lack of effect may be due to the capacity of the residual maternal kidney to fulfill the excretory needs of the organism to the extent that the foetuses may have been protected from excessive excretory demands.

Nevertheless, it is important to learn something of the physiological activity of the foetal kidney if the relation between function and growth is to be understood. In a comparative study of prenatal excretion in various mammals, Bremer (1916) found that the mesonephros usually handles the excretory needs of the organism until it eventually degenerates in later development as the kidney proper (metanephros) becomes functionally active. The size of the allantois varies in proportion to the duration and function of the mesonephros. In the pig, sheep, and cat, the mesonephros persists until the kidney itself is mature enough to take over the excretory needs of the foetus. In the rat, guinea pig, rabbit, and human being, the mesonephros regresses before the kidney is ready to function. In fact, the rat mesonephros never develops functional glomeruli. In these latter animals, therefore, the placenta is modified, by virtue of specialized epithelial membranes associated with the foetal capillaries, into an excretory organ capable of eliminating waste products at least until the kidney becomes functional.

The onset of kidney function in the rat occurs some time prior to the last two days of gestation. Wells (1946d) showed that if the foetal ureter is ligated, both it and the associated renal pelvis become distended during the next day or two. Analysis of the foetal urine collected in this way showed it to be more dilute than that derived from the mother (Daly, *et al.*, 1947). If an organ is capable of functioning, its work output is adjusted to the demands. It follows, therefore, that increased demands for excretion should stimulate greater functional activity in the kidney. In foetal rats, Wells (1946b) has demonstrated that urine production is accelerated following the subcutaneous injection of urea *in utero*, or as a result of ligating the renal pedicles of the mother. Thus, the foetal kidney is apparently capable of functional compensation but whether or not it undergoes compensatory growth is still problematical.

The obvious way to answer this question is to perform unilateral nephrectomy in the embryo or foetus. Ferris (cited by Weiss, 1955) attempted this in 12- to 13- day- old chick embryos by cauterizing one metanephros. During the subsequent two days there occurred a 70 per cent rise in mitotic activity in the opposite metanephros (at a stage when this organ was assumed to be in a prefunctional state). Such an operation has not been successfully performed in the mammalian embryo except by genetic mutation. In a study of the descendants of irradiated mice, Bagg (1925) noted that when one kidney was congenitally absent, the solitary remaining kidney in the adults was typically hypertrophic. Similar mice examined within 24 hours after birth, however, possessed single kidneys of normal dimensions, indicating that renal hypertrophy does not commence until some time after parturition. It is at this time that the kidneys become vitally essential organs, for mice totally lacking both kidneys survive and develop normally in other respects until a day or two after birth. Indeed, Gluecksohn-Schoenheimer (1943) observed that in homozygotes of the Sd strain of mice, in which both kidneys were missing, "severe urinary malformations appear not to have affected viability before birth, since the segregation ratio of normal and abnormal at birth was very close to that expected". Apparently such abnormalities relate to whether or not the upper end of the ureters differentiate, for the metanephros was never encountered in mice in which the renal pelvis had failed to develop (Gluecksohn-Schoenheimer, 1945). Conversely, Goldstein (1957) described a case of a teratogenic rat embryo (produced by treatment with trypan blue) in which there occurred only one unilateral kidney to which two ureters were connected. But since this "single" kidney had grown to twice the size of those in normal litter mates it is very possible that it represented two fused kidneys instead of a single hypertrophic one.

Thus, most of the evidence derived from foetal animals indicates that normal renal growth is associated with ordinary levels of physiological needs, and that compensatory growth does not occur until functional demands become extreme. During prenatal development the excretory functions of the mother apparently preclude the necessity for compensatory renal hypertrophy in mammalian foetuses with only one kidney. Not until after birth do the functional demands become sufficiently compelling to bring about compensatory growth of the kidney. The chick embryo, incidentally, does not enjoy the benefits of placental dependence on the maternal system. Accordingly, it must do all of its own excretory work throughout development, with the result that the loss of one kidney would be more acutely felt and reacted to than in mammalian embryos. Thus, comparisons between oviparous and viviparous development from this point of view may be especially fruitful.

Still unexplored are the possible relationships between other foetal and maternal organs. Potentially rewarding fields of research lie in the investigation of such tissues as the blood, lymphatic system, and exocrine organs. The report by Vyasov, et. al. (1962), that removal of one maternal rat lung on the eighth day of gestation results in an enlargement of foetal lungs on the sixteenth day to 126 per cent of control weights, should be verified in view of its obvious relationship to the possible role of function in growth control.

Alternatively, the reactions of foetal tissues to the injections of homologous tissue preparations into the mother may be worth investigating, especially in view of Gluecksohn-Waelsch's (1957) apparently successful attempt to produce central nervous system

R

abnormalities in 8 to 9 per cent of the embryos of pregnant mice injected with brain emulsions. If such a result is attributable to the deleterious effects of maternal immunization against tissue-specific antigens, there may still be some justification for again attempting to confirm the claim by Guyer and Smith (1918) that antibodies against lens can cause *in utero* anomalies in lens development in rabbits and mice (despite the unsuccessful attempts by Finlay (1924) and Huxley and Carr-Saunders (1924) to repeat these experiments). Since antibodies are known to be transmitted from mother to offspring in certain mammals (e.g. mouse, rat, guinea pig, rabbit, human), the development of many tissues and organs might be profitably investigated from this point of view.

XV

The Functional Demand Theory of Growth Regulation

AN abundance of evidence has led inescapably to the thesis that reduction in the mass of an organ is indirectly responsible for compensatory growth by creating excessive demands for increased functional activity on the part of the residual tissues. If this is indeed the case, it must follow that functional overload in the absence of partial ablation should also initiate compensatory growth responses. Conversely, if the loss of tissue is not accompanied by extra functional burdens on homologous organs, then the latter should not be stimulated to grow. Sufficient information is now available with reference to many organs and tissues to reach a convincing conclusion as to the fundamental role of function in regulating compensatory, regenerative, and perhaps even normal growth (cf. Walter and Addis, 1939). Accordingly, various tissues, organs, and systems capable of compensatory growth will be considered *seriatim* from this point of view, in order to determine how their growth might be affected by functional requirements. Nowhere have these principles been more eloquently interpreted than in the writings of Boycott (1932) on the subject of adaptive growth.

Liver

It is difficult to decide which of the many functions of the liver is the one by which its growth might be controlled. The liver is the site where many plasma proteins are synthesized, including albumin, α- and β-globulins, and fibrinogen. In addition, it produces heparin, prothrombin, and hypertensinogen. Strategically located between the alimentary canal and the general systemic circulation, the liver carries on numerous metabolic degradations and conversions in the course of processing the end products of digestion. When necessary, it detoxifies noxious substances. It also serves as a major storage site for glycogen and fats. Judging from its histological architecture and its embryonic origin, however, the primary function of the liver appears to be the elaboration and secretion of bile. Therefore, the

259

liver is fundamentally an exocrine organ, and as such, it is logical to regard this aspect of hepatic physiology as a possible factor in the regulation of the size of the liver.

Perhaps the simplest way to investigate this relationship is to ligate the bile duct, a technique which is physiologically crude but which yields some interesting results. Cameron, *et al.* (1957) described the early occurrence of necrosis in occluded rabbit bile ducts, followed by the onset of proliferation in duct epithelium as soon as 12 to 17 hours afterwards, together with evidence of the formation of new bile duct buds. By the second day, proliferative activity was common in the hepatic parenchymal cells, a fact subsequently corroborated in the rat by MacDonald and Pechet (1961). This hyperplastic response resembled that occurring in liver regeneration following partial hepatectomy, except that it lasted for a longer time. Indeed, if the rat liver is simultaneously subjected to partial ablation and biliary obstruction, the mitotic response of regeneration proceeds normally at first (Weinbren, 1953) but persists longer than in unobstructed regenerating controls (Ferguson, *et al.*, 1949). If part of the biliary system is occluded in the rabbit, Schalm, *et al.* (1956) reported atrophy of the affected portion of the liver, accompanied by compensatory regeneration of the unobstructed part.

Whether these various effects of bile duct obstruction on the liver are the result of mechanical pressure or the specific effects of bile, still remains to be resolved. The toxicity of bile, according to Horrall and Carlson (1928) resides in the presence of sodium glucocholate and sodium taurocholate. Solopaev (1957) found that intact livers were unaffected in rats fed diets containing fresh dog's bile, but that partially hepatectomized livers of such animals regenerated about twice as fast as in controls on normal diets. When fed daily in the diet to rabbits, bile caused some peripheral lobular atrophy during the first week, followed by proliferation of bile duct epithelial cells, and eventually by cirrhosis after a few months (Holsti, 1956). Wilson (1955) observed a stimulation of mitotic activity in the livers of mice fed diets containing ox gall for six to seven days. In mice with livers induced to regenerate by CCl_4 injury, 0·5 per cent desiccated ox gall in the diet caused abnormal mitotic figures to occur, perhaps due to imperfect formation of spindle fibres. These effects of bile were believed by Wilson (1955) to be accentuated by its passage through the enterohepatic circulation, which is responsible for the repeated absorption and secretion of bile components. The necessity for such additional secretory activity by the liver may constitute a functional overload to which the subsequent hyperplastic response is attributed. There may therefore be some basis for relating liver regeneration to bile secretion, but to be convincing, considerably more evidence will be required.

Nevertheless, the relation between liver growth and nutrition is well established. High protein diets are known to stimulate liver growth (MacKay, et al., 1928; Campbell and Kosterlitz, 1950), as does the administration of biotin or choramine (Wilson and Leduc, 1949, 1950). Leduc (1949) has shown in mice that inanition inhibits liver mitoses, decreases cell size, and depletes cytoplasmic basophilia; these effects are reversed by refeeding. In rats maintained on a low protein diet, liver regeneration after partial hepatectomy was retarded, according to experiments by Higgins and Ingle (1939). Such results, however, cannot be unequivocally interpreted as specific for the liver inasmuch as similar effects of starvation have been noted in the kidney, too (see below).

Nevertheless, the liver is first and foremost a digestive organ. As such, its functioning depends in large measure upon the supply of venous blood delivered to it from the digestive tract via the hepatic portal vein. Thus, the liver is strategically interposed between the digestive tract and the rest of the body and is therefore in a position to process the materials which come to it from the gut. The venous blood from the hepatic portal vein, together with the arterial blood entering by way of the hepatic artery, leave the liver through the hepatic vein, which empties into the vena cava. This arrangement makes it possible to deprive the liver of its venous circulation, thus impairing many of its functions, while leaving the arterial blood flow intact. Rous and Larimore (1920) occluded the portal circulation to part of the liver in rabbits and noted that the affected lobes underwent a gradual atrophy. Moreover, the unobstructed part of the liver hypertrophied in compensation. If the portal vein is partially ligated in rats also subjected to partial hepatectomy, Stephenson (1932) found that regeneration occurred to only 76 per cent of the control values. Similarly, when the hepatic portal vein is anastomosed to the posterior vena cava (Eck fistula) so that the venous blood bypasses the liver, regeneration is also inhibited and chronic liver insufficiency may result (Mann and Magath, 1922). These experiments emphasize the importance of the portal circulation in maintaining function and growth of the liver.

Owing to the extensive investigations of Glinos (1956a,b, 1958a,b), already reviewed in Chapter XIII, a widely accepted view of liver growth regulation involves the effects of plasma protein concentrations. Since hepatic mitosis is stimulated by plasmapheresis, and inhibited by artificially raising the concentrations of plasma proteins (as by restricted fluid intake), there is reason to suspect that liver cells might be stimulated to multiply concomitant with the demands for greater synthetic and secretory activity needed to replenish depleted plasma proteins. How each of the different proteins might affect such a process, indeed, to what extent liver growth is governed by one or all of the manifold hepatic functions, is an intriguing facet of the problem of liver regeneration in particular and growth regulation in general.

Kidney

The most obvious function of the kidney is that of excretion, which represents a collection of subsidiary processes involving the elimination or resorption of numerous substances. In addition, the kidney plays a leading role in maintaining proper water balance in the body, and is especially important in regulating blood-pressure. Again we are confronted with the problem of determining which of these functions mediates renal growth.

A striking consequence of partial nephrectomy is the physiological compensation of the remaining kidney tissue. Although there is a transient rise in the blood urea concentration (Karsner, *et al.*, 1932; Allen, *et al.*, 1935; McCance and Morrison, 1956), there is usually no reduction in the normal output of urine (Sacerdotti, 1896; Schilling, 1905; Pearce, 1908; Karsner, *et al.*, 1915). Nevertheless, Karsner, *et al.* (1932) found that the remaining kidneys of dogs were deficient for approximately a month after unilateral nephrectomy in their abilities to excrete injected urea, presumably because their normal functional reserve capacities were being utilized to compensate physiologically for the reduced renal mass. When the proportion of kidney mass removed is so large that the remaining tissue does not have the capacity to meet the excretory needs of the body, then alterations in the composition of the urine are noted. Bradford (1898–99) observed that when two-thirds to three-quarters of the total renal mass of dogs was excised, the water content of the urine rose proportionately, presumably because of limited capabilities for reabsorption.

The rate of glomerular filtration depends upon a variety of factors, not the least of which are the rates and pressures of blood flow through the glomerular capillaries. In the frog, Richards and Schmidt (1924) noted that individual glomeruli open and close at intervals of 10 to 30 seconds. In the rabbit, Khanolkar (1922) found that "the various units of which the kidney is composed are not all active during moderate activity of the organ. In other words, the exigencies of everyday life during health demand the activity of only a proportion of the kidney units, at any particular moment." He concluded "that the active units are active to their utmost limits; that whenever the amount of work to be accomplished is increased, this is met by an increased number of units being thrown into activity and not by an increased activity of the active units". Later investigations of rabbit kidneys showed that the number of patent glomeruli at any one moment varies between 40 and 80 per cent of the total number (Hayman and Starr, 1925), and that within 24 hours after unilateral nephrectomy the number of open glomeruli in the remaining kidney had increased to 91 to 99 per cent, an effect which lasted for at least 10 days (Moore and Lukianoff, 1929). It would be valuable to learn how soon after operation this physiological compensation takes place, for only 2 hours after uninephrectomy Fajers (1957b) failed to detect any functional alterations in the residual rabbit kidney, including glomerular filtration rate, effective renal plasma flow, urinary output, and per cent water and sodium excretion. Further studies along these lines should yield precisely the kind of information that is needed to elucidate the primary cause of compensatory renal hyperplasia.

To determine if the growth response of the remaining kidney is attributable to reduction in renal mass *per se* or the consequent functional overload, it is necessary to increase the latter without removing any kidney tissue. This can be achieved by rendering one kidney non-functional. When one ureter is severed, allowing the urine to drain into the peritoneal cavity and thence to be reabsorbed, the extra burden on the contralateral kidney is not reflected in a growth response such as that which occurs following unilateral nephrectomy. Simpson (1960) found no increase in renal P^{32} uptake between 36 and 48 hours after such an operation in rats, and concluded that the stimulus for compensatory renal hypertrophy "is some factor other than a dialysable substance in the urine". In agreement with this, there is no rise in mitotic activity in either kidney 48 hours after transection of one ureter (Goss and Rankin, 1960). Royce (1963) has reported similar results, and has suggested that the lack of effect might be due to peritoneal inflammation associated with ureteroperi-toneostomy. He showed that if a talc suspension is introduced into the peritoneal cavities of uninephrectomized rats, compensatory hypertrophy of the remaining kidneys is inhibited.

When one ureter is deviated to the duodenum in rats, Block, et al. (1953) observed no enlargement of the opposite kidney, and concluded that excretory work is not causally related to renal growth. Fortner and Kiefer (1948), however, claimed that unilateral uretero-duodenostomy in dogs sometimes resulted in contralateral renal hypertrophy. Hartman (1933) raised the concentration of excretory products in the body by grafting the urinary bladder to isolated segments of the ileum in dogs. During the subsequent two months, the kidneys became enlarged as a result of tubular proliferation, but thereafter underwent degenerative changes. It was concluded that "increased excretory work must be considered as a probable major factor in the hypertrophy and subsequent degeneration of the kidneys, burdened through reabsorption with large excesses of normal urinary constituents".

Hartman (1933) also tested the effects of direct injections of concentrated human urine into dogs but only succeeded in causing death with 24 hours. Similar experiments on rats have been attempted by Goss (unpublished). Intravenous or intraperitoneal injections of filtered rat or human urine, administered three times over a two-day period in doses of 1 to 2 millilitres per 100 grammes body weight caused no significant changes in renal mitosis (as compared with saline-injected controls). In view of such negative results, any definite conclusion as to the possible role of urinary constituents in mediating compensatory renal hypertrophy must be held in abeyance pending the acquisition of more convincing evidence.

Perhaps the most logical approach to the problem of how kidney size regulation might be related to excretory work is to analyse the individual urinary components, of which urea is of course the most important. Excretory demands can be experimentally increased by feeding an animal excessive protein or by direct administration of urea. Conversely, starvation might be expected to have opposite effects on the kidneys. The latter conditions were studied by Sacer-dotti (1896), who noted that enlargement of the remaining kidney after uninephrectomy was inhibited in fasting animals. More recently, Hall and Hall (1952) reported that compensatory renal hypertrophy was retarded in starving rats. In a study of renal mitotic activity,

Williams (1962a) has shown that inanition reduces the incidence of cell division in normal rat kidneys as well as in those undergoing compensatory renal hyperplasia. Royce (1963) has confirmed that compensatory renal hypertrophy is incompatible with starvation.

Increased protein intake imposes an added burden on the kidneys which must excrete extra amounts of nitrogenous waste products. Osborne, et al. (1927) maintained rats on high protein diets which caused a 50 per cent enlargement of the kidneys within a week. Such rats drank excessively and were extremely diuretic. Upon returning the animals to a normal diet the hypertrophic kidneys underwent "compensatory atrophy". MacKay, et al. (1927) pursued similar studies by measuring the weights of kidneys of rats on normal compared with high (18 per cent v. 70 per cent) protein diets. Young rats, between 26 and 70 days old, had kidneys enlarged 50 per cent as a result of the excessive protein intake. The kidneys of old animals, however, from 346 to 400 days of age, were only slightly affected by such a diet, perhaps because the renal nephrons undergo hypertrophy with advancing age to compensate for the normal loss of renal tissue. Old animals may, therefore, be incapable of further renal growth if maximum physiological efficiency is to be maintained (see Chapter IV). The effect of high protein diets is apparently specific for the kidneys, for Leathem (1945) fed rats on diets containing 78 per cent casein and noted renal hypertrophy, but no enlargement of other organs such as the pituitary, thyroid, adrenal, testes, seminal vesicles, prostate, or spleen. As might be expected, however, the liver is also induced to enlarge as a result of excess protein intake (MacKay, et al., 1928; Campbell and Kosterlitz, 1950). Apparently, the form in which the protein is administered makes little difference, for Baxter and Cotzias (1949) succeeded in causing reversible enlargement of the kidneys by the intraperitoneal injection of gelatin, albumin, or globulin. Similar effects have been noted in residual kidneys following contralateral nephrectomy. High protein diets stimulate extra compensatory growth (Smith and Moise, 1927; Allen and Mann, 1935; MacKay, et al., 1938) and protein-free diets suppress such enlargement (Mandel, et al., 1950). The latter study is of particular interest. Although the increase in weight, protein content, and RNA in compensatory kidneys was markedly reduced 30 hours after uninephrectomy in protein-starved rats (see Table 6), thus accounting for the decrease in cellular hypertrophy, the rise in the renal DNA content was not adversely affected by protein deprivation. This would

	Normal diet	Protein-free diet
	%	%
Increase in kidney weight	41	6
Increase in renal protein	39	12
Increase in RNA	42	14

TABLE 6. Effect of protein content of diet on compensatory growth of rat kidney 30 hours after uninephrectomy (Mandel, et al., 1950). Restriction of protein intake seriously retards compensatory renal growth.

indicate that hyperplasia *per se* might not depend upon protein availability, but that other aspects of growth (e.g. hypertrophy) might be seriously affected by it.

If the growth-promoting effects of high protein intake on the kidney are solely attributable to the need to excrete extra amounts of nitrogenous waste products, it should follow that urea ought to exert comparable influences. Curiously enough, this is not necessarily the case. Osborne, *et al.* (1927) reported enlargement of rat kidneys to moderate extents after a week on diets containing 18 to 28 per cent urea, but the response was considerably less than in rats fed equivalent quantities of proteinaceous nitrogen. These observations were later confirmed by MacKay, *et al.* (1931), but in other investigations no effect of urea on the kidneys was noted. When fed five grams of urea per day for up to nine months, rabbits exhibited no alterations in renal histology although they excreted twice the normal amounts of urea (Newburgh, 1919). In rats, Emge (1921) fed urea in doses increasing from 5·5 to 17 per cent for as long as 16 months, but could find no adverse effects on the histological or cytological features of the kidneys. When urea was injected into dogs by Hartman (1933), the chief effects were convulsions, coma, and degeneration of the kidneys. No renal hypertrophy occurred. Baxter and Cotzias (1949) injected urea intraperitoneally into rats and also failed to obtain enlargement of the kidneys. Therefore, there is little convincing evidence that kidney growth is directly related to how much urea it is called upon to excrete.

The discrepancy between the above effects of protein as opposed to urea is not easily explained. The simplest interpretation would involve the extra nutritional qualities of protein which might account for its greater growth-promoting effects. However, the apparent specificity for liver and kidney (suggesting deamination), coupled with the observation by Baxter and Cotzias (1949) that casein hydrolysate fails to affect kidney size when injected intraperitoneally (in contrast to the efficacy of whole proteins), argues against an explanation based on nutritional factors alone.

Other urinary constituents have been less extensively analysed for their possible effects on kidney growth. With reference to carbohydrates, Allen and Mann (1935) reported a slight increase in compensatory renal hypertrophy in uninephrectomized rats and rabbits injected intraperitoneally with 20 per cent sucrose solutions. However, Steuart (1958) found no such influence when gauged in terms of renal proliferation after 48 hours. Therefore, it is doubtful that these compounds are causally related to the regulation of kidney size.

The remaining major ingredient of the urine is salt, of which most kinds have no effect on renal size. Osborne, et al. (1927) fed rats a variety of salts in concentrations up to 22 per cent and observed no indications of kidney growth. NaCl, however, in doses from 18 to 25 per cent did cause renal enlargement, a fact which has been corroborated by Goss and Rankin (1960) who found a twofold increase in renal mitotic activity in rats maintained on 1 per cent NaCl drinking water for five days. When such animals were then deprived of one kidney, the resultant 48-hour mitotic peak was markedly reduced, which may perhaps be explained by the prior occurrence of growth during the compulsory salt regimen, thus rendering further compensatory responses less necessary. Nevertheless, Allen and Mann (1935) had previously shown that when uninephrectomized animals were fed diets containing 15 per cent NaCl, subsequent compensatory hypertrophy was unaffected. Given water *ad libitum*, however, these animals could easily excrete excess salt, whereas rats forced to drink only salt water could not so easily eliminate the salt. Hence, the above discrepancies regarding the effect of NaCl may possibly be explained in terms of how much sodium is actually retained in the body. As will be elaborated below, this appears to be related to a number of factors which affect renal growth and physiology, including desoxycorticosterone secretion, the juxtaglomerular apparatus and the regulation of blood-pressure.

The one urinary constituent which seems to have been most neglected in studies of renal growth responses, namely, water, may conceivably be the most important. The kidney is first and foremost concerned with maintaining an appropriate water balance in the body. In terrestrial vertebrates, one of the chief functions of the kidney is to conserve water, which is done by reabsorption from the glomerular filtrate. Mediated by the antidiuretic hormone, this process accounts for much of the work done by the kidneys. Indeed, the efficiency of the kidney can be expressed in terms of its competence to excrete a concentrated urine, which is proportional to the amount of water that it is capable of reabsorbing. Thus, it could be argued that the need to retain more water, in case of excess salt intake, might promote growth of the kidney through the action of the antidiuretic hormone. However, the direct effects of this hormone on kidney growth have not been experimentally investigated, nor is it known if uninephrectomy affects its secretion.

It has been abundantly proved that the pituitary exerts a renotrophic effect through its influence on the function and growth of the kidney. The size of the kidney in rats, for example, decreases after hypophysectomy (Smith, 1930; Selye, 1941), which may be explained by the marked reduction in mitotic activity (Goss and Rankin, 1960; McCreight and Sulkin, 1962b). Nor can the 40 per cent decline in kidney weight two weeks after hypophysectomy (Fontain and Veil, 1947), be accounted for entirely by the decreased systemic growth rate, since the *relative* weight of the kidney under these circumstances also falls (Fontaine, 1947). Just as the normal growth of the kidney is promoted by the pituitary, so also is compensatory growth. Thus, the enlargement of the kidneys that normally ensues a high protein diet is prevented by hypophysectomy (Leathem, 1945). Even when the loss of body weight that normally accompanies hypophysectomy is avoided by forced feeding, the relative weight of the kidney still remains depressed (Levine, 1944).

Growth of kidneys in response to partial ablation is also dependent on the pituitary. Indeed, the effect of hypophysectomy is so pronounced as to have led some investigators to conclude that compensatory renal hypertrophy is totally abolished when the pituitary is missing, especially when compared with intact controls. Most studies, however, have revealed a slight enlargement of residual kidneys in comparison with hypophysectomized controls possessing intact kidneys, indicating that growth is usually obscured by the normal decrease in kidney size after loss of the pituitary (Selye, 1941; Fontaine and Veil, 1946; Braun-Menendez and Houssay, 1949; Astarabadi and Essex, 1953; Astarabadi, 1963b). The "compensating" kidney, therefore, regresses less than do intact kidneys in hypophysectomized animals. The proliferative aspects of compensatory growth are likewise strikingly diminished by hypophysectomy, although there still persists a narrow margin of response between experimental and control kidneys (Goss and Rankin, 1960; McCreight and Sulkin, 1962b). Even when hypophysectomy is postponed until two weeks after uninephrectomy, the already hypertrophic kidney undergoes atrophy (Astarabadi, 1962a). Not only does the pituitary affect the kidney, but there is a reciprocal relationship between kidney and pituitary that has been demonstrated by the studies of Wrete (1946), who noted that the weight of the mouse pituitary gland enlarges following removal of one kidney.

It is possible that the stimulating influence of the pituitary on the kidney might be indirectly mediated via hormones from other endocrine glands secreted in response to hypophyseal trophic hormones. Thyroxine, for example, causes renal hypertrophy (Herring, 1917; MacKay and MacKay, 1931; Walter and Addis, 1939; Selye, *et al.*, 1945) and increases the mitotic index (Herlant, 1949; Pisi and Cavalli, 1955). Thyroidectomy results in a reduction of kidney weight (MacKay and MacKay, 1931; Walter and Addis, 1939) but does not affect compensatory renal hypertrophy (McQueen-Williams and Thompson, 1939; Zeckwer, 1946). Apparently the influence of the thyroid on kidney growth, therefore, is neither essential nor organspecific, but is mediated through its general effect on metabolic rate. This view is supported by Landauer's (1937) report of renal enlargement in fowl with heightened metabolic rates as a result of the loss of feathers. Hence, it is not surprising that thyrotrophic hormone administered to normal or hypophysectomized rats exerts a renotrophic effect (Hay, *et al.*, 1946).

Selye (1941) has emphasized the renotrophic action of certain steroid hormones, including oestrogen, testosterone, and progesterone. Accordingly, the stimulatory effects of FSH and luteinizing hormones which he has demonstrated, are most probably attributed to the steroids they cause to be secreted. The administration of ACTH, according to experiments by Simpson, *et al.* (1946), causes no enlargement of the kidneys, nor can it restore renal size in hypophysectomized rats (Astarabadi, 1962b) even after excision of one kidney (Astarabadi, 1963a). Consistent with this is the fact that cortisone is antagonistic to compensatory renal growth (Hall and Hall, 1952; Goss and Rankin, 1960). Growth hormone exerts some stimulatory effects on kidney growth (Kochakian and Stettner, 1948), apparently accounted for by enlargement of the convoluted tubules (Selye and Stone, 1946). However, Astarabadi (1962b) failed to restore the normal size of kidneys, rendered abnormally small in hypophysecto- mized rats, by giving growth hormone, although crude pituitary extracts were effective. But in subsequent experiments (Astarabadi, 1963b) it was shown that growth hormone administered to unineph- rectomized, hypophysectomized rats not only stimulated compen- satory renal hypertrophy (to approximately half the rate in controls) but also promoted body growth to almost the same extent. Growth hormone may therefore be important for kidney growth but it can hardly be regarded as a specific renotrophic hormone.

The general stimulatory effect that the pituitary has on the growth of the kidney is paralleled by its influence on renal physiology. This is clearly illustrated by the generalized circulatory disturbances resulting from hypophysectomy, which in turn affect kidney function. Thus, it has been shown that cardiac output is reduced after the pituitary is removed, which leads in turn to a decline in renal plasma flow (Heinbecker, et al., 1941; White, et al., 1947; Goodkind, et al., 1957; Bojs, et al., 1962). This depresses the glomerular filtration rate, which is the basic process of renal function (deBodo, et al., 1951; Goodkind, et al., 1957; Bojs, et al., 1962). These inhibitory results are largely attributable to the absence of growth hormone, for its administration to hypophysectomized dogs tends to reverse the above effects (White, et al., 1949; deBodo, et al., 1951). Thus, the mutual dependence of renal function and growth on the pituitary emphasizes the importance of the relationship between these two processes. The pituitary may therefore be regarded as an important link in the sequence of processes by which kidney size is regulated, but there is as yet no evidence that it is anything but a secondary factor which in turn responds to more fundamental governing mechanisms. Thus, the existence of a *specific* hormone, such as "renotrophin" as proposed by Braun-Menendez (1952), is very problematical.

The mechanisms by which blood-pressure is regulated include the kidneys as important organs which affect and are affected by hyper- tension. Therefore, it is possible that the growth of the kidneys might be influenced directly or indirectly by these factors. As the source of renin, derived from the juxtaglomerular cells, and as the major organs controlling the composition of the plasma, the kidneys exert profound influences on blood-pressure. The latter, in turn, is in large part responsible for the rate of glomerular filtration, which cannot go on unless the pressure of blood in the glomerular capillaries exceeds that of the filtrate. Nowhere are these principles better illustrated than in the effects of partial renal ischaemia. If the rate of blood flow through one or both kidneys is experimentally restricted (e.g. by reducing the diameter of the renal arteries with Goldblatt clamps), there occurs a striking rise in the systemic blood-pressure (Goldblatt, *et al.*, 1934; Wilson and Byrom, 1939, 1941). Similar hypertensive effects can be produced by encapsulating kidneys with silk, or by inducing hydronephrosis by the ligation of one or both ureters (Harrison, *et al.*, 1936; Megibow, *et al.*, 1942; Floyer, 1957). In all such cases the flow of blood through the kidney is interfered with and the blood-pressure in the general circulation becomes elevated.

The responses of the kidneys themselves to such treatments are particularly interesting. When one renal artery is partially constricted, the affected kidney becomes reduced in size (Drury, 1932; Pickering and Prinzmetal, 1938; Block, *et al.*, 1953) and develops into what Selye (1946) and Selye and Stone (1946) called an "endocrine" kidney. The local drop in blood-pressure renders the ischaemic kidney incapable of carrying on effective glomerular filtration, with the result that the now useless nephron tubules are gradually converted into cords of cells as their lumens become obliterated. Because the kidney has two main functions, one excretory and one endocrine, the loss of the former function, coupled with the histological impression created by the collapse of the tubules, have suggested that such ischaemic kidneys may have been converted to endocrine organs. Although they do indeed secrete renin, it is not the former tubule cells that are engaged in this process (Simonsen, 1950). The intact contralateral kidney, however, undergoes compensatory enlargement (Drury, 1932; Pickering and Prinzmetal, 1938), but not so much as that which occurs after unilateral nephrectomy (Selye and Stone, 1946). It also exhibits pathological vascular lesions which further restrict the renal blood flow and aggravate the already existing hypertension, thus creating a vicious circle (Wilson and Byrom, 1939, 1941). Encapsulation of one kidney in silk likewise results in the hypertrophy of the opposite kidney (Heinbecker, 1948), and the same effect, accompanied by glomerular enlargement, is also produced by unilateral hydronephrosis which follows the ligation of one ureter (Hinman, 1922; Arataki, 1927; Saphir, 1927).

In the hydronephrotic kidney there is a mitotic response which is not evident until after 24 hours (Herlant, 1948). It reaches a maximum in two to three days (Fautrez and Roels, 1954; Herlant, 1948; Goss and Rankin, 1960) and eventually returns to normal by the third week (Herlant, 1948). Meanwhile, the destructive effects of hydronephrosis proceed as the kidney becomes increasingly distended. Eventually such changes become irreversible, but before this happens, Hinman and Butler (1923) claimed that in order for the hydronephrotic kidney of the dog to repair itself, "the stimulus of compulsory function" is required. "If left in partnership with the normal kidney, which meanwhile has undergone compensatory hypertrophy, atrophy will replace the initial repair, an atrophy in the nature of a disuse atrophy."

The intact kidney opposite to the hydronephrotic one likewise exhibits a mitotic response. This has been detected on the second post-operative day by Herlant (1948) and Goss and Rankin (1960) and on the third day by Fautrez and Roels (1954). Occurring prior to any obvious destruction of tissue in the hydronephrotic kidney, this proliferation must be compensating for the functional inadequacy of the opposite ligated kidney, not for its reduction in mass.

The factors which all of the above conditions have in common are ischaemia, hypertension, and compensatory renal enlargement. The possibility that these may be causally related is worth exploring. Hypertension is clearly brought on by renal ischaemia and the attending renal insufficiency. According to Heinbecker (1948), "hypertension is regarded as the reaction of the body to any inadequacy of renal tubular function. It is part of the mechanism for compensating with increased blood flow the deficiency of the renal tubular mass. Renin is regarded as the substance released by the kidney tubules which not only constrict vessels outside the kidney directly, but also stimulates the eosinophile cells of the glandular hypophysis and thereby increases the cardiac output and renal tubular function".

If it is granted that renin is secreted by the juxtaglomerular cells, then the relation of these to renal ischaemia, and hence hypertension, will be important to establish. Goormaghtigh (1939) first described the increase in number and granulation of juxtaglomerular cells following constriction of the renal artery in rabbits and dogs. Hartroft (1957) described the degranulation of the cells in the opposite intact kidneys. Comparable results have been obtained following encapsulation of one kidney (Dunihue, 1941) or occlusion of one ureter (Hartroft, 1957), in the sense that the granulation of the affected kidney is consistently greater than that of the contralateral one. Tobian, et al. (1958) demonstrated that such changes are reversible, for the granulation in the juxtaglomerular cells of the untreated kidney increases when its renal artery is also constricted, or when the opposite ischaemic kidney is excised. Thus, the physiological relationship between hypertension and the degree of juxtaglomerular granulation is inescapable. Indeed, granulation can be increased or decreased by artificially lowering or raising the blood-pressure pharmacologically (Hartroft, 1953). Moreover, Tobian, et al. (1959) successfully reduced the juxtaglomerular granulation by perfusing isolated rat kidneys for four hours with blood at high pressures (167 to 192 mm.Hg), whereas perfusion at low pressures (82 to 85 mm.Hg) caused no changes. On the strength of these results, it was proposed that the juxtaglomerular cells operate as baroreceptors, regulating their rates of secretion in inverse proportion to the degree of arterial blood-pressure. Accordingly, Tobian (1960) concludes that the amount of juxtaglomerular granulation is directly proportional to secretory activity, and that lowered blood-pressure decreases the extent to which the juxtaglomerular cells surrounding the afferent arterioles of the glomeruli are stretched. Presumably, "relaxed" juxtaglomerular cells are stimulated to secrete renin, which brings about a rise in blood pressure. Under normal conditions this has a homoeostatic effect on systemic blood-pressure, but when the kidney is rendered *locally* hypotensive by experimental means the result is a miscalculated response which overcompensates by causing hypertension. It is this that presumably exposes the juxtaglomerular cells of the opposite intact kidney to excessive arterial pressures and causes their degranulation (cf. Hartroft, 1957; Tobian, et al., 1958). It also explains the much greater reduction in the renin content of the normal contralateral kidney than in the ischaemic one (Blaquier, et al., 1961).

Other factors, as outlined in figure 46, have also been shown to be correlated with the degrees of granulation of the juxtaglomerular cells and therefore are presumed to be causally related to the regulation of blood-pressure, although their exact mechanisms of action remain obscure. The sodium concentration in the plasma, for example, bears an inverse relationship to the juxtaglomerular granulation (Pitcock and Hartroft, 1958). Hence, sodium deficiencies result in increased granulation of the juxtaglomerular cells (Hartroft and Hartroft, 1953;

s

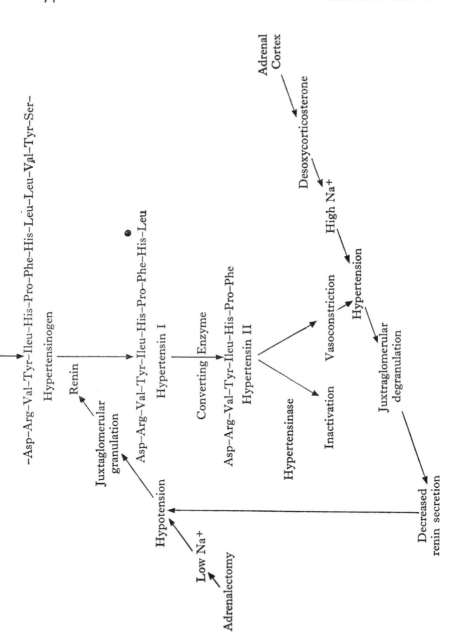

Figure 46. Generalized outline of the physiological regulation of blood pressure, showing relationship of sodium

Tobian, *et al.*, 1948; Newmark, *et al.*, 1959; Fisher and Klein, 1963), whereas excess NaCl intake is followed by degranulation (Hartroft and Hartroft, 1952, 1953). This in turn may be related to the adrenal cortex, for adrenalectomy not only results in sodium depletion, but also is followed by an increase in the juxtaglomerular granulation (Tobian, *et al.*, 1958; Newmark, *et al.*, 1959). These effects are attributable to desoxycorticosterone which, when secreted in sufficient amounts, is responsible for sodium retention by the kidneys and also brings about degranulation of the juxtaglomerular cells (Hartroft and Hartroft, 1952, 1953; Dunihue and Robertson, 1957; Tobian, *et al.*, 1959; Wiedman, *et al.*, 1958). The latter effect, however, depends upon the presence of sufficiently high sodium levels in the blood, for when desoxycorticosterone is administered to sodium-deficient rats, the increased juxtaglomerular granulation normally caused by low levels of sodium is not prevented by the presence of the hormone (Hartroft and Hartroft, 1952, 1953).

How these various correlated observations are to be arranged in a sequence of causally related events is an interesting subject for speculation. Almost certainly, the role of the adrenal cortex is to regulate the sodium balance in the body, which is lowered by adrenalectomy and raised by desoxycorticosterone. This may directly affect blood-pressure in direct proportion to the sodium level. The altered blood-pressure then stimulates the stretch receptors of the juxtaglomerular apparatus in such a way that hypotension may cause increased granulation and renin secretion, while hypertension has opposite effects. Such an interpretation is consistent with the fact that total adrenalectomy reduces blood-pressure (Blalock and Levy, 1937; Diaz and Levy, 1939; Gaudino, 1944; Zweifach, *et al.*, 1947) and that this can be circumvented by providing the animal with either excess salt, desoxycorticosterone, or both (Zweifach, *et al.*, 1947). In normal animals, injections of desoxycorticosterone also exert a hypertensive effect (Prado and Valle, 1952; Skelton, 1953; Salgado, 1954) but only when there is a sufficiency of sodium (Selye and Stone, 1946).

How the growth of the kidney might be related to these manifold factors by which blood-pressure is regulated can be investigated in several ways. Some circumstantial evidence discussed by Goss and Rankin (1960) would indicate that a causal relationship might exist. Various experimental interventions that tend to elevate blood-pressure also promote renal growth, and vice versa. Administration of desoxycorticosterone, which raises blood-pressure and causes renal enlargement, also increases the mitotic response in compensatory renal hyperplasia. Compulsory NaCl intake likewise produces hypertensive effects as well as renal proliferation. Ligation of one ureter, which causes ipsilateral hydronephrosis, also stimulates cell division in both kidneys, perhaps in response to the attendant hypertension. Whether the extra high level of mitotic activity in the hydronephrotic kidney is caused directly by the intratubular pressure of confined urine or indirectly by the resultant ischaemia cannot be positively determined. Although neither the presence nor absence of a mitotic response in kidneys made ischaemic by arterial construction has been reported, the eventual reduction in kidney size following such procedures might indicate that ischaemia *per se* is not responsible for proliferation. Yet even if the hyperplasia associated with unilateral hydronephrosis is caused by mechanical pressure, the vicarious, albeit reduced, reaction of the opposite intact kidney can be explained only by other factors presumably related to the accompanying hypertension. Conversely, experimental treatments which tend to reduce blood-pressure have been found to decrease compensatory hyperplasia. This has been demonstrated by the direct approach, i.e. by decreasing the volume of blood, as well as by hypophysectomy or adrenalectomy, all of which diminish blood-pressure and reduce compensatory renal hyperplasia.

It is possible that the foregoing data represent only fortuitous correlations between blood-pressure regulation and the control of kidney size. Such arguments cannot prove conclusively that compensatory renal hypertrophy occurring after uninephrectomy is mediated by effects on the blood-pressure, no matter how suggestive the correlation may be. The difficulty is that unilateral nephrectomy is not known to raise the blood-pressure even though it brings about enlargement of the opposite kidney. Moreover, the various methods cited above by which hypertension (and renal mitosis) are promoted, do not act on the blood-pressure soon enough for the latter to affect the relatively prompt hyperplastic reaction that typically occurs in the kidney. Since compensatory renal hyperplasia is itself the consequence of preceding reactions (e.g. DNA synthesis, alterations in enzyme activities), it is obvious that its ultimate cause must be sought very soon after operation, probably within the first 12 hours. Inasmuch as hypertension does not occur during this period, it cannot be regarded as a cause of renal hyperplasia, but rather as a result of perhaps some common stimulus to both processes. There is reason to believe that this common stimulus may be the physiological demands for excessive sodium excretion.

This conclusion is based upon the following observations concerning the relation between the adrenal cortex and renal mitosis. According to Goss and Rankin (1960) adrenalectomy abolishes the mitotic response in the residual kidney 48 hours after uninephrectomy. Williams (1962a), however, performed similar experiments and observed only a slight (26 per cent) reduction in the mitotic responses of the compensating kidneys, whereas Astarabadi (1963a) reported a 53 per cent increase in compensatory renal hypertrophy over control levels, as determined by weight measurements two weeks after unilateral nephrectomy and bilateral adrenalectomy. In otherwise intact rats, Williams (1962a) found that total adrenalectomy had no effect on normal mitosis 32, 40 or 48 hours later. The above disparity, in which Williams (1962a) and Astarabadi (1963a) found little influence of adrenalectomy on renal hyperplasia, while Goss and Rankin (1960) reported marked inhibition of compensatory renal hyperplasia in rats subjected to simultaneous bilateral adrenalectomy and unilateral nephrectomy, can be logically explained on the basis of salt intake. The former two investigators maintained their adrenalectomized animals on saline drinking water, but the latter did not. When these experiments were repeated (Goss, unpublished) on two groups of rats kept on either saline or fresh drinking water, compensatory renal hyperplasia occurred only in the former group, not in the salt-depleted rats. The adrenals, then, are necessary for renal hyperplasia only in so far as desoxycorticosterone promotes the retention of sodium. If salt is exogenously supplied after adrenalectomy, their loss does not affect the kidneys.

These results may be taken to indicate that the sodium concentration in the blood may play a major role in determining the growth rate of the kidneys. It appears to be the single common agent relating compensatory renal hyperplasia to such diverse factors as hypertension, desoxycorticosterone, and juxtaglomerular degranulation. Hence, sodium, and possibly other electrolytes, may turn out to be key factors in controlling the growth of the kidneys.

Endocrine Glands

No other organs illustrate better than do the endocrine glands the causal relationship between function and growth, for the factors that regulate secretory activity also govern the size of the gland. Some endocrine glands, e.g. adrenal cortex, gonads, and thyroid, depend upon trophic hormones to stimulate their function and growth. The anterior pituitary, however, which is the source of these trophic hormones, is in turn controlled by the hormones produced by its target organs. Still other glands, such as the parathyroid and islets of Langerhans, are apparently under the direct influence of calcium and carbohydrate, respectively. Thus, each gland is automatically induced to grow when stimulated to secrete. Indeed, in the absence of such influences they characteristically undergo atrophy.

The secretion of cortisone by the inner zones (fasciculata and reticularis) of the adrenal cortex occurs under the influence of ACTH produced by the cells of the anterior pituitary. The reciprocal relationship between these two hormones is maintained via the hypothalamus where specialized cells secrete a third hormone that is carried directly to the anterior pituitary by the portal circulation. Secretory activity by the hypothalamus normally occurs only when the concentration of cortisone in the circulation falls below a critical inhibitory level. Thus, cortisone does not directly affect the cells of the anterior pituitary that normally secrete ACTH. A lesion in the hypothalamus is enough to cause adrenal atrophy and prevent compensatory hypertrophy after unilateral adrenalectomy (Bachrach and Kordon, 1958). As has been discussed in Chapter XII, Davidson and Feldman (1962) have demonstrated that tiny crystals of hydrocortisone (insufficient to exert a systemic effect) when implanted into the hypothalamus will reduce or inhibit compensatory adrenal hypertrophy, whereas control crystals of cholesterol in the hypothalamus, or hydrocortisone in the anterior pituitary, are both without effect.

This endocrinological *ménage à trois* maintains the cortisone in the system at a level predetermined by factors not clearly understood. Presumably such levels are regulated by the bodily demands for cortisone. Stress, for example, acts as a non-specific stimulus for cortisone secretion and thereby promotes adrenal enlargement. Such an influence could operate by raising the threshold of hypothalamic sensitivity to cortisone, and indeed may account for the interposition of the hypothalamus in the feedback control of cortisone secretion by the anterior pituitary.

The gonads bear a similar relationship to the hypothalamus and anterior pituitary. Growth and secretion by the gonads are both initiated by gonadotrophic stimuli from the pituitary which in turn are under the control of the hypothalamus. The direct sensitivity of the latter to oestrogen and testosterone has been demonstrated by Davidson and Sawyer (1961) who were able to induce ovarian and testicular atrophy by implanting crystals of the appropriate hormones into the hypothalamus (but not by implants elsewhere in the brain, nor in the pituitary). Indeed, Lisk (1960) was able to cause testicular atrophy by hypothalamic implants of oestrogen, indicating the apparent inability of the hypothalamic cells to distinguish between the two sex hormones. As in the case of the adrenal cortex, atrophy can also be produced by hypothalamic lesions (Lisk, 1960). The opposite effect can be induced by preventing hormonal communication between the gonads and the hypothalamus, as has been achieved by intrasplenic grafts of gonads in otherwise castrated animals. Since the liver degrades the steroid hormones carried to it by the portal circulation, the hypothalamus remains "unaware" of the existence of the intrasplenic gonadal grafts, and in the absence of inhibitory influences stimulates gonadotrophic secretion by the pituitary. Chronic exposure to such effects results in the development of luteomata and granulosa cell tumours in the ovarian grafts after several months (Biskind and Biskind, 1949) and interstitial cell tumours in testicular transplants (Sundell, 1957). Theoretically, comparable results might be expected in the case of intrasplenic grafts of the adrenal cortex, but only excessive hypertrophy in the absence of tumour formation has been reported (Bernstein and Biskind, 1957).

The rate of sex hormone secretion may normally be rather variable. The degree of such modulations closely parallels the changes in gonadal mass. This is less common in males, except when there is a well-defined breeding season at which time testosterone secretion is increased and the testes enlarge. In the female, the vicissitudes of the oestrous cycle usually reflect the cyclical alterations in the secretion of gonadotrophic hormones. Thus, superimposed on the homoeostatic regulation of gonadal size and secretion may be the familiar rhythms of reproductive activity. These may be of intrinsic origin, as in polyoestrous females, or they may be timed by extrinsic environmental influences (e.g. seasonal fluctuations in daylengths). In either case, it is probable that such rhythms are imposed on the pituitary-gonadal axis by nervous influences on the hypothalamus which alter the sensitivity of the latter to gonadal steroids. That the resultant cycles of functional activity are accompanied by parallel changes in gonadal size testifies to the causal relationship between growth and functional demand in these organs.

The thyroid, like the gonads and adrenal cortex, is also stimulated to secrete and to grow by the anterior pituitary gland. Accordingly, hypophysectomy results in thyroid atrophy (Smith, 1930) and prevents compensatory thyroid hypertrophy (Houssay, *et al.*, 1932; Magdalena, 1935). It is possible that the thyroid-pituitary feedback relationship is mediated via the hypothalamus, as in the previously discussed cases. Reichlin (1957) has showed that when hypothalamic lesions are inflicted on rats from which three-quarters of the thyroid has been removed, compensatory hypertrophy may be reduced or abolished and the rate of iodine uptake by the gland diminished. Conversely, the thyrotrophic stimulus from the pituitary may be heightened by reductions in thyroxine output, such as may occur following partial thyroidectomy as well as in the cases of iodine deficiency or thiouracil administration. The results are essentially the same. Excessive thyrotrophic hormone promotes growth as it stimulates secretion. Indeed, when the latter is impossible, the goiterogenic influence is all the more exaggerated. In the case of thiouracil-induced cretin rats in which the thyroids may become up to nine times the normal size, partial ablation is not followed by compensatory hypertrophy of the remnant (Horn and LoMonaco, 1958) presumably because the pituitary is already stimulated to secrete maximal amounts of thyrotrophic hormone. Indeed, 50 per cent ablation of an organ that is already many times its natural size still leaves a super-abundance of that tissue *in situ*. Hence, there would be no need for compensation.

As in the cases previously discussed, the balance between thyroid and pituitary is adjusted to the demands of the body for thyroxine. Thus, enforced reduction of metabolic rates, as occurs in rats maintained at simulated high altitudes, causes the thyroid glands to become smaller (Harclerode, *et al.*, 1962). Alternatively, Landauer (1937) showed that the natural loss of feathers in frizzle fowl, or the plucking of feathers from normal birds, caused the thyroids to enlarge. By raising the basal metabolic rate to compensate for these conditions, a demand for excessive thyroid activity is created which accounts for the increase in size. Such effects can be prevented by keeping the fowl warm.

If trophic hormones of pituitary origin are responsible for growth of their target organs, then the anterior pituitary should itself be subject to hormonal growth promotion concomitant with the stimulation of its own secretory activities. Accordingly, it might be predicted that extirpation or inactivation of the target organs should bring about enlargements of the pituitary, whereas the administration of supplemental target organ hormones ought to reduce pituitary size. Furthermore, such effects would be expected to find expression in the appropriate cell types of the anterior pituitary. Unfortunately, this is a subject that has not received the experimental attention it deserves, but there have been some reports that lend support to the above ideas. The development of "castration" cells in the pituitary glands of gonadectomized animals may be taken to indicate that excessive demands for their secretory activity results in their hypertrophy and hyperplasia (Pomerat, 1940). Comparable studies with reference to other target organs would be of obvious theoretical value.

Several hormones are apparently not trophically affiliated with other endocrine glands. Instead, they are associated functionally with the regulation of certain ions or other compounds in the blood, the concentrations of which in turn govern the rate of hormone secretion. Such mutual influences are evident not only in the secretory activities of these glands, but also in their growth.

The parathyroid gland is a case in point. Although its compensatory hypertrophy has not been studied following partial ablation, its response to physiological demands leaves little doubt as to what the outcome of such an investigation would be. Normally concerned with maintaining the proper calcium concentration in the blood, the parathyroid hormone is secreted whenever soluble calcium needs to be replenished. The size of the parathyroid gland is proportional to such physiological demands. Marine (1914) maintained fowl on calcium-deficient diets and observed that their parathyroids subsequently became enlarged, an effect that was reversed when returned to a normal diet. Luce (1923) reported that the enlargement of the parathyroids of calcium-deficient rats was the result of hyperplasia, not cellular hypertrophy. If the calcium content of the blood is reduced by administering excess phosphate, parathyroid hyperplasia also results (Drake, et al., 1937; Pierre, et al., 1939). That this is caused by low blood calcium rather than high phosphate was conclusively proved by Ham, et al. (1940) who noted no responses of the parathyroid to high or low phosphate when the calcium level in the blood was held constant. The opposite effect, namely, parathyroid hypoplasia, has been reported by Pierre, et al. (1939) following the administration of calcium gluconate to rabbits. These growth responses of the parathyroid are accompanied by alterations in the rate of hormone secretion. Patt and Luckhardt (1942) perfused canine parathyroid glands with normal or with decalcified blood and then injected the perfusate into normal dogs. The decalcified perfusate caused an elevation of the recipients' serum calcium levels, whereas normal blood was without effect.

Parathyroid hyperplasia is also related to chronic renal insufficiency such as occurs in association with nephritis. Castleman and Mallory (1937) reported this from clinical observations and suggested that it may be attributed to the retention of phosphate which in turn would cause hypocalcaemia. Experimentally, parathyroid hyperplasia and hypertrophy have been produced in the rat by removing all or most of the kidney mass (Platt, 1950; Morrison, 1962) or by ligating both ureters (Baker, 1945). It will be important to correlate these results with detailed studies of the blood composition during such experiments.

In the same category with the parathyroid glands are the islets of Langerhans, the β-cells of which secrete insulin. It was shown by Woerner (1938) that the continuous infusion of glucose into guinea pigs stimulated the secretion of insulin by the β-cells as indicated by the depletion of their granules. Subsequently there occurred a proliferation of β-cells, augmented by their de novo differentiation from duct cells. Evidence previously cited in Chapter XIV, concerning the hypertrophy of the islets of Langerhans in the foetuses of diabetic mothers, further supports the contention that function and growth of the β-cells are promoted by the same physiological stimulus, namely, hyperglycaemia.

However, other investigations have yielded results that may cast doubt on such a straightforward explanation. Allen (1922a), for example, noted degeneration rather than compensatory hyperplasia of islet β-cells following removal of large fractions of the pancreas. Regeneration of new islets from proliferating duct cells may occur under these conditions, however. When animals were treated with excess glucose, or rendered hyperglycaemic by diets rich in carbohydrates, Allen (1922b) was not able to detect cytological evidence (e.g. vacuolation) of hypersecretory activity in the islet cells. Therefore, partial pancreatectomy and artificially induced hyperglycaemia did not cause the same changes in the islets of Langerhans. Muggia (1927) was also unable to stimulate compensatory hypertrophy of the islets by increasing the body's demands for insulin. In fact, he found that hyperglycaemia caused a reduction in the sizes of the islets of Langerhans, whereas hypoglycaemia brought about their hypertrophy. The rationale by which these results might be explained, however, continues to elude us.

The secretion of desoxycorticosterone is not known to be controlled by a trophic hormone from another gland. Therefore, it is possible that it may be under the direct influence of the serum electrolyte concentration. As a major factor in promoting the retention of sodium by the kidneys, the rate of desoxycorticosterone secretion is therefore inversely proportional to the sodium concentration in the serum. Accordingly, Deane, et al. (1948) and Newmark, et al. (1959) have shown that the zona glomerulosa, from which desoxycorticosterone is secreted, becomes hypertrophic in animals maintained on sodium-deficient diets.

Exocrine Glands

The various exocrine glands of the body afford some convenient opportunities for analysing the relationships between function and growth. With much in common anatomically, yet representing wide spectra of secretory products and functions, valuable information can be gathered by comparing the results of similar experimental procedures on glands of diverse physiological functions. Perhaps the simplest, though not the most satisfactory, method of investigation involves duct ligation. Although this blocks function, it also leads to a number of undesirable, non-specific side effects. A better approach is to stimulate or inhibit secretory activity by hormonal or nervous pathways equivalent to those by which function is normally regulated. If these promote or retard growth according to whether secretion is stimulated or inhibited, respectively, they would constitute compelling evidence in favour of the functional demand theory of growth regulation. Finally, it has been possible in some cases to stimulate growth or function artificially by the use of drugs. Such methods might reveal if growth can be promoted in the absence of increased function, and vice versa.

Some of these experimental principles can be illustrated by the exocrine pancreas. Direct ligation, for example, results in degeneration of the acini, followed by their eventual regeneration (Grauer, 1926). The more immediate response to ligation has been investigated by Augustine (1963), who determined that two days after separating the distal half of the pancreas from the proximal half by a ligature, there was a threefold and twofold increase in the pancreatic mitotic activity in each half, respectively. It is possible that the distal (ligated) half was responding to direct effects of duct occlusion, while the proximal half was compensating for the incapacitated distal portion.

Another approach to the problem has been explored by Chernick, *et al.* (1948) who fed chicks on raw soy-bean which contains a trypsin inhibitor. Such animals not only exhibited enlargements of the pancreas, but their pancreatic proteolytic enzyme content was also increased. These results suggest the possibility that growth and function of the pancreas might occur in response to the reduced efficacy of the enzymes secreted, and that such a response might be elicited either by a selective deficiency in any one enzyme, or by a general deficiency in all of them.

To investigate the effect of functional activity *per se* on pancreatic growth, Augustine (1963) injected rats with pilocarpine, a drug that typically stimulates generalized exocrine secretory activity. After two days of such treatment, however, mitotic activity in the pancreas was found not to have risen above normal control levels. These results suggest that it is not the increased function of an organ that stimulates growth, but something occurring earlier, such as the original physiological stimulus for increased activity, which in this case was by-passed by pilocarpine.

Comparable studies with pilocarpine have been carried out by Alho (1961) on the rat salivary glands. Despite the efficacy of the drug in stimulating excessive salivation, there was no increase in mitotic activity over control levels, either in intact glands or in remaining glands following unilateral ablation. Representing another instance of increased function unaccompanied by mitotic stimulation, evidence such as this may constitute an important clue as to the precise nature of growth-regulating factors.

Another drug, which in a sense exerts the opposite effects on salivary glands, is isoproterenol:

$$HO-\underset{OH}{\underbrace{}}$$

HO

$$HO-\langle\rangle-CHCH_2NHCH(CH_3)_2$$
$$\phantom{HO-\langle\rangle-C}|$$
$$\phantom{HO-\langle\rangle-}OH$$

Injected daily into rats or mice, this compound causes a remarkable enlargement of the salivary glands that is proportional to the dose administered and reversible upon cessation of injections (Wells, 1962). As seen in Plates 15.1 and 15.2, the salivary acinar cells become hypertrophic and hyperplastic under the influence of isoproterenol. This drug is specific for salivary glands, and has no effect on other exocrine organs such as the external lachrymal glands (Brown-Grant, 1961). According to Selye, et al. (1961), hypertrophic salivary glands may become five times larger than normal after seventeen days of treatment. Wells (1962) reported that isoproterenol also stimulates secretory activity by the salivary glands five to ten minutes after intraperitoneal injection (300 mg./kg.) in rats, and that increased glandular weight was evident after three days. Brown-Grant (1961) noted that glandular enlargement under these conditions involved increases in cytoplasmic secretory granules and hypertrophy of acinar cells. Hyperplasia of salivary glands is also induced by isoproterenol, according to the observations of Selye, et al. (1961).

Still another influence on salivary gland growth has recently been reported by Ershoff and Bajwa (1963). They fed young rats on diets containing various proteolytic enzymes (trypsin, chymotrypsin, papaine) and noted that after twelve days the submaxillary glands (but not the parotids) had become hypertrophic. Histologically, these changes were accompanied by enlargement of the acini and their constituent cells. Obviously it will be important to learn to what extent these enzymes stimulate saliva secretion, and whether or not the rate of cell division in the affected glands is accelerated.

The salivary glands have also been subjected to a number of other experimental treatments which have yielded additional information concerning their growth potentials under various physiological conditions. Ligation of the duct, for example, results in atrophy of the acinar cells during the first post-operative week as secretory activity is suppressed (Rabinovitch, et al., 1952; Bhaskar, et al., 1956), after which the histology of the gland remains essentially unchanged (although reversible) for periods up to one year (Junqueira, et al., 1954). These changes have been studied in detail by Standish and Shafer (1957) who described an increase in acinar granulation one day after ligation, together with a depolarization of the duct cells. By the third day, inflammation of the gland was evident, the cytoplasmic granules of the acinar cells had disappeared, the acini were smaller, and the cuboidal epithelium lining the now distended ducts exhibited considerable mitotic activity which lasted through the ninth day. The net result of such alterations is an increase in the ratio of ducts to acini in the atrophic gland, the rationale of which is not easily explained.

Probably the most significant research thus far reported on salivary glands is that related to their physiological association with the incisor teeth and the nervous system. It has been found that if the lower incisors of rats are repeatedly amputated twice a week at the gum line, the submandibular salivary glands become enlarged as much as 12 per cent after only 24 hours (Wells and Munson, 1960), and at the end of a month they may have doubled their size (Wells, et al., 1959). This effect is not produced if the upper incisors are amputated instead, and when only one lower incisor is amputated repeatedly the response occurs almost entirely in the ipsilateral submandibular gland (Wells, et al., 1959). The hypertrophic glands decrease in size if the incisor amputations are stopped. This hypertrophic response is diminished but not abolished by hypophysectomy (Wells, et al., 1959) and is not induced by other kinds of trauma such as ulceration of the oral mucosa adjacent to the lower incisors (Wells and Munson, 1950). Histologically, the hypertrophic effect involves swelling of the serous and mucous acini, including enlargement of nuclei and nucleoli, but no increase in tubular dimensions (Wells, et al., 1959; Handelman and Wells, 1963).

The foregoing data suggest that the growth of the salivary glands might be profoundly affected by nervous influences. Indeed, this was demonstrated in 1941 by Lacassagne and Caussé, who described atrophy of the sublingual and submandibular glands in mice after severing the corda tympani which is the source of their innervation. Not only was this a unilateral effect, but it was followed by compensatory hypertrophy of the glands on the non-operated side. In the rat, Wells, et al. (1961) reported that excision of the superior cervical sympathetic ganglion resulted in loss of weight by the ipsilateral submandibular gland and prevented its hypertrophy after repeated amputation of the lower incisor. On the logical assumption, therefore, that submandibular growth might be sympathetically mediated Wells (1960) treated rats with barbital or chlorisondamine, which are ganglionic blocking drugs, or dibenamine, an adrenergic inhibitor, and found that the submandibular hypertrophy that normally ensues incisor amputation was arrested. Similar results were obtained by treatment with agents such as reserpine or bretylium tosylate, which reduce the capacity of sympathetic nerves to release norepinephrine (Wells, *et al.*, 1961).

Thus, there are two well-documented means by which the salivary glands can be induced to undergo hypertrophy, namely, by repeatedly amputating the lower incisors or by injecting isoproterenol. The former is clearly mediated via the sympathetic nervous system, but isoproterenol acts independently of submandibular innervation, exerting its hypertrophic effect bilaterally despite unilateral ganglionectomy (Wells, 1962). In this sense, then, isoproterenol is a sympathomimetic drug, yet its action cannot be strictly equated with sympathetic stimulation inasmuch as its effect on the submandibular gland is additive when administered to rats also subjected to incisor amptutation (Wells, 1962). Exactly how diets rich in proteolytic enzymes (Ershoff and Bajwa, 1963) can induce salivary gland hypertrophy is not known.

One can only speculate as to the significance of the incisor-submandibular gland relationship. Yet the only possible conclusion is the most obvious one, namely, that the mechanism that has evolved for regulating the size of the gland, and therefore its functional capacity, accommodates to the physiological demands for salivation by monitoring the rate of food intake in terms of nervous stimulation from the incisors. Why such a relationship should exclude participation of the upper incisors, or why it should be unilateral, must remain in the realm of the arcane.

In less striking ways the growth of other exocrine glands can be shown to depend upon functional relationships. The orbital glands of the rat illustrate this principle in a negative sense by not responding to contralateral extirpation with compensatory hyperplasia. In contrast, Teir (1951) has demonstrated that they decrease in size when their eye is removed, and undergo cystic degeneration following duct ligation. With reference to the mammary glands the enlargement concomitant with functional reactivation that occurs with parturition is too well known to require reiteration. Duct ligation of lactating mammary glands causes degenerative changes, as is usual with exocrine glands, characterized by decreased RNA and DNA contents (Tucker and Reece, 1963).

An especially interesting effect of function on size regulation has been discovered by Ellis, *et al.* (1963) with reference to the avian salt glands (Plate 8.5). Capable of concentrating and eliminating excess NaCl, these glands are most highly developed in marine birds, but also exist as more rudimentary organs in non-marine species. Studies on domestic ducklings have revealed that by the fourth day after hatching the central ducts begin to develop radially arranged secretory tubules. Under normal conditions these elongate and gradually differentiate into terminal segments where proliferation occurs, plus more central regions composed of principal cells capable of secretion. In this way, the lobules into which the salt gland is subdivided slowly increase in diameter. Ellis, *et al.* (1963) have studied the effects of compulsory salt regimens on the rate and extent of salt gland development in ducklings. From the fourth post-hatching day, experimental birds were allowed access only to one per cent NaCl for 12 out of every 24 hours, while controls were given fresh water *ad libitum*. After only three days of such treatment, it was noted that the development of the salt glands had been noticeably accelerated. The lobules became conspicuously enlarged owing to increases in the width and length of the secretory tubules. The differentiation of the principal (secretory) cells was also advanced beyond that of control glands. After only four days of treatment the glands of the salt-loaded ducklings were able to function, as indicated by the production of a saline effluent from the external nares. Eventually, the experimental glands grew to more than twice the size of the control ones as a result of the accelerated proliferation of peripheral tubule cells and hypertrophy of the differentiated secretory cells. It was concluded that increased functional demands, in the form of osmotic load, stimulate growth and differentiation in the salt glands, leading to their precocious maturation. It would be logical to predict, therefore, that if one salt gland were removed the occurrence or absence of compensatory hypertrophy of the opposite one would depend upon whether or not the bird was subjected to a salt intake sufficiently high to create a functional demand. In the case of this gland, therefore, the inseparability of growth and physiological activity is manifest.

Respiratory Organs

The process of respiration involves a number of organs and tissues such that alterations in respiratory demands are reflected in a variety of functionally related growth responses. These may be initiated in either of two ways, namely, by reducing the mass of the tissue or organ concerned, or by exposure to hypoxic conditions. In either case, the resultant compensatory growth can most logically be interpreted as a response to the body's increased demands for oxygen.

This principle is illustrated by the mammalian lung, which many investigators have shown capable of compensatory growth following surgical reduction. Cohn (1939), for example, removed part of the lung from 14-day-old rats and reported the eventual restoration of the normal relative amount of lung tissue in the body by compensatory enlargement of the residual portions. More recently, Birkun (1958) reported that unilateral pneumectomy stimulates hyperplasia in the remaining lung. It is probable that such phenomena are reactions to increased respiratory demands on the tissues of the lung, but the exact biochemical pathways connecting the cause with the effect remain obscure.

Experiments on the gills of larval amphibians have revealed the extent to which respiratory organs can become modified by physiological conditions (figure 47). A number of different investigations

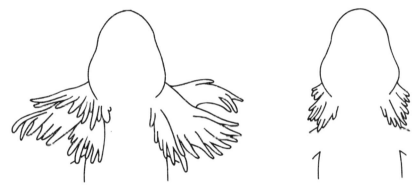

Figure 47. Effect of oxygen tension on gill development in larval *Salamadra maculosa*. When raised under hypoxic conditions, gills become greatly enlarged (left); gills of larvae raised in an atmosphere rich in oxygen are considerably reduced in size (right). (After Drastich, 1925.)

have demonstrated that the gills of larvae raised under low oxygen tensions become greatly enlarged, while high oxygen tensions exert inhibitory effects on gill development (Drastich, 1925; Bond, 1960; Boell, et al., 1962). Under the former conditions, Bond (1960) has attributed the excessive growth of the gills (up to three times the normal surface area) to increases in the numbers and sizes of cells, as well as the development of more numerous filaments on elongated gills. It was suggested that the blood-pressure might be inversely

T

related to oxygen tension, thereby stimulating growth of the gills in media low in oxygen concentration by the mechanical effects of increased pressure. In support of such a conclusion are the observations of Stickney and Van Liere (1953) that hypertension is induced in mammals maintained in hypoxic atmospheres. Moreover, Opitz (1951) has reported that exposure of rats to high altitudes brought about a proliferation and elongation of retinal capillaries and an increase in capillary diameters in the liver and brain.

In addition to the above effects, erythropoiesis is also modified by the respiratory requirements of the organism. This is dramatically illustrated by comparing the blood of man, essentially a sea-level creature, with animals such as the llama and vicuna which have evolved adaptations to high altitude habitats (Dill, 1938). The latter animals possess haemoglobin molecules with an inherently greater affinity for oxygen than in sea-level animals, in addition to which they have two to three times as many red blood corpuscles per cubic millimetre of blood as does the human, although their erythrocytes are smaller. Such genetic adaptations to high altitude provide an interesting perspective in which to view the physiological adaptations to high altitude that have been observed in man. In a study reported by Huff, et al. (1951) on humans transferred from Lima, Peru to Morococha at an altitude of 14,900 feet, it was observed that during the first ten-day acclimatization period there was a twofold increase in the rate of iron turnover, a decrease in the total volume of plasma, but no increase in red cell mass until somewhat later. In no case, however, did the red cell mass rise to levels typical of the native population.

The reverse situation was investigated in natives of Morococha who were moved to Lima. During the first ten days, their blood volumes remained unaltered, but the rates of iron turnover declined to one-tenth of their normal values. There was also a 10 per cent decrease in red cell mass due in part to reduced rates of erythropoiesis and in part to accelerated rates of red cell destruction. Presumably these modulations would eventually adjust to a new constant level of red cell balance commensurate with the new environment.

Hurtado, et al. (1945) have shown that in humans polycythaemia occurs under conditions of hypoxia at elevated altitudes. Its severity is proportional to the duration and degree of hypoxia. Conversely, Fried, et al. (1957) exposed rats to atmospheres rich in oxygen and noted a decreased rate of erythropoiesis. These conditions, however, do not preclude the capacity to respond to erythropoietin. Indeed, such animals exhibit exaggerated erythropoietic reactions to the injection of plasma from anaemic animals. Hodgson and Tohá (1954) showed that in rabbits rendered temporarily anaemic by bleeding, the resultant high concentration of erythropoietin in the plasma that is normally responsible for accelerating erythropoiesis is virtually abolished when such animals are exposed to 100 per cent oxygen. Therefore, the most direct reaction to alterations in oxygen availability appears to be in the production of erythropoietin.

Yet it is not the presence or absence of oxygen *per se* that is important; rather, it is its availability in relation to the demand by the body's tissues that determines the rate of erythropoietin production. This supply and demand relationship has been incisively outlined by Jacobson, *et al.* (1957b), who have classified the several conditions under which erythropoietin production may be increased or decreased:

I—*Conditions promoting erythropoietin production*
  A. Normal O_2 supply, increased O_2 demand:
    1. Dinitrophenol
    2. Triiodothyronine

  B. Decreased O_2 supply, normal O_2 demand:
    1. Bleeding
    2. Phenylhydrazine
    3. Hypoxia

II—*Conditions depressing erythropoietin production*
  A. Normal O_2 supply, decreased O_2 demand:
    1. Starvation
    2. Hypophysectomy

  B. Increased O_2 supply, normal O_2 demand:
    1. Transfusion-induced polycythaemia
    2. Hyperoxia

As shown in the above outline, erythropoietin production is increased whenever the demand for oxygen exceeds the supply, and it is decreased under the reverse conditions. Whether the connection between erythropoietin production on the one hand, and oxygen supply versus oxygen demand on the other, is mediated somehow by all tissues of the body or is relegated to a single tissue acting in a "sensory" capacity is beyond the scope of our present knowledge. The only educated guess that one can hazard is that if decreased oxygen tension causes an elevation of blood-pressure (Stickney and Van Liere, 1953) then the juxtaglomerular apparatus might be related to the production of erythropoietin by the kidneys. Goldfarb and Tobian (1963), however, failed to detect a decrease in juxtaglomerular granulation to parallel the diminished erythropoietin concentration in the plasma of rats exposed to high oxygen tensions.

Lymphatic System

The lymphoid tissues of the body include a miscellany of cell types, but in general are concerned with protecting the body from the intrusions of foreign materials. Thus, animals raised under germ-free conditions have very poorly developed lymphoid organs, a fact which suggests that exposure to foreign substances might normally stimulate growth and differentiation in this system. The investigations of Coons, *et al.* (1955) and Leduc, *et al.* (1955) illustrate this point especially well. Treatment of rabbits with antigen, they found, stimulates lymphoid stem cells to differentiate into mature plasma cells, which are identifiable by their inclusion of antigen as localized by fluorescent antibodies. These cells are numerous a day after injection of antigen, but decrease thereafter. Upon exposure to a second antigenic injection one month later, however, there occurred a remarkably greater increase in their population owing to the hyperplasia apparently induced by the antigen. It would appear that the primary response conditions the system to react more violently to the next exposure to the same antigen. Presumably there are relatively few cells of the specific type that are responsive to the antigen when it is first injected. These cells may then proliferate and differentiate into mature plasma cells capable of synthesizing antibodies complementary to the antigen which initiated their production. These descendants of the originally stimulated cells are thereafter susceptible to secondary responses. By virtue of the larger initial number of such antigen-specific plasma cells, secondary immune reactions are typically more vigorous than primary ones, not only as measured by the promptness and magnitude of the antibody responses, but also in terms of the hyperplastic reaction of affected lymphoid tissues.

As in many other systems, function in lymphatic organs can be suppressed by replacement of end product. Uhr and Baumann (1961) have found that antibody production is inhibited if exogenous antibody is administered to animals as much as five days after exposure to specific antigen. These results suggest that antibody synthesis is quantitatively adjusted to the amount of end product already in the system.

In his clonal selection theory of acquired immunity, Burnet (1959) has recognized this antigen-stimulated proliferation of antibody-producing cells as the means by which clones of cells specific for a given antigen are produced. Concomitantly, such cells are induced to synthesize antibodies, thus linking their growth with the physiological demand for their functional activity. Clearly, the antigen in this case is responsible for initiating antibody synthesis. In doing so, it must communicate its molecular specificity to that of the antibody. Numerous studies with antimetabolites have demonstrated that such a pathway includes the vital processes of protein synthesis and nucleic acid synthesis. It remains obscure, however, whether DNA replication, in addition to RNA synthesis, is an essential step in the transfer of molecular specificity. If it is, then there would exist a logical explanation of why hyperplasia should accompany immunological reactions. If DNA replication should be indispensible for the induction of specific protein synthesis, which is such an integral part of cell differentiation and function, then it would lead almost inevitably to cell division as an unavoidable by-product of, not an essential step in, the stimulation of functional activity.

Nervous System

Although mature neurons are in general incapable of division, there is a little evidence that the adult central nervous system is not as developmentally static as it is often believed to be. Although overt mitotic activity is very rarely observed, the occasional uptake of tritiated thymidine by cells of the central nervous system testifies to their ability to synthesize new DNA, whether or not this leads to cell division. In young adult mice, for example, Messier, et al. (1958) described the common occurrence of mitotic activity in ependymal tissues in contrast to the rare incorporation of tritiated thymidine into cells of the grey matter. Inasmuch as these labelled cells were usually neuroglial in nature, it can be concluded that they may sometimes undergo divisions in the process of differentiating into neurons, which would account for the occasional labelling of the latter. If DNA synthesis occurs in already mature neurons, it may give rise to polyploid conditions instead of leading to cytokinesis.

To study the effects of localized injuries on the incorporation of tritiated thymidine into cells of the central nervous system, Altman

(1962) injected label directly into the brains of rats and detected its subsequent uptake by the glial cells in the vicinity of the wound. Since some neurons were also found to be labelled, it is probable that they may have arisen from undifferentiated cells that were capable of division before becoming mature. In addition to the occurrence of labelled cells in the immediate site of traumatization, others were encountered at some distance from the lesion in areas functionally associated with it. Moreover, there were indications of labelled cells in the uninjured opposite side of the brain in regions corresponding to the contralateral location of the lesion. Thus, the relationship of such growth responses to functional considerations is strongly implicated. In the apparent absence of mitosis in mature neurons, such evidence again raises the question of why DNA synthesis is associated with enhanced functional activities, even if it cannot result in cell proliferation.

Growth responses in the central nervous system are most prominently exhibited in immature animals with neuroblasts still capable of division. Experiments on embryos have demonstrated the capacity of the nervous system to undergo compensatory hypertrophy following contralateral ablation of parts of the brain (Kollros, 1953). Moreover, in adult lower vertebrates certain parts of the brain are even able to replace excised regions by morphogenetic regeneration. In the adults of higher vertebrates, however, nervous regeneration is restricted largely to peripheral fibres. In such cases, the size of the regenerating fibres vary in proportion to the functional demands of the end organs with which they become connected, thus illustrating the causal relationship between growth and physiological activity, even when cell division is no longer possible (Sanders and Young, 1946).

Within the brain the proportional size relationships are also dependent upon the peripheral connections with sensory and motor organs. This has been experimentally investigated with reference to the eye and the limb. Larsell (1931) recorded the decreased size of the optic lobe associated with the extirpated eye of tadpoles, and White (1948) noted a proportional relationship between the size of the eye and that of the optic tectum in teleost embryos. Similar effects (figure 48) have been observed on the brachial region of the embryonic chick spinal cord following ablation of the wing bud (Bueker, 1947; Simmler, 1947; Barron, 1948). Conversely, neural hyperplasia can be caused by grafting extra limb buds (Hamburger, 1939). Exaggerated versions of the latter phenomenon can be induced in embryonic ganglia innervating transplanted mouse sarcomata or treated with specific nerve growth factors extracted from such diverse sources as sarcoma, salivary glands, or snake venom (Levi-Montalcini and Angeletti, 1961). Yet as important and interesting as this curious phenomenon may be, its true significance with respect to the normal development of the nervous system still eludes us.

Figure 48. Cross-section through the spinal cord of chick from which the right limb had been removed in the 48- to 60-hour embryo. Development is retarded on the side lacking the normal number of terminal connections. (After Bueker, 1947.)

Muscle

The hypertrophy and atrophy of skeletal muscle fibres are familiar results of use and disuse, respectively. Few tissues in the body would appear to exemplify more convincingly the relationship between function and growth, yet it is important to recognize the distinction between functional activity and functional demand in attempting to comprehend the nature of compensatory hypertrophy of muscles. The amount of contractile activity of a muscle fibre is equivalent to the frequency with which it is stimulated by nervous impulses. Under chronic conditions, this is proportional to the degree of hypertrophy that results. Conversely, denervation causes paralysis and atrophy. Thus, it is not possible to determine from this information if the growth response (or its absence) is caused by the contractile activity *per se* or by nervous factors unrelated to contractile stimulation.

The crucial experiment in this regard was alluded to by Bizzozero in 1894. "Division of the sciatic nerve," he wrote, "leads to atrophy of the muscles of the leg, but the process of wasting can be retarded by frequent electric stimulation of the muscles whose nerve supply has been destroyed, and it is fair to assume that a like effect might be produced by stimulation of a different kind. In such cases it is not the stimulation applied by us that regulates the nutrition of the muscular fibre; we only induce certain conditions which rouse the latter to functional activity, and for this purpose it must modify its metabolism and its nutrition." Thus, it is not the nerve fibres themselves that are responsible for muscle hypertrophy, but the stimulation they provide for contractile activity.

Whether or not smooth muscle fibres adhere to the same principles cannot yet be determined. The most dramatic instance of smooth muscle growth occurs in the pregnant uterus in which there occurs an augmentation of muscle fibres together with extreme enlargement of pre-existing ones. Alterations such as these are attributable in part to the mechanical effects of stretching. To what extent they are also affected by hormonal and nervous influences would be a provocative but difficult area for future experimentation.

Uterus

In addition to the above attributes, the uterus contains a number of tissue layers each of which is capable of considerable modulations when conditions demand. In general, the uterus appears to be profoundly affected by a combination of mechanical and hormonal factors which influence its growth and enlargement. With reference to the oestrous cycle, the uterus is subjected to increasing concentrations of oestrogen that stimulate proliferation among the endometrial cells. This is followed after ovulation by further endometrial hypertrophy as progesterone exerts its effects. If further stimulated by implantation, the endometrium will be induced to develop into placental tissues. Even in the absence of fertilization, the sensitivity of the progestational endometrium can be experimentally demonstrated by traumatization, by which it is stimulated to grow into a deciduoma. This response represents an overcompensation by the endometrial stroma which persists only as long as enough progesterone is secreted to sustain it. Regression of the deciduoma occurs following degeneration of the corpora lutea, which illustrates the marked dependence of the uterus on ovarian hormones. Nevertheless, a single remaining horn of the uterus in the rat will not exhibit compensatory hypertrophy following excision of the opposite horn (Addis and Lew, 1940), although it is capable of remarkable regenerative properties after being slit open lengthwise (Selye and McKeown, 1934). In addition, the uterus is especially responsive to mechanical factors as represented, for example, by the expansion that occurs during pregnancy. This effect can be duplicated by experimental hydrometria, whereby the uterus is distended and mitotic proliferation induced (Reynolds, 1949). Comparable effects of luminal distension in other hollow organs have already been described with reference to the gall bladder and urinary bladder (Chapter V).

Heart

The histological attributes of cardiac hypertrophy involve the enlargement of cardiac muscle fibres without concomitant increases in their vascularization (figure 28). Consequently, there arise serious problems of supplying the innermost regions of the muscle fibres with adequate concentrations of metabolites. Although this may lead to adverse results in extreme circumstances, the hypertrophic reaction of cardiac muscle fibres normally represents the consequences of functional compensation necessitated by increased work loads. The latter invariably involve elevations in blood-pressure. Even the normal form of the heart, with the left ventricle surpassing the right one in size, may well reflect a morphological adaptation to the functional discrepancies between the systemic and pulmonary circulations. Indeed, it is no coincidence that in cardiac hypertrophy the greatest enlargement occurs in the left ventricle where the effects of hypertension are most acute (Chanutin and Barksdale, 1933).

The dependence of the heart on blood pressure can be demonstrated in both positive and negative ways. Hypophysectomy, for example, has been shown to cause a 17 per cent decrease in heart weight during a five-day period in the rat (Beznak, 1952), while the blood-pressure dropped from an average of 117 to 83 mm.Hg. (Beznak, 1954). Cardiac hypertrophy, however, is promoted by hypertension whether the latter is induced by chronic renal insufficiency following sub-total nephrectomy (Chanutin and Ferris, 1932; Morrison, 1962), desoxycorticosterone injections (Knowlton, *et al.*, 1946; Salgado, 1954), glomerulonephritis (Karsner, *et al.*, 1925), renal encapsulation (Herrmann *et al.*, 1941), constriction of the renal artery (Byrom and Dodson, 1949), or aortic constriction (Eyster, 1927; Beznak, 1952, 1954). This last method is by far the most effective means of inducing cardiac hypertrophy, perhaps because it is the most direct. Eyster (1927) found that it was only necessary to constrict the ascending thoracic aorta of dogs for three to six days with rubber bands in order to cause cardiac hypertrophy. Beznak (1952) achieved the same results in rats by placing a silver ring around the aorta immediately below the diaphragm. This procedure resulted in the exclusive enlargement of the left ventricle by 38 per cent, thus causing a 25 per cent overall increase in heart weight in only five days. When combined with hypophysectomy, however, the hypertrophic effects of aortic constriction are entirely abolished; indeed, 11 per cent cardiac atrophy occurred (as opposed to 17 per cent atrophy in rats only hypophysectomized).

Supporting Tissues

With functions of a mechanical nature, it is not unexpected that skeletal elements and their associated tissues should react developmentally to the stresses and strains of mechanical pressures. Although bones have intrinsic morphogenetic potentialities, the expression of which is not well understood, their basic shapes are capable of being modified by modulating factors. Skeletal remodelling depends upon the turnover of materials that accounts for the constant erosion and deposition of osseous substances. Under normal conditions, the sizes and dimensions of bones are maintained by the equivalent rates and distributions of both of these destructive and constructive processes. It is when the patterns of calcification and decalcification do not coincide that the morphology of the bone is changed. This can be made to occur by subjecting bones to mechanical forces applied from abnormal directions. According to Wolff's law, this causes the bones to grow away from the source of the pressure, not by bending but by differential resorption of bone from the near side and its deposition on the far side. Such reactions tend to reinforce the structure of the bone in locations where it is most needed to resist the pressure. A similar result is achieved by tendons, for example, in which the thickness is directly related to the forces exerted along the longitudinal axis (Buck, 1953). These and other examples illustrate how supporting tissues have evolved developmental processes by which they can best modify their inherent structures in accordance with the functional requirements imposed upon them.

Wound Healing

From the functional point of view, wound healing may be interpreted as a developmental response to the interruption of physiological activities caused by localized injuries. No matter what tissues may be involved, a morphological wound must have functional consequences. Thus, the morphological terms in which wound healing is usually regarded are expressions of *physiological* as well as *anatomical* repair. Since localized injuries disrupt both form and function, it is quite possible that the latter is responsible for initiating healing. If the local demands for the resumption of normal function are indeed the chief stimuli for wound repair, then this is no more than a special case of compensatory growth. The only difference is that in wound healing the functional demands are localized while in compensatory growth they are distributed generally. Thus, a localized incision in the liver, for example, may remove some of the lobes or it may result in no reduction in hepatic mass, depending on how it is oriented. In the former case, a generalized hyperplastic response characteristic of liver regeneration would occur, presumably resulting from "injuries" distributed more or less evenly throughout all of the reacting population of cells. Such injuries would not be the direct result of the original incision, but would be equivalent to the functional deficiencies accompanying the reduction in liver mass. On the other hand, the hepatic wound that does not remove liver tissue elicits only a localized response in the immediate region of injury. This means that the various histological entities of the liver that have been directly affected (e.g. lobule, parenchymal cords, bile ducts) will tend to repair themselves.

The problem here, as it is in skin wounds, is to determine what is the nature of the wound healing stimulus. It is difficult to find satisfaction in explanations that rely solely on morphological factors, such as the so-called innate tendency of epithelia to establish continuity with themselves. This kind of interpretation may be an accurate statement of the end result of a process, but hardly reveals the mechanism. As has been indicated in Chapter V, what is needed is a more meaningful approach to the problem of local wound healing, one that embraces functional and morphological considerations. Although experimental proof is lacking, it is very possible that the several developmental processes which add up to wound healing— migration, proliferation, differentiation, etc.—may be initiated by the functional interruptions that are inseparable from the anatomical disruptions of localized injuries. The answer to this might be sought in studies of wounds healing in organs with more definitively understood physiological activities than those which characterize the integument. Furthermore, it should be possible to determine how the spatial limits of a wound are correlated with the regional extents of the healing response. Inasmuch as the functional interruption may sometimes extend beyond the limits of actual physical injury, it might be possible to draw some significant conclusions from studies designed to learn with which of these areas the healing response coincides.

It is conceivable, therefore, that cells might be capable of responding to a variety of functional deficiencies. Those which result in generalized compensatory hyperplasia in residual homologous tissues following partial ablation may be of a rather different nature from those caused by local injuries. In the liver, for example, generalized regeneration after partial hepatectomy may perhaps be initiated by decreases in plasma protein concentrations, while localized healing reactions may be in response to interrupted flow of bile in the bile capillaries. Alternatively, the systemic factors that initiate compensatory renal hyperplasia following unilateral nephrectomy are distinct from those which bring about wound repair in a single damaged nephron. If this kind of reasoning is valid, then it is logical to conclude that there is no one function on which a cell's mitotic potential is dependent. Every cell is engaged in many processes, some specialized and others of a general nature. Presumably, demands upon any one of these functions may suffice to initiate processes leading to duplication. The specificity of compensatory growth reactions is clearly related to specialized functions shared in common by homologous tissues. Wound healing, however, which is restricted to the immediate neighbourhood of an injury but which can occur in any traumatized tissue, is perhaps more commonly associated with the generalized physiological activities of the affected cells. Were it experimentally possible to inflict wounds without stimulating healing processes, or to initiate healing in the absence of wounds, then it might be possible some day to clarify some of these problems.

Regeneration

The phenomenon of appendage regeneration is not without its functional attributes. Once an amputation stump has been closed by cicatrization, the most indispensable factor required for the initiation of regrowth is its innervation. In the absence of nerves, regeneration does not occur in such appendages as limbs, tails, fins, and barbels of amphibians and fishes. Normally, however, the greatest concentration of nerve endings is in the epidermis overlying the stump. Here they appear to be causally related to the establishment of conditions conducive to blastema formation. In denervated structures only scar tissue, in the absence of a blastema, is produced. Thus, the trophic influence of nerves is most important during the early phases of regeneration. Once differentiation and morphogenesis are under way, the presence of nerves is no longer required for the qualitative replacement of the lost appendage. However, the size ultimately attained may be reduced in regenerates subjected to delayed denervation.

The mechanism by which the trophic influence of nerves operate is still not completely understood. It does not depend upon the existence of central connections because limbs innervated solely by ganglia which have been isolated from the spinal cord by transection of the dorsal roots are still capable of regeneration. Intact neurons, however, are essential. Their fibres must be present in sufficient quantities to exceed the minimum threshold required for successful regeneration. The chemical nature of the trophic nerve influence has been most successfully investigated by means of microperfusion techniques devised by Singer (1960). By the infusion of various drugs into blastemas, these studies have revealed that acetylcholine, or a related compound, is probably the agent by which the trophic influence of nerves on amphibian limb regeneration is mediated. This, then, is clearly related to the functional role of nerves, and establishes the dependence of blastema development on the assurance of eventual functional competence.

The specific target of this nerve influence appears to be the epidermis. This conclusion is dictated in part by the process of elimination, for the regeneration of individual tissues in an appendage (e.g. bone, muscle) can proceed in the absence of nerves. Moreover, no specific mesodermal component has ever been shown to be essential for regeneration so long as some other source of cells is available to give rise to the blastema proper. Epidermis, however, represents a *sine qua non* of regeneration. In addition, it is the most highly innervated tissue in the regenerating appendage. The studies of Thornton (1954) have shown that the site of the greatest concentration of nerve fibres determines where the blastema shall develop, an event that is predictable by the thickening of the epidermal layer in that location. It is possible, therefore, that the nerves exert their trophic influences on the epidermis and that the latter in turn induces the accumulation of blastema cells from the underlying dedifferentiating mesoderm.

By virtue of this dependence on the presence of nerves, the regeneration of nerveless appendages is effectively precluded. Since the regeneration of such structures would be without function and therefore wasteful, it would have had no selective advantage during vertebrate evolution. But if there are any structures that do not depend upon nerves for their functional competence, by the same rationale one would expect their regeneration not to be affected by trophic nerve influences. This is the case with reference to most internal organs, and also applies to the annual regrowth of deer antlers (Wislocki and Singer, 1946). Moreover, in the normal ontogeny of appendages, development proceeds in the absence of nerves. Indeed, if the brachial region of the spinal cord is excised, fore-limb growth still occurs, giving rise to "aneurogenic" limbs. In urodele amphibians, Yntema (1959) has shown that aneurogenic or sparsely innervated limbs, unlike denervated ones, are capable of regeneration. More recently, Steen and Thornton (1963) have demonstrated that aneurogenic limbs covered with normal skin do not regenerate when amputated through the grafted skin, but that replacement of the mesodermal tissues with those from normally innervated limbs does not prevent regeneration. Indeed, such mesodermal grafts, when labelled with tritiated-thymidine, can be shown to be the source of blastema cells. Therefore, it appears to be the skin which normally responds to the trophic influence of nerves in regeneration.

Perhaps these interesting facts can be explained in terms of functional considerations. The function of the limb bud is different from that of the fully developed limb. The former does not depend upon sensory and motor structures in order to be of value to the organism. Its only function is to grow and to develop, and these processes can be carried on without nerves. In contrast, the normal adult limb has sensory and motor functions, processes which are nerve-dependent. The known facts dictate that during the normal development of the limb bud, there is reached a stage of maturity at which the presence of nerves becomes indispensable for regeneration. If nerves are never allowed to enter the embryonic limb, the latter never becomes addicted to them in the developmental sense. As an interesting example of the relationship between growth and function, this represents one of the potentially significant problems currently ripe for solution in the field of regeneration.

XVI

Conclusion

It has been abundantly demonstrated that many kinds of growth, both normal and experimentally induced, are stimulated by the physiological demands for increased functional activity. Trophic hormones, for example, promote growth of their target organs at the same time they stimulate secretory activity. Similarly, the rate of erythropoiesis rises in response to increased demands for oxygen, renal hyperplasia follows the need to excrete excess sodium, lymphatic organs enlarge when challenged antigenically, and muscles become hypertrophic when called upon to work harder. Comparable changes can often be effected by reducing the mass of an organ, provided this results in increased functional demands upon the residual tissues of the same kind elsewhere in the body. If it does, then compensatory hypertrophy occurs. However, if the effects of the loss are only locally felt, then the growth response is a spatially restricted one. Thus, the process of wound healing reflects the functional disturbances caused by anatomical injuries to the many kinds of tissues in which this type of repair can occur. Even the regeneration of appendages in lower vertebrates owes its success to the presence of nerves, without which normal function of the regenerate would be impossible; for similar reasons, the regeneration of the newt lens depends on the presence of the retina.

The cases cited above are samples from the broad spectrum of growth phenomena which are stimulated by functional demands. Yet inasmuch as they may all be logically regarded as special cases of normal developmental processes, it follows that normal growth in post-embryonic organisms may also be controlled by the necessities for physiological activity. In renewing tissues, the rate of cellular turnover is clearly governed by functional demands such that the total mass of differentiated products remains constant and optimal. Expanding organs differ from the former in that they normally lose little or none of their cellular mass. Except under conditions of partial ablation, therefore, these organs do not have to replenish lost cells. Accordingly, they lack germinative zones and exhibit only minimal rates of mitotic activity. In a growing post-embryonic animal, expanding organs need enlarge only fast enough to keep pace with the increasing size of the body. As soon as the latter exceeds the optimum physiological relationship between organ and body as expressed in relative weight, then it is the demands of the body for increased function that brings about further growth. Experimental animals reared in the artificial absence of selected functional demands typically exhibit atrophy of the appropriate organs. Thus, germ-free environments yield animals with poorly developed lymphatic organs, while salamander larvae raised in a hyperoxic atmosphere have diminutive gills. Though disuse may typically induce atrophy, it does not lead to the total abolition of organs or tissues.

For obvious reasons, functional considerations cannot govern the development of embryonic structions in a prefunctional state. Therefore, what controls embryonic growth before functional demands take over is not understood. In large measure, this is a problem of differentiation, for by definition a prefunctional structure is one that is not yet completely differentiated. Thus, embryonic development is an expression of the individual's genetic endowment. It is the latter that determines what kinds of organs and tissues shall differentiate, and what morphogenetic relationships they shall bear one to another. Presumably, the capacity to grow in response to functional demands is also an attribute inherited by most of the cells of the body. How much the various organs of the body actually express their potentials for growth, however, is determined by the physiological requirements placed upon them after they have differentiated to the point of functional competence.

Few cell types perform only single functions, despite their specializations. The problem arises, therefore, as to which of several functions is the one or ones that control growth. Do all of the specialized physiological activities of a tissue play equal roles in regulating growth, or are the interests of all represented by just one, and if so, what considerations could have dictated its selection? More specifically, we do not yet know if liver cells are stimulated to multiply by demands for the synthesis of bile (and if so, which component(s) thereof?) or plasma proteins (fibrinogen, globulins, albumin, etc.?). Proliferative activity among the tubule cells of the kidney is known to be sensitive to the need to excrete excess sodium, but is it also susceptible to the innumerable other substances these cells are called upon to handle? Of the variety of enzymes synthesized by the pancreatic acinar cells, the secretion of which one(s) promotes hyperplasia? Answers to these questions cannot be obtained by the conventional methods of studying compensatory hyperplasia following partial ablation of the organs concerned. Rather, it will be necessary either to subject organs to selected physiological demands to learn which ones become translated into growth, or to study the atrophy-producing effects of substitution therapy whereby one or another of an organ's functions can be by-passed.

An especially interesting aspect of hypertrophy is the problem of whether or not there is a limit to the size to which an organ or tissue can be induced to grow. Following partial ablation, the residual mass of an organ enlarges enough to restore the original functional efficiency. However, if subjected to chronic functional demands, an organ may become excessively enlarged. This is especially true of endocrine glands under the constant stimulation of trophic hormones. Intrasplenic grafts of steroid-secreting glands, for example, typically become hyperplastic under the influence of excess trophic stimulation. In the case of the ovary, this can eventually lead to tumour formation. The thyroid can be made hypertrophic by excessive stimulation of thyrotrophic hormone, as occurs in animals treated with thiouracil. It is interesting, however, that when half of the goiterous thyroid is excised from rats treated with thiouracil, no compensatory enlargement occurs in the remaining half. Apparently the goiterous growth represents either the highest rate of thyrotrophic hormone secretion by the pituitary or the maximum size to which thyroid tissue can be stimulated to grow no matter how great the excess of thyrotrophic hormone. In general, therefore, it would appear that many organs are capable of considerably more growth than they ordinarily manifest, but whether or not the maximum size of a tissue or organ is really unlimited, and how this might relate to the nature of cancer, must remain undetermined for now.

Functional demand and functional activity are so inseparably associated that it is difficult to study one in the absence of the other. Yet it is important to learn if growth is stimulated by the enhanced activity of a cell, or by the factors that initiated this activity in the first place. Such evidence as is thus far available indicates that functional activity *per se* does not promote growth. Exocrine glands artificially stimulated to hypersecretory activity by pilocarpine, for example, do not undergo hyperplasia as a result. A rise in the oxygen-carrying activity of red blood-cells does not stimulate erythropoiesis.

U

On the contrary, these activities might be logically expected to depress growth lest there be a superabundance of cells available to perform a given task.

Thus, there are compelling reasons to attribute growth stimulation to those physiological factors which *promote* increased functional activity and which are themselves activated by functional insufficiencies. The physiological feedbacks by which proper functional levels are maintained serve also to regulate organ and tissue growth as an accessory mechanism of controlling function. Although nerves and hormones are the chief means of maintaining or stimulating functional output by effector organs, there are many other factors, each appropriate to a specific function, by which growth can be regulated. The level of sodium in the blood governs the growth and function of kidneys, adrenal zona glomerulosa and avian salt glands; calcium regulates the size and secretory activity of the parathyroid glands; the relation between the body's demands for oxygen and its availability affect the entire respiratory mechanism, including the rate of erythropoiesis; blood-pressure determines the workload of the heart, and thus influences cardiac size; and antigens promote proliferation among the same cells that they induce to synthesize antibodies. There are as many growth-controlling mechanisms as there are physiological means of initiating functional activity.

How are functional demands related to growth and DNA synthesis? The intracellular mechanisms linking these events appear to involve the balance between enzyme activities and substrate availability. Potter and Auerbach (1959) have pointed out that "seemingly purposeful mechanisms exist for altering the enzyme pattern of cells in a way that makes them better suited to the environment in which they find themselves". According to these authors, excessive availability of substrate tends to promote the production or activation of more enzymes specific for catalysing the conversion of that substrate into its end product. This is persumably achieved by initiating specific RNA production at activated gene loci, together with the subsequent synthesis of specific enzymes on the ribosomes. The end product thus formed may be regarded as being equivalent to functional activity. In this sense, then, the end product tends to inhibit further function, perhaps by suppressing the operation of the enzyme-forming system, as suggested by Potter and Auerbach (1959), but more likely by reducing the original functional demands.

These general principles account for the modulations of functional activity characteristic of all cells under varying conditions of physiological demands. Theoretically, functional insufficiency may therefore be defined as a state in which the amount of substrate exceeds that of the product. This condition may be brought about by any factors that create a functional demand, including the partial ablation of an organ. Thus, the deficiency of the product reduces the normal inhibition of enzyme activity while the increase in the substrate handled by the system enhances enzyme activity. Together, these effects promote the activation and synthesis of the appropriate enzymes, and account for the *physiological* compensation that is so characteristic of homoeostatic systems. The *hypertrophic* compensation that accompanies physiological demands characteristically includes DNA synthesis. The resultant increase in mass enhances the functional output of the organ by accelerating the rate at which substrates are converted into end products.

If functional demands are equivalent to substrate superabundance, how does the latter stimulate growth at the same time it initiates enzyme synthesis? Somehow, the substrate would appear to promote DNA replication concomitant with the production of more (or even new?) enzymes. The ultimate explanation of this correlation resides in the phylogenetic logic of evolving both systems simultaneously. Together, they constitute quantitative and qualitative means of achieving the same end, namely, physiological efficiency. The proximate explanation, however, must be sought in the mechanisms by which gene activation occurs under the influence of substrate molecules. How this activation might be related to the synthesis of new DNA will hopefully be the next breakthrough in the problem of growth regulation.

References

ABERCROMBIE, M., 1957. Localized formation of new tissue in an adult mammal. *Symp. Soc. Exp. Biol.*, **11**, 235–254.

ABERCROMBIE, M., and AMBROSE, E. J., 1962. The surface properties of cancer cells: *A review. Cancer Res.*, **22**, 525–548.

ABERCROMBIE, M., and HARKNESS, R. D., 1951. The growth of cell populations and the properties in tissue culture of regenerating liver of the rat. *Proc. Roy. Soc. B.*, **138**, 544–561.

ADDIS, T., and LEW, W., 1940. The restoration of lost organ tissue. The rate and degree of restoration. *J. Exp. Med.*, **71**, 325–334.

ADDIS, T., MYERS, B. A., and OLIVER, J., 1924. The regulation of renal activity. IX. The effect of unilateral nephrectomy on the function and structure of the remaining kidney. *Arch. Int. Med.*, **34**, 243–257.

ADIBI, S., PASCHKIS, K. E., and CANTAROW, A., 1959. Stimulation of liver mitosis by blood serum from hepatectomized rats. *Exp. Cell Res.*, **18**, 396–398.

AKAMATSU, N., 1923. Über Gewebkulturen von Lebergewebe. *Virchow's Arch.*, **240**, 308–311.

ALHO, A., 1961. Regeneration capacity of the submandibular gland in rat and mouse. *Acta Path. Microbiol. Scand., Suppl.*, **149**, 1–84.

ALLEGRI, A., FOREST, M., and RIZZOLINI, G. F., 1954. La rigenerazione epatica nei ratti in parabiosi. *Arch. Sci. Med.*, **97**, 248–260.

ALLEN, E., 1923. Ovogenesis during sexual maturity. *Am. J. Anat.*, **31**, 439–481.

ALLEN, F. M., 1922a. The pathology of diabetes. 1. Hydropic degeneration of islands of Langerhans after partial pancreatectomy. *J. Metab. Res.*, **1**, 5–41.

ALLEN, F. M., 1922b. The pathology of diabetes. 4. The role of hyperglycaemia in the production of hydropic degeneration of islands. *J. Metab. Res.*, **1**, 75–88.

ALLEN, R. B., BOLLMAN, J. L., and MANN, F. C., 1935. Effect of resection of large fractions of renal substance. *Arch. Path.*, **19**, 174–184.

ALLEN, R. B., and MANN, F. C., 1935. Experiments on compensatory renal hypertrophy. *Arch. Path.*, **19**, 341–363.

ALOV, I. A., and SEMENOVA, N. F., 1958. Activation of the division and growth of cells during regeneration. *Bull. Exp. Biol. Med. (English translation)*, **46**, 1137–1142.

ALOV, I. A., and ZHIRNOVA, A. A., 1957. Changes in the cell nucleic acids content in protein activation of mitosis. *Doklady Akad. Nauk SSSR (English translation)*, **114**, 484–486.

ALSTON, W. C., and THOMSON, R. Y., 1963. Humoral and local factors in liver regeneration. *Cancer Res.*, **23**, 901–905.

ALTMAN, J., 1962. Are new neurons formed in the brains of adult mammals? *Science*, **135**, 1127–1128.

ANDRES, G., 1955. Growth reactions of mesonephros and liver to intravascular injections of embryonic liver and kidney suspensions in the chick embryo. *J. Exp. Zool.*, **130**, 221-250.

ANGERVALL, L., 1959. Alloxan diabetes and pregnancy in the rat. Effects on offspring. *Acta Endocr., Suppl.*, **44**, 1-86.

ANGERVALL, L., 1962. Adrenalectomy in pregnant rats. Effects on offspring. *Acta Endocr.*, **41**, 546-560.

ANNAU, E., MANGINELLI, A., and ROTH, A., 1941. Increased weight and mitotic activity in the liver of tumor-bearing rats and mice. *Cancer Res.*, **11**, 304-306.

ARAI, H., 1920. On the cause of the hypertrophy of the surviving ovary (albino rat) after semi-spaying and on the number of ova in it. *Am. J. Anat.*, **28**, 59-79.

ARATAKI, M., 1926. Experimental researches on the compensatory enlargement of the surviving kidney after unilateral nephrectomy (albino rat). *Am. J. Anat.*, **36**, 437-450.

ARATAKI, M., 1927. Experimental researches on the compensatory enlargement of the surviving kidney after hydronephrosis (albino rat). *Am. J. Anat.*, **38**, 71-88.

ARGYRIS, T. S., 1961. Effect of unilateral nephrectomy or damage on mitotic activity in the contralateral kidney. *Am. Zool.*, **1**, 434.

ARGYRIS, T. S., and ARGYRIS, B. F., 1959. Stimulation of hair growth during skin regeneration. *Devel. Biol.*, **1**, 269-280.

ASDELL, S. A., 1924. Some effects of unilateral ovariotomy in rabbits. *Brit. J. Exp. Biol.*, **1**, 473-486.

ASTARABADI, T., 1962a. The regression in size of the hypertrophic remaining kidney after hypophysectomy in rats. *Quart. J. Exp. Physiol.*, **47**, 93-97.

ASTARABADI, T., 1962b. Some experimental evidence for the dependence of the kidney on the pituitary gland. *Acta Endocr., Suppl.*, **67**, 169.

ASTARABADI, T., 1963a. The effect of hypophysectomy, adrenalectomy and ACTH administration on compensatory renal hypertrophy in rats. *Quart. J. Exp. Physiol.*, **48**, 80-84.

ASTARABADI, T., 1963b. The effect of growth and lactogenic hormones on renal compensatory hypertrophy in hypophysectomized rats. *Quart. J. Exp. Physiol.*, **48**, 85-92.

ASTARABADI, T. M., and ESSEX, H. E., 1953. Effect of hypophysectomy on compensatory renal hypertrophy after lateral nephrectomy. *Am. J. Physiol.*, **173**, 526-534.

ASTWOOD, E. B., SULLIVAN, J., BISSEL, A., and TYSLOWITZ, R., 1943. Action of certain sulphonamides and thiourea upon the function of the thyroid gland of the rat. *Endocr.*, **32**, 210-225.

ATERMAN, K., 1952a. Some local factors in the restoration of the rat's liver after partial hepatectomy. I. *Arch. Path.*, **53**, 197-208.

ATERMAN, K., 1952b. Some local factors in the restoration of the rat's liver after partial hepatectomy. II. "Watery vacuolation": Its relation to the vacuolation of anoxia. *Arch. Path.*, **53**, 209-216.

ATERMAN, K., 1961. Electron microscopy of the rat liver cell after partial hepatectomy. *J. Path. Bact.*, **82**, 367-369.

AUB, J. C., 1950. Regeneration of the liver in old age. *Trans. 10th Conf. on Problems of Ageing*, J. Macy Foundation, New York, p. 17.

AUERBACH, E., 1952. An inhibiting effect observed in the course of normal wound healing. *Proc. Soc. Exp. Biol. Med.*, **81**, 294–296.

AUGUSTINE, J. M., 1963. Compensatory growth of the exocrine pancreas in the rat. *Thesis, Brown University*.

BABAEVA, A. G., 1961. An experimental study of the regeneration capacity of the outer orbital gland in rats. In *Regeneration and Cell Division in Animals* (Liosner, L. D., and Dobrokhotov, V. N., eds.) Edition of Moscow University, **2**, 75–84.

BACHRACH, D., and KORDON, C., 1958. Suppression de l'hypertrophie surrénalienne compensatrice à la suite de lésions hypothalamiques chez le rat. *C. R. Acad. Sci.*, **247**, 2462–2464.

BAGG, H. J., 1925. Hereditary abnormalities of the viscera. I. A morphological study with special reference to abnormalities of the kidneys in the descendants of X-rayed mice. *Am. J. Anat.*, **36**, 275–311.

BAKER, B. L., 1945. The structural response of the parathyroid glands to ureteral ligation or bilateral nephrectomy. *Anat. Rec.*, **93**, 125–143.

BARNUM, C. P., JARDETZKY, C. D., and HALBERG, F., 1957. Nucleic acid synthesis in regenerating liver. *Texas Rep. Biol. Med.*, **15**, 134–147.

BARRON, D. H., 1948. Some effects of amputation of the chick wing bud on the early differentiation of the motor neuroblasts in the associated segments of the spinal cord. *J. Comp. Neurol.*, **88**, 93–127.

BAXTER, J. H., and COTZIAS, G. C., 1949. Effects of proteinuria on the kidney. Proteinuria, renal enlargement, and renal injury consequent on protracted parenteral administration of protein solutions in rats. *J. Exp. Med.*, **89**, 643–668.

BAXTER, J. S., 1946. The growth cycle of the cells of the adrenal cortex in the adult rat. *J. Anat.*, **80**, 139–146.

BECKER, N. H., and OGAWA, K., 1959. Changes in desoxyribose nucleic acid per nucleus in renal compensatory hypertrophy in the rat. *J. Biophys. Biochem. Cytol.*, **6**, 295–297.

BEIDLER, L. M., NEJAD, M. S., SMALLMAN, R.L., and TATEDA, H., 1960. Rat taste cell proliferation. *Fed. Proc.*, **19**, 302.

BELOFF, R. H., 1959. An immunochemical analysis of the developing chick lens. *J. Exp. Zool.*, **140**, 493–518.

BENSLEY, S. H., and WOERNER, C. A., 1938. The effects of continuous intravenous injection of an extract of the alpha-cells of the guinea pig pancreas on the intact guinea pig. *Anat. Rec.*, **72**, 413–434.

BERNSTEIN, D. E., 1950. Autotransplantation of adrenal gland in the spleen and mesentery of rats. *Proc. Soc. Exp. Biol. Med.*, **73**, 175–176.

BERNSTEIN, D. E., and BISKIND, G. R., 1957. Autotransplantation of the adrenal of the rat to the portal circulation: induced adrenal hypertrophy and its prevention by oöphorectomy. *Endocr.*, **60**, 575–577.

BERNSTORF, E. C., 1951. Incomplete hepatic inactivation of hormone produced by intrasplenically grafted ovary in the mouse. *Endocr.*, **49**, 302–309.

BERTALANFFY, L. VON, and PIROZYNSKI, J., 1952. Ontogenetic and evolutionary allometry. *Evolution*, **6**, 387–392.

BEZNAK, M., 1952. The effect of the pituitary and growth hormone on the blood-pressure and on the ability of the heart to hypertrophy. *J. Physiol.*, **116**, 74–83.

BEZNAK, M., 1954. The behaviour of the weight of the heart and the blood pressure of albino rats under different conditions. *U. Physiol.*, **124**, 44–63.

BHASKAR, S. N., BOLDEN, T. E., and WEINMANN, J. P., 1956. Experimental obstructive adenitis in the mouse. *J. Dent. Res.*, **35**, 852–862.

BIGGS, P. M., and PAYNE, L. N., 1959. Cytological identification of pro-liferating donor cells in chick embryos injected with adult chicken blood. *Nature*, **184**, 1594.

BILLMAN, F., and ENGEL, R., 1939. Vikariierender Einsatz fetaler Neben-nieren in der Schwangerschaft bein nebennierenlosen Hund. *Klin. Wchnschr.*, **18**, 599–600.

BIRKUN, A. A., 1958. Intrapulmonary compensatory processes after large operations of the lungs (Compensatory hypertrophy of the lungs). *Arkh. Patol.*, **20**, 41–48. (in Russian).

BISKIND, G. R., and BISKIND, M. S., 1948. Atrophy of ovaries transplanted to the spleen in unilaterally castrated rats; proliferative changes following subsequent removal of intact ovary. *Science*, **108**, 137–138.

BISKIND, G. R., and BISKIND, M. S., 1949. Experimental ovarian tumors in rats. *Am. J. Clin. Path.*, **19**, 501–521.

BISKIND, G. R., and KORDAN, B., 1949. Effect of pregnancy on rat ovary transplanted to spleen. *Proc. Soc. Exp. Biol. Med.*, **71**, 67–68.

BIZZOZERO, E., 1903. Sull'ipertrofia compensatoria delle ghiandole salivari. *Arch. Sci. Med.*, **27**, 423–432.

BIZZOZERO, G., 1894. An address on the growth and regeneration of the organism. *Brit. Med. J.*, **1**, 728–732.

BLALOCK, A., and LEVY, S. E., 1937. Studies on the aetiology of renal hyper-tension. *Ann. Surg.*, **106**, 826–847.

BLAQUIER, P., BOHR, D. F., TAQUINI, A. C., Jr., and HOOBLER, S. W., 1961. Renin and angiotensinase content of the kidney of normal and renal hypertensive rats. *Proc. Soc. Exp. Biol. Med.*, **108**, 711–715.

BLOCK, M. A., WAKIM, K. G., and MANN, F. C., 1953. Appraisal of certain factors influencing compensatory renal hypertrophy. *Am. J. Physiol.*, **172**, 60–66.

BLOMQVIST, K., 1957. Growth stimulation in the liver and tumour develop-ment following intraperitoneal injections of liver homogenates in the rat. *Acta Path. Microbiol. Scand., Suppl.*, **121**, 1–65.

BLUMENFELD, C. M., 1938. Periodic and rhythmic mitotic activity in the kidney of the albino rat. *Anat. Rec.*, **72**, 435–443.

BLUMENTHAL, H. T., and LOEB, L., 1942. Parallelism in the response of thyroid and parathyroid to various hormones and hormone-like substances. *Endocr.*, **30**, 502–510.

BOELL, E. J., GREENFIELD, P., and HILLE, B., 1962. The respiratory function of gills in the larvae of *Amblystoma punctatum. Devel. Biol.*, **7**, 420–431.

BOHNE, A. W., OSBORN, R. W., and HETTLE, P. J., 1955. Regeneration of the urinary bladder in the dog following total cystectomy. *Surg. Gynec. Obstet.*, **100**, 259–264.

BOJS, G., FALKHEDEN, T., SJØGREN, B., and VARNAUSKAS, E., 1962. Haemodynamic studies in man before and after hypophysectomy. *Acta Endocr.* **39**, 308–322.

BOLLMAN, J. L., and MANN, F. C., 1936. The physiology of the impaired liver. *Ergebn. Physiol.*, **38**, 445–492.

BOLLUM, F. J., and POTTER, V. R., 1959. Nucleic acid metabolism in regenerating rat liver. VI. Soluble enzymes which convert thymidine to thymidine phosphates and DNA. *Cancer Res.*, **19**, 561–565.

BOND, A. N., 1960. An analysis of the response of salamander gills to changes in the oxygen concentration of the medium. *Devel. Biol.*, **2**, 1–20.

BOND, C. J., 1906. An inquiry into some points in uterine and ovarian physiology and pathology in rabbits. *Brit. Med. J.*, **2**, 121–127.

BONSER, G. M., and ROBSON, J. M., 1940. The effects of prolonged oestrogen administration upon male mice of various strains: development of testicular tumours in the strong A strain. *J. Path. Bact.*, **51**, 9–22.

BORSOOK, H., 1959. On the mucoprotein erythropoietic factor. In *The Kinetics of Cellular Proliferation* (F. Stohlman, ed.), pp. 357–358.

BOXER, G. E., and SHONK, C. E., 1958. Deoxyribose-5-phosphate metabolism by normal liver and malignant hepatoma. *J. Biol. Chem.*, **233**, 535–540.

BOYCOTT, A. E., 1910. A case of unilateral aplasia of the kidney in a rabbit. *J. Anat. Physiol.*, **45**, 20–22.

BOYCOTT, A. E., 1929. The blood as a tissue: hypertrophy and atrophy of the red corpuscles. *Proc. Roy. Soc. Med.*, **23**, 1–25.

BOYCOTT, A. E., 1932. Hypertrophy and atrophy. *Univ. Coll. Hosp. Mag.*, **17**, 56–66.

BOYCOTT, A. E., 1934. Regeneration of red corpuscles. *Trans. Roy. Soc. Trop. Med. Hyg.*, **27**, 529–532.

BRACCO, R., 1939. Modificazioni istologiche del fegato e delle ghiandole linfatiche dopo splenectomia (Ricerche sperimentali). *Riv. Patol. Sper.*, **23**, 41–57.

BRADFORD, J. R., 1898–99. The results following partial nephrectomy and the influence of the kidney on metabolism. *J. Physiol.*, **23**, 415–496.

BRAMBELL, F. W. R., 1958. The passive immunity of the young mammal. *Biol. Rev.*, **33**, 488–531.

BRANSTER, M. J., and MORTON, R. K., 1956a. Some biochemical characteristics of isolated whole cells from animal tissues. *Austral. J. Sci.*, **19**, 72–73.

BRANSTER, M. J., and MORTON, R. K., 1956b. Comparative rates of synthesis of diphosphopyridine nucleotide by normal and tumour tissue from mouse mammary gland: studies with isolated nuclei. *Biochem. J.*, **63**, 640–646.

BRAUER, A., 1926. Regeneration of transitional epithelium. *Anat. Rec.*, **33**, 137–146.

BRAUN, G. A., MARSH, J. B., and DRABKIN, D. L., 1962. Synthesis of plasma albumen and tissue proteins in regenerating liver. *Metab. Clin. Exp.*, **11**, 957–966.

BRAUN-MENÉNDEZ, E., 1952. Hypertension and the relation between body weight and kidney weight. *Acta Physiol. Latino-americana*, **2**, 1–32.

BRAUN-MENÉNDEZ, E., and HOUSSAY, H. E. J., 1949. Hypertrophie compensatrice du rein chez la rat hypophysectomisée. *C. R. Soc. Biol.*, **143**, 1255–1256.

BREMER, J. L., 1916. The interrelations of the mesonephros, kidney and placenta in different classes of animals. *Am. J. Anat.*, **19**, 179–209.

BRENNER, R. M., 1963. Radioautographic studies with tritiated thymidine of cell migration in the mouse adrenal after a carbon tetrachloride stress. *Am. J. Anat.*, **112**, 81–96.

BREUHAUS, H. C., and MCJUNKIN, F. A., 1932. Effect of macerated kidney on the mitotic rate of kidney epithelium. *Proc. Soc. Exp. Biol. Med.*, **29**, 894–895.

BRØNSTED, H. V., 1954. The time-graded regeneration field in planarians and some of its cyto-physiological implications. In *Recent Developments in Cell Physiology* (J. A. Kitching, ed.), Proc. 7th Symp. Colston Res. Soc., pp. 121–138.

BROWN-GRANT, K., 1961. Salivary gland growth in the isopropyl-noradrenaline treated mouse. *Nature*, **191**, 1076–1078.

BRUES, A. M., DRURY, D. R., and BRUES, M. C., 1936. A quantitative study of cell growth in regenerating liver. *Arch. Path.*, **22**, 658–673.

BRUES, A. M., and MARBLE, B. B., 1937. An analysis of mitosis in liver regeneration. *J. Exp. Med.*, **65**, 15–27.

BRUES, A. M., TRACY, M. M., and COHN, W. E., 1944. Nucleic acids of rat liver and hepatoma: Their metabolic turnover in relation to growth. *J. Biol. Chem.*, **155**, 619–633.

BUCHER, N. L. R., 1958. In *Liver Function, A Symposium on Approaches to the Quantitative Description of Liver Function* (Brauer, R. W., ed.), *Am. Inst. Biol. Sci. Publ.* No. 4, Washington, D.C., p. 433.

BUCHER, N. L. R., 1963. Regeneration of mammalian liver, *Int. Rev. Cytol.*, **15**, 245–300.

BUCHER, N. L. R., DI TROIA, J. F., and SWAFFIELD, M. N., 1961. DNA synthesis during hepatic regeneration in rats of various ages. *Fed. Proc.*, **20**, 286.

BUCHER, N. L. R., and GLINOS, A. D., 1950. The effect of age on regeneration of rat liver. *Cancer Res.*, **10**, 324–332.

BUCHER, N. L. R., SCOTT, J. F., and AUB, J. C., 1951. Regeneration of the liver in parabiotic rats. *Cancer Res.*, **11**, 457–465.

BUCHER, N. L. R., and SWAFFIELD, M. N., 1962. The threshold of response to partial hepatectomy in rats as determined by incorporation of labelled thymidine into DNA. *Fed. Proc.*, **21**, 300.

BUCK, R. C., 1953. Regeneration of tendon. *J. Path. Bact.*, **66**, 1–18.

BUEKER, E. D., 1947. Limb ablation experiments on the embryonic chick and its effect as observed on the mature nervous system. *Anat. Rec.*, **97**, 157–174.

BULLOUGH, W. S., 1962. The control of mitotic activity in adult mammalian tissues. *Biol. Rev.*, **37**, 307–342.

BULLOUGH, W. S., and LAURENCE, E. B., 1960a. The control of epidermal mitotic activity in the mouse. *Proc. Roy. Soc. B.*, **151**, 517–536.

BULLOUGH, W. S., and LAURENCE, E. B., 1960b. The control of mitotic activity in mouse skin. Dermis and hypodermis. *Exp. Cell Res.*, **21**, 394–405.

BURKE, W. T., 1962. Changes in hepatic metabolism associated with carcinogenesis or regeneration in rat liver. *Cancer Res.*, **22**, 10–14.

BURNET, M., 1959. *The Clonal Selection Theory of Acquired Immunity.* Vanderbilt University Press, Nashville.

BURROWS, R. B., 1938. Variations produced in bones of growing rats by parathyroid extracts. *Am. J. Anat.*, **62**, 237–290.

BUTCHER, E. O., 1948. Adrenal autotransplants with hepatic portal drainage in the rat. *Endocr.* **43**, 30–35.

BYROM, F. B., and DODSON, L. F., 1949. The mechanism of the vicious circle in chronic hypertension. *Clin. Sci.*, **8**, 1–10.

CALMAN, R. M., and MURRAY, J., 1950. The transfer of antibodies across the placenta. *Endeavour*, **10**, 27–32.

CALVA, E., and COHEN, P. P., 1959. Carbamyl phosphate-aspartate transcarbamylase activity in regenerating rat liver. *Cancer Res.*, **19**, 679–683.

CAMERON, G. R., 1952. *Pathology of the Cell.* Oliver and Boyd, Edinburgh.

CAMERON, G. R., GRIFFITHS, D. B., and HASAN, S. M., 1957. Liver necrosis following obstruction of the common bile duct. *J. Path. Bact.*, **74**, 327–333.

CAMERON, G. R., and KARUNARATNE, W. A. E., 1936. Carbon tetrachloride cirrhosis in relation to liver regeneration. *J. Path. Bact.*, **42**, 1–21.

CAMERON, G. R., and RHEE, K-S., 1959. Compensatory hypertrophy of the spleen: A study of splenic growth. *J. Path. Bact.*, **78**, 335–350.

CAMPBELL, R. M., and KOSTERLITZ, H. W., 1950. The effects of growth and sex on the composition of the liver cells of the rat. *J. Endocr.*, **6**, 308–318.

CARDELL, B. S., 1953. Hypertrophy and hyperplasia of the pancreatic islets in new-born infants. *J. Path. Bact.*, **66**, 335–346.

CAREY, E. J., 1921. Studies in the dynamics of histogenesis. Tension of differential growth as a stimulus to myogenesis. VII. The experimental transformation of the smooth bladder muscle of the dog, histologically into cross-striated muscle and physiologically into an organ manifesting rhythmicality. *Am. J. Anat.*, **29**, 341–378.

CARMICHAEL, E. S., and MARSHALL, F. H. A., 1908. On the occurrence of compensatory hypertrophy in the ovary. *J. Physiol.*, **36**, 431–434.

CARNOT, P., 1913. Sur l'hypertrophie compensatrice du rein après néphrectomie unilatérale. *C. R. Soc. Biol.*, **74**, 1086–1088.

CARNOT, P., and DEFLANDRE, C., 1906a. Sur l'activité hémopoïétique du sérum au cours de la régénération du sang. *C. R. Acad. Sci.*, **143**, 384–386.

CARNOT, P., and DEFLANDRE, C., 1906b. Sur l'activité hémopoïétique des différents organes au cours de la régénération du sang. *C. R. Acad. Sci.*, **143**, 432–435.

CARNOT, P., and MAY, R. M., 1938. La régénération du rein chez le rat étudiée au moyen de la colchicine. *C. R. Soc. Biol.*, **128**, 641–643.

CARNOT, P., and TERRIS, E., 1926. Sur la cicatrisation de plaies cutanées par les extraits d'embryons ou de peau régénérée. *C. R. Soc. Biol.*, **95**, 655–657.

CASTLEMAN, B., and MALLORY, T. B., 1935. The pathology of the parathyroid gland in hyperparathyroidism. A study of 25 cases. *Am. J. Path.*, **11**, 1–72.

CATER, D. B., HOLMES, B. E., and MEE, L. K., 1956. Cell division and nucleic acid synthesis in the regenerating liver of the rat. *Acta Radiol.*, **46**, 655–667.

CATER, D. B., HOLMES, B. E., and MEE, L. K., 1957. The effect of growth hormone upon cell division and nucleic acid synthesis in the regenerating liver of the rat. *Biochem. J.*, **66**, 482–486.

CHANUTIN, A., and BARKSDALE, E. E., 1933. Experimental renal insufficiency produced by partial nephrectomy. II. Relationship of left ventricular hypertrophy, the width of cardiac muscle fibres and hypertension in the rat. *Arch. Int. Med.*, **52**, 739–751.

CHANUTIN, A., and FERRIS, E. B., 1932. Experimental renal insufficiency produced by partial nephrectomy. I. Control diet. *Arch. Int. Med.*, **49**, 767–787.

CHANUTIN, A., HORTENSINE, J. C., COLE, W. S., and LUDWIG, S., 1938. Blood plasma proteins in rats following partial hepatectomy and laparotomy. *J. Biol. Chem.*, **123**, 247–256.

CHERNICK, S. S., LIPKOVSKY, S., and CHAIKOFF, I. L., 1948. A dietary factor regulating the enzyme content of the pancreas. Changes induced in the size and proteolytic activity of the chick pancreas by the ingestion of raw soybean meal. *Am. J. Physiol.*, **155**, 33.

CHRISTENSEN, B. G., and JACOBSEN, E., 1949. Studies on liver regeneration. *Acta Med. Scand., Suppl.*, **234**, 103–108.

CHRISTIANSON, M., and JONES, C. I., 1957. The interrelationships of the adrenal glands of mother and foetus in the rat. *J. Endocr.*, **15**, 17–42.

CLAYTON, R. M., 1954. Localization of embryonic antigens by antisera labelled with fluorescent dyes. *Nature*, **174**, 1059.

COCK, A. G., and SIMONSEN, M., 1958. Immunological attack on new-born chickens by injected adult cells. *Immunology*, **1**, 103–110.

COETZEE, M. L., and WELLS, L. J., 1957. Hypophysis-adrenal system in the fetal rat. Effects of hydrocortisone, cortisone, DCA, adrenatectomy and maternal hypophysectomy upon the hypophysis. *Am. J. Anat.*, **101**, 419–442.

COHEN, P. P., and HEKHUIS, G. L., 1941. Transamination in tumors, fetal tissues, and regenerating liver. *Cancer Res.*, **1**, 620–626.

COHN, R., 1939. Factors affecting the post-natal growth of the lung. *Anat. Rec.*, **75**, 195–206.

CONTOPOULOS, A. N., McCOMBS, R., LAWRENCE, J. H., and SIMPSON, M. E., 1957. Erythropoietic activity in the plasma of patients with polycythemia vera and secondary polycythemia. *Blood*, **12**, 614–619.

CONTOPOULOS, A. N., VAN DYKE, D. C., and SIMPSON, M. E., 1956. Increased erythropoietic stimulant in plasma of pregnant rats. *Proc. Soc. Exp. Biol. Med.*, **93**, 424–428.

COOLEY, L. M., and GOSS, R. J., 1958. The effects of transplantation and X-irradiation on the repair of fractured bones. *Am. J. Anat.*, **102**, 167–182.

COONS, A. H., LEDUC, E. H., and CONNOLLY, J. M., 1955. Leukocytes involved in antibody formation. *J. Exp. Med.*, **102**, 49–60.

COPENHAVER, W. M., 1930. Results of heteroplastic transplantation of anterior and posterior portions of the heart rudiment in Amblystoma embryos. *J. Exp. Zool.*, **55**, 298–318.

COULOMBRE, A. J., 1956. The role of intraocular pressure in the development of the chick eye. I. Control of eye size. *J. Exp. Zool.*, **133**, 211–225

COULOMBRE, A. J., and COULOMBRE, J. L., 1963. The growth of the lens of the embryonic chick eye. *Anat. Rec.*, **145**, 219–220.

COULOMBRE, J. L., and COULOMBRE, A. J., 1963. Lens development: fiber elongation and lens orientation. *Science*, **142**, 1489–1490

COURRIER, R., COLOGNE, A., and BACLESSE, M., 1951. Action de la cortisone administrée à la mère sur la surrénale du foetus de rat. *C. R. Acad. Sci.*, **233**, 333–336.

COWDRY, E. V., 1942. Ageing of individual cells. In *Problems of Ageing* (Cowdry, E. V., ed.), Williams and Wilkins, 2nd ed., pp. 616–663.

CRAFTS, R. C., and MEINEKE, H. A., 1957. Decreased oxygen need as a factor in anemia of hypophysectomized animals. *Proc. Soc. Exp. Biol. Med.*, **95**, 127–131.

CREUTZFELD, W., 1951. Experimentelle Untersuchungen über die Regenerationsfähigkeit des Inselapparates (Pankreasresektion am alloxandiabetischen Hund). *Zellforsch. Mikrosk. Anat.*, **35**, 47–61.

CROISILLE, Y., 1958. Action de différents extraits d'organes sur l'embryon de poulet et sur des organes embryonnaires cultivés *in vitro*. *Arch. d'Anat. Micr. Morph. Expér.*, **47**, 359–400.

DALY, H., WELLS, L. J., and EVANS, G., 1947. Experimental evidence of the secretion of urine by the fetal kidney. *Proc. Soc. Exp. Biol. Med.*, **64**, 78–80.

D'AMOUR, F. E., 1931. Effect of estrin injections on the anterior lobe. *J. Biol. Chem.*, **92**, lxxxv–lxxxvi.

DAVIDSON, J. M., and FELDMAN, S., 1962. Adrenocorticotrophin secretion inhibited by implantation of hydrocortisone in the hypothalamus. *Science*, **137**, 125–126.

DAVIDSON, J. M., and SAWYER, C. H., 1961. Effects of localized intracerebral implantation of oestrogen on reproductive function in the female rabbit. *Acta Endocr.*, **37**, 385–393.

DAVIDSON, J. N., 1943. Wound hormones. *Edinburgh Med., J.*, **50**, 70–84.

DAVIS, M. E., and PLOTZ, E., 1954. The effects of cortisone acetate on intact and adrenalectomized rats during pregnancy. *Endocr.*, **54**, 384–395.

DAVISON, J., 1959. Studies on the form of the amphibian red blood-cell. *Biol. Bull.*, **116**, 397–405.

DAWSON, A. B., 1940. Cell division in relation to differentiation. *Growth*, *Suppl.*, pp. 91–106.

DEANE, H. W., SHAW, J. H., and GREEP, R. O., 1948. The effect of altered sodium or potassium intake on the width and cytochemistry of the zona glomerulosa of the rat's adrenal cortex. *Endocr.*, **43**, 133–153.

DEBODO, R., SCHWARTZ, I. L., GREENBERG, J., KURTZ, M., EARLE, D. P., Jr., and FARBER, S. J., 1951. Growth hormone and water metabolism in hypophysectomized dogs. *Fed. Proc.*, **10**, 33–34.

DEBURGH, P. M., 1957. Coenzyme synthesis in regenerating and virus-infected liver. *Austral. J. Sci.*, **20**, 86.

DEBURGH, P. M., and MILLER, J. F. A. P., 1955. Cellular control in virus infection. *Nature*, **175**, 550.

DEGROOT, J., and FORTIER, C., 1959. Quantitative and histological aspects of adrenal cortical regeneration in the male albino rat. *Anat. Rec.*, **133**, 565–570.

DeLanney, L. E., and Ebert, J. D., 1962. On the chick spleen: origin; patterns of normal development and their experimental modification. *Contrib. to Embryol. No. 255*, **37**, 57–85.

DeMello, R. F., 1940. Synergie des hormones des glandes sexuelles au cours d'expériences de greffe et de parabiose. *C. R. Soc. Biol.*, **123**, 213–216.

Dempster, W. J., 1954. Some aspects of skin regeneration. *XV° Congr. Soc. Internat. Chir., Bruxelles*, pp. 528–541.

Detwiler, S. R., 1932. Growth acceleration and regulation in heteroplastic spinal-cord grafts. *J. Exp. Zool.*, **61**, 245–277.

Diaz, J. T., and Levy, S. E., 1939. Studies on experimental hypertension in the rat. *Am. J. Physiol.*, **125**, 586–592.

Dill, D. B., 1938. *Life, Heat and Altitude*. Harvard University Press, Cambridge.

Doljanski, F., 1960. The growth of the liver with special reference to mammals. *Int. Rev. Cytol.*, **10**, 217–241.

Doljanski, L., and Auerbach, E., 1944. Effect of cell growth activating tissue extracts locally applied, on experimental skin wounds. *Proc. Soc. Exp. Biol. Med.*, **55**, 112–113.

Domm, L. V., and Juhn, M., 1927. Compensatory hypertrophy of the testes in brown leghorns. *Biol. Bull.*, **52**, 458–473.

Donaldson, H. H., 1924. *The rat*. Memoirs of the Wistar Inst. of Anat., No. 6, Philadelphia.

Doncaster, L., and Marshall, F. H. A., 1910. The effects of one-sided ovariotomy on the sex of the offspring. *J. Gen.*, **1**, 70–72.

Doniach, I., and Weinbren, K., 1952. The development of inclusion bodies in the cells of the rat's liver after partial hepatectomy. *Brit. J. Exp. Path.*, **33**, 499–505.

Drabkin, D. L., 1947. Liver regeneration and cytochrome C metabolism. Influence of amount of tissue excised and of diet, with a note on accompanying changes in liver nucleic acids. *J. Biol. Chem.*, **171**, 395–408.

Drake, T. G., Albright, F., and Castleman, B., 1937. Parathyroid hyperplasia in rabbits by parenteral phosphate administration. *J. Clin. Invest.*, **16**, 203–206.

Drastich, L., 1925. Über das Leben der Salamadra-Larven bei hohem und neidrigem Sauerstoffpartialdruck. *Z. Vergleich. Physiol.*, **2**, 632–657.

Drury, D. R., 1932. Production of renal insufficiency by surgical procedure. *Proc. Soc. Exp. Biol. Med.*, **29**, 856–857.

Dunihue, F. W., 1941. Effect of cellophane perinephritis on the granular cells of the juxtaglomerular apparatus. *Arch. Path.*, **32**, 211.

Dunihue, F. W., and Robertson, W. van B., 1957. The effect of desoxycorticosterone acetate and of sodium on the juxtaglomerular apparatus. *Endocr.*, **61**, 293–299.

Du Noüy, L., 1936. *Biological Time*. Methuen and Co., Ltd., London.

Ebert, J. D., 1953. Selective incorporation of radioactivity from proteins of labelled chorioallantoic grafts of adult chicken tissues with proteins of homologous tissues of host chick embryos. *Anat. Rec.*, **117**, 523.

3I8 ADAPTIVE GROWTH

EBERT, J. D., 1958. Immunological analysis of development. In *The Chemical Basis of Development* (McElroy, W. D., and Glass, B., eds.), The Johns Hopkins Press, Baltimore, pp. 526–545.

EBERT, J. D., 1959. The Acquisition of Biological Specificity. In *The Cell* (Brachet, J., and Mirsky, A. E., eds.), 1, 619–694.

EDWARDS, J., 1940. The effect of unilateral castration on spermatogenesis. *Proc. Roy. Soc. London, B*, 198, 407–421.

EGUCHI, G., 1963. Electron microscopic studies on lens regeneration. I. Mechanism of depigmentation of the iris. *Embryologia*, 8, 45–62.

EGUCHI, G., and ISHIKAWA, M., 1960. ^{32}P-uptake by dorsal and ventral halves of the iris at the beginning of lens regeneration in the newt. *Embryologia*, 5, 219–226.

EGUCHI, G., and ISHIKAWA, M., 1963. Alkaline phosphatase in the dorsal and the ventral halves of the iris during early stages of lens-regeneration in the newt. *Embryologia*, 7, 295–305.

EGUCHI, Y., 1960. Experimental studies on the adrenal cortex of the mouse-fetus. I. Effects of maternal adrenalectomy on the adrenal of the fetus based on histology and volume determination. *Embryologia*, 5, 206–218.

ELIASSON, N. A., HAMMARSTEN, E., REICHARD, P., AQVIST, S., THORELL, B., and EHRENSVÄRD, G., 1951. Turnover rates during formation of proteins and polynucleotides in regenerating tissue. *Acta Chem. Scand.*, 5, 431–444.

ELLIS, R. A., GOERTEMILLER, C. C., Jr., DeLELLIS, R. A., and KABLOTSKY, Y. H., 1963. The effect of a salt water regimen on the development of the salt glands of domestic ducklings. *Devel. Biol.*, 8, 286–308.

EMERY, F. E., 1931. Changes in the ovary and oestrus cycle following the removal of one ovary in albino rats. *Physiol. Zool.*, 4, 101–110.

EMGE, L. A., 1921. A cytological study of the kidney cell in long continued hyperfunction with relation to hypertrophy in the mitochondrial apparatus. *Stanford Univ. Publ., Med. Sci.*, 1, 103–124.

ENESCO, M., and LEBLOND, C. P., 1962. Increase in cell number as a factor in the growth of the organs and tissues of the young male rat. *J. Emb. Exp. Morph.*, 10, 530–562.

ERSHOFF, B. H., and BAJWA, G. S., 1963. Submaxillary gland hypertrophy in rats fed proteolytic enzymes. *Proc. Soc. Exp. Biol. Med.*, 113, 879–881.

ERSLEV, A. J., 1953. Humoral regulation of red cell production. *Blood*, 8, 349–357.

ERSLEV, A. J., 1955. Erythropoietic function in dilution anemia. *Blood*, 10, 616–622.

ERSLEV, A. J., 1958. Erythropoietic function in uremic rabbits. *Arch. Int. Med.*, 101, 407–417.

ERSLEV, A. J., 1959. The effect of anemic anoxia on the cellular development of nucleated red cells. *Blood*, 14, 386–398.

ERSLEV, A. J., 1960. Erythropoietic function in uremic rabbits. II. Effect of nephrectomy on red cell production and iron metabolism. *Acta Haemat.*, 23, 226–235.

ERSLEV, A. J., and HUGHES, J. R., 1960. The influence of environment on iron incorporation and mitotic division in a suspension of normal bone marrow. *Brit. J. Haemat.*, 6, 414–432.

ERSLEV, A. J., and LAVIETES, P. H., 1954. Observations on the nature of the erythropoietic serum factor. *Blood*, **9**, 1055–1061.

EVENS, R. G., and MARTIN, J. M., 1963. A quantitative study of pancreatic regeneration in rats. *Fed. Proc.*, **22**, 604.

EYSTER, J. A. E., 1927. Cardiac dilatation and hypertrophy. *Trans. Assoc. Am. Physic.*, **42**, 15–21.

FAJERS, C. M., 1957a. On compensatory renal hypertrophy after unilateral nephrectomy. 1. Akaryometric study. *Acta Path. Microbiol. Scand.*, **41**, 25–33.

FAJERS, C. M., 1957b. On compensatory renal hypertrophy after unilateral nephrectomy. 2. The immediate effect of unilateral nephrectomy as judged by some renal function tests and karyometric studies in hydrated rabbits. *Acta Path. Microbiol. Scand.*, **41**, 34–43.

FANKHAUSER, G., 1955. The role of nucleus and cytoplasm. In *Analysis of Development* (Willier, B. H., Weiss, P., and Hamburger, V., eds.), Sect. IV, Ch. 1, pp. 126–150.

FANKHAUSER, G., VERNON, J. A., FRANK, W. H., and SLACK, W. V., 1955. Effect of size and number of brain cells on learning in larvae of the salamander, *Triturus viridescens*. *Science*, **122**, 692–693.

FAUTREZ, J., CAVELLI, G., and PISI, E., 1955. Variations in the amounts of deoxyribonucleic acid in the cell nuclei and its correlation with mitotic activity: compensatory hypertrophy of the kidney. *Nature*, **175**, 684–685.

FAUTREZ, J., and ROELS, H., 1954. Mitose et synthèse d'acide désoxyribonucléique. Le cas des mitoses provoquées dans le tube contourné du rein par l'hydronephrose unilatérale. *Arch. Biol.*, **65**, 459–496.

FELL, H. B., 1957. In discussion of: Gaillard, P. J., Morphogenesis in animal tissue cultures. *J. Nat. Cancer Inst.*, **19**, 601–602.

FELL, H. B., and MELLANBY, E., 1953. Metaplasia produced in cultures of chick ectoderm by high vitamin A. *J. Physiol.*, **119**, 470–488.

FELS, E., and DeEANDI, F. F., 1943. Hepatectomia parcial y embarazo. *Rev. Soc. Argent. Biol.*, **19**, 309–313.

FERGUSON, C. C., ROGERS, C. S., and VARS, H. M., 1949. Liver regeneration in the presence of common bile duct obstruction. *Am. J. Physiol.*, **159**, 343–350.

FERGUSON, L., and KIRSCHBAUM, A., 1954. Effect of gonadotrophic hormone on cross-strain grafting of ovaries between inbred strains of mice. *Anat. Rec.*, **118**, 298.

FILMANOWICZ, E. V., and GURNEY, C. W., 1959. A study of the kinetics of erythropoiesis. *J. Lab. Clin. Med.*, **54**, 813–814.

FILMANOWICZ, E. V., and GURNEY, C. W., 1961. Studies on erythropoiesis. XVI. Response to a single dose of erythropoietin in polycythemic mice. *J. Lab. Clin. Med.*, **57**, 65–72.

FINERTY, J. C., 1952. Parabiosis in physiological studies. *Physiol. Rev.*, **32**, 277–302.

FINLAY, G. F., 1924. The effect of different species' lens antisera on pregnant mice and rats and their progeny. *Brit. J. Exp. Biol.*, **1**, 201–213.

FIROR, W. M., and GROLLMAN. A., 1933. Studies in the adrenal. I. Adrenalectomy in mammals with particular reference to the white rat (Mus norvegicus). *Am. J. Physiol.*, **103**, 686–698.

FISHBACK, F. C., 1929. A morphologic study of regeneration of the liver after partial removal. *Arch. Path.*, **7**, 955–977.

FISHER, B., FISHER, E. R., and SAFFER, E., 1963. Investigations concerning the role of a humoral factor in liver regeneration. *Cancer Res.*, **23**, 914–920.

FISHER, E. R., and KLEIN, H. Z., 1963. Effect of renal hypertension in sodium deficient rats on juxtaglomerular index and zona glomerulosa. *Proc. Soc. Exp. Biol. Med.*, **113**, 37–39.

FISHER, J. W., SANZARI, N. P., BIRDWELL, B. J., and CROOK, J., 1962. The role of the kidney in erythropoietin production. In *Erythropoiesis* (Jacobson, L. O., and Doyle, M., eds.), Grune and Stratton, New York, pp. 78–86.

FISHER, N. F., 1924. Regeneration of pancreas from pancreatic duct. *J. Am. Med. Assn.*, **83**, 502–503.

FLICKINGER, R. A., LEVI, E., and SMITH, A. E., 1955. Some serological experiments relating to the embryonic development of the lens. *Physiol. Zool.*, **28**, 79–85.

FLINT, J. M., 1910. Compensatory hypertrophy of the small intestine following resection of large portions of the jejunum and ileum. *Trans. Connecticut State Med. Soc.*, **1910**: 283–335.

FLOYER, M. A., 1957. Role of the kidney in experimental hypertension. *Brit. Med. Bull.*, **13**, 29–32.

FONTAINE, T., 1947. Sur le mécanisme de la régression rénale à la suite de l'hypophysectomie chez le rat. *C. R. Soc. Biol.*, **141**, 569–571.

FONTAINE, T., and VEIL, C., 1946. Hypertrophie rénale compensatrice chez le rat hypophysoprive. *C. R. Soc. Biol.*, **140**, 159–162.

FONTAINE, T., and VEIL, C., 1947. Hypertrophie rénale compensatrice chez le rat hypophysoprive. *Arch. Sci. Physiol.*, **1**, 49–61.

FORSGREN, E., 1929. The anatomical qualities of the liver during the various stages of its functional activities. *J. Morph.*, **47**, 519–529.

FORTNER, J. G., and KIEFER, J. H., 1948. Ureteroduodenal anastomosis. *J. Urol.*, **59**, 31–37.

FOWLER, I., and CLARKE, W. M., 1959. The inhibition of lens-inducing capacity of the optic vesicle with adult lens antisera. *Anat. Rec.*, **133**, 277.

FOWLER, I., and CLARKE, W. M., 1960. Development of anterior structures in the chick after direct application of adult lens antisera. *Anat. Rec.*, **136**, 194–195.

FOWLER, W. M., and BARER, A. P., 1942. Rate of hemoglobin regeneration in blood donors. *J. Am. Med. Assoc.*, **118**, 421–427.

FRANCK, G., 1958. Activité mitotique et dosages cytophotométriques des acides désoxyribonucléiques dans le rein en hypertrophie compensatrice chez le jeune rat. *C. R. Soc. Biol.*, **152**, 1841–1844.

FRANCK, G., 1960. Étude du métabolisme et de la synthèse des acides désoxyribonucléiques au cours de l'hypertrophie compensatrice du rein chez le rat jeune, par cytophotométrie, caryométrie et histautoradiographie. *Arch. Biol.*, **71**, 489–525.

FREEMAN, G., and OVERTON, J., 1961. Lens regeneration from the cornea of *Xenopus laevis*. *Am. Zool.*, **1**, 448–449.

FRIED, W., PLZAK, L. F., JACOBSON, L. O., and GOLDWASSER, E., 1957. Studies on erythropoiesis. III. Factors controlling erythropoietin production. *Proc. Soc. Exp. Biol. Med.*, **94**, 237–241.

FRIEDRICH-FREKSA, H., and ZAKI, F. G., 1954. Spezifische Mitose-Auslösung in normaler ratten Leber durch Serum von partiell hepatektomierten Ratten. *Z. Naturf.* **96**, 394–397.

FRITZSON, P., 1962. The relation between uracil-catabolizing enzymes and rate of rat liver regeneration. *J. Biol. Chem.*, **237**, 150–156.

FUKUTANI, K., 1959. Further studies on the effects of the removal of the chief lymphoid organs. *Folia Anatomica Japonica*, **34**, 43–63.

FURST, S. S., ROLL, P. M., and BROWN, G. W., 1950. On the renewal of the purines of the desoxypentose and pentose nucleic acids. *J. Biol. Chem.*, **183**, 251–266.

FURUTA, W. J., 1947. An experimental study of lymph node regeneration in rabbits. *Am. J. Anat.*, **80**, 437–505.

GANONG, W. F., and HUME, D. M., 1955. Effect of hypothalamic lesions on steroid-induced atrophy of adrenal cortex in the dog. *Proc. Soc. Exp. Biol. Med.*, **88**, 528–533.

GARDNER, W. A., Jr., and TABER, E., 1963. The demonstration of nonsteroid gonadal inhibiting substance elaborated by the ovary of the brown leghorn. *Anat. Rec.*, **145**, 231.

GARDNER, W. U., 1943. Spontaneous testicular tumors in mice. *Cancer Res.*, **3**, 759–766.

GAUDINO, N. M., 1944. Las suprarrenales en la hipertesion arterial nefrogena. *Rev. Soc. Argent. Biol.*, **20**, 470–486.

GAUTHIER, G. F., and PADYKULA, H. A., 1963. Comparative cytological studies of the heterogeneity of skeletal muscle fibres. *Anat. Rec.*, **145**, 232.

GLINOS, A. D., 1956a. Mechanism of growth control in liver regeneration. *Science*, **123**, 673–674.

GLINOS, A. D., 1956b. Inhibition of liver cell division and serum protein changes induced by dehydration in partially hepatectomized rat. *Fed. Proc.*, **15**, 76.

GLINOS, A. D., 1958a. Liver regeneration and liver function. In *Liver Function, A Symposium on Approaches to the Quantitative Description of Liver Function* (Brauer, R. W., ed.), Am. Inst. Biol. Sci. Publ., No. 4, Washington, D.C., pp. 425–431.

GLINOS, A. D., 1958b. The mechanism of liver growth and regeneration. In *A Symposium on the Chemical Basis of Development* (McElroy, W., and Glass, B., eds.), Baltimore, pp. 813–842.

GLINOS, A. D., and GEY, G. O., 1952a. Humoral factors involved in the induction of liver regeneration in the rat. *Proc. Soc. Exp. Biol. Med.*, **80**, 421–425.

GLINOS, A. D., and GEY, G. O., 1952b. Alteration of the growth response of tissue cells *in vitro* in serum from partially hepatectomized rats. *Cancer Res.*, **12**, 265.

GLOCK, G. E., and McLEAN, P., 1957. Levels of oxidized and reduced diphosphopyridine nucleotide and triphosphopyridine nucleotide in tumours. *Biochem. J.*, **65**, 413–416.

GLUECKSOHN-SCHOENHEIMER, S., 1943. The morphological manifestations of a dominant mutation in mice affecting tail and urogenital system. *Genetics*, **28**, 341–348.

x

GLUECKSOHN-SCHOENHEIMER, S., 1945. The embryonic development of mutants of the Sd-strain in mice. *Genetics*, **30**, 29–38.

GLUECKSOHN-WAELSCH, S., 1957. The effect of maternal immunization against organ tissues on embryonic differentiation in the mouse. *J. Emb. Exp. Morph.*, **5**, 83–92.

GOLDBLATT, H., LYNCH, J., HANZAL, R. F., and SUMMERVILLE, W. W., 1934. Studies on experimental hypertension. I. The production of persistent elevation of systolic blood-pressure by means of renal ischemia. *J. Exp. Med.*, **59**: 347–380.

GOLDEN, J. B., and SEVRINGHAUS, E. L., 1938. Inactivation of estrogenic hormone of the ovary by the liver. *Proc. Soc. Exp. Biol. Med.*, **39**, 361–362.

GOLDFARB, B., and TOBIAN, L., 1963. Effect of high O_2 concentration on erythropoietin and renal juxtaglomerular cells. *Proc. Soc. Exp. Biol. Med.*, **113**, 35–36.

GOLDHABER, P., 1958. Preliminary observations on bone isografts within diffusion chambers. *Proc. Soc. Exp. Biol. Med.*, **98**, 53–56.

GOLDSTEIN, D. J., 1957. Trypan blue indiced anomalies in the genito-urinary system of rats. *S. African J. Med. Sci.*, **22**, 13–22.

GOLDWASSER, E., JACOBSON, L. O., FRIED, W., and PLZAK, L., 1957. Mechanism of erythropoietic effect of cobalt. *Science*, **125**, 1085–1086.

GOODCHILD, C. G., 1956. Reconstitution of the intestinal tract in the adult leopard frog, Rana pipiens Schreber. *J. Exp. Zool.*, **131**, 301–328.

GOODKIND, M. J., DAVIS, J. O., BALL, W. C., and BAHN, R. C., 1957. Alterations in cardiovascular and renal hemodynamic function following hypophysectomy in the dog. *Am. J. Physiol.*, **188**, 529–537.

GOORMAGHTIGH, N., 1939. Existence of an endocrine gland in the media of renal arterioles. *Proc. Soc. Exp. Biol. Med.*, **42**, 688–689.

GORDON, A. S., NERI, R. O., SIEGEL, C. D., DURNFEST, B. S., HANDLER, E. S., LOBUE, J., and EISLER, M., 1960. Evidence for circulating leucocytosis-inducing factor (LIF). *Acta Haemat.*, **23**, 323–341.

GORDON, A. S., PILIERO, S. J., KLEINBERG, W., and FREEDMAN, H. H., 1954. A plasma extract with erythropoietic activity. *Proc. Soc. Exp. Biol. Med.*, **86**, 255–258.

GORDON, A. S., PILIERO, S. J., MEDICI, P. T., SIEGEL, C. D., and TANNENBAUM, M., 1956. Attempts to identify site of production of circulating "erythropoietin". *Proc. Soc. Exp. Biol. Med.*, **92**, 598–602.

GORDON, A. S., WINKERT, J. W., DORNFEST, B. S., LoBUE, J., and CRUSCO, A., 1959. Properties of the urinary erythropoietic stimulating factor (ESF). In *The Kinetics of Cellular Proliferation* (Stohlman, F., ed.), pp. 332–343.

GORDON, W. H., 1936. Compensatory hypertrophy and hyperplasia of islands of Langerhans *in utero*; congenital hypoglycemia due to hyperinsulinism. *Ohio State Med. J.*, **32**, 540–542.

GOSS, R. J., 1961. Factors affecting lens regeneration in the newt. In *Annual Report of the Director of the Department of Embryology*, Carnegie Inst. Wash. Year Book 60, pp. 430–431.

GOSS., R. J., 1963a. Effects of maternal nephrectomy on foetal kidneys. *Nature*, **198**, 1108–1109.

Goss, R. J., 1963b. Mitotic responses of the compensating rat kidney to injections of tissue homogenates. *Cancer Res.*, **23**, 1031–1035.

Goss, R. J., and Rankin, M., 1960. Physiological factors affecting compensatory renal hyperplasia in the rat. *J. Exp. Zool.*, **145**, 209–216.

Gourevitch, M., 1951. Isolement du facteur croissance cellulaire dans la réparation des plaies expérimentales du rat. Rôle de l'age. *C. R. Soc. Biol.*, **145**, 1472–1474.

Grant, R., 1945. Rate of replacement of the surface epithelial cells of the gastric mucosa. *Anat. Rec.*, **91**, 175–185.

Grauer, T. P., 1926. Regeneration in the pancreas of the rabbit. *Am. J. Anat.*, **38**, 233–253.

Gray, S. H., 1929. The effect of potassium iodide, thyroid extract and anterior pituitary extract upon regeneration and early compensatory hypertrophy of the thyroid gland. *Am. J. Path.*, **5**, 415–423.

Greenbaum, A. L., Greenwood, F. C., and Harkness, R. D., 1954. Glutamic dehydrogenase and glutamic-aspartic transaminase in regenerating liver of the rat. *J. Physiol.*, **125**, 251–262.

Greene, R. R., Burrill, M. W., and Ivy, A. C., 1941. Experimental intersexuality: the effects of combined estrogens and androgens on the embryonic sexual development of the rat. *J. Exp. Zool.*, **87**, 211-232.

Greenwald, G. S., 1962. Temporal relationship between unilateral ovariectomy and the ovulatory response of the remaining ovary. *Endocr.*, **71**, 664–666.

Gurd, F. N., Vars, E. M., and Ravdin, I. S., 1948. Composition of the regenerating liver after partial hepatectomy in normal and protein-depleted rats. *Am. J. Physiol.*, **152**, 11–21.

Gurney, C. W., and Pan, C., 1960. Studies on erythropoiesis. XIII. A comparison of methods of bioassay of erythropoietin in human plasma. *J. Lab. Clin. Med.*, **55**, 67–72.

Guthrie, M. J., 1954. The structure of intrasplenic ovaries in mice. *Anat. Rec.*, **118**, 305.

Guyer, M. F., and Smith, E. A., 1918. Studies on cytolysins. I. Some pre-natal effects of lens antibodies. *J. Exp. Zool.*, **26**, 65–82.

Hagerman, D. D., and Villee, C. A., 1960. Transport functions of the placenta. *Physiol. Rev.*, **40**, 313–330.

Halbert, S. P., and Fitzgerald, P. L., 1958. Studies on the immunologic organ specificity. *Am. J. Ophthal.*, **46**, 187–195.

Halbert, S. P., Locatcher-Khorazo, D., Swick, L., Witner, R., Seegal, B., and Fitzgerald, P. L., 1957. Homologous immunological studies of ocular lens. I. *In vitro* observations. *J. Exp. Med.*, **105**, 439-452.

Halbert, S. P., Manski, W., and Auerbach, T., 1960. Lens antigens in relation to evolution. *Anat. Rec.*, **136**, 204–205.

Hall, C. E., and Hall, O., 1952. Growth effects of desoxycorticosterone and cortisone with special reference to renal hypertrophy. *Proc. Soc. Exp. Biol. Med.*, **79**, 536–538.

Ham, A. W., Littner, N., Drake, T. G., Robertson, E. C., and Tisdall, F. F., 1940. Physiological hypertrophy of the parathyroids, its cause and its relation to rickets. *Am. J. Path.*, **16**, 277–286.

HAMBURGER, V., 1939. Motor and sensory hyperplasia following limb-bud transplantation. *Physiol. Zool.*, **13**, 268–284.

HAMBURGH, M., SOBEL, E. H., KOBLIN, R., and RINESTONE, A., 1962. Passage of thyroid hormone across the placenta in intact and hypophysectomized rats. *Anat. Rec.*, **144**, 219–225.

HAMMARSTEN, E., 1951. Turnover rates during formation of proteins and polynucleotides in regenerating tissues. *Ciba Found. Conf. on Isotopes in Biochem.* (Wolstenholme, G. E. W., ed.), pp. 203–212.

HAMMOND, J., 1925. *Reproduction in the rabbit.* Oliver and Boyd, London.

HANDELMAN, C. S., and WELLS, H., 1963. Morphological and histochemical studies of experimentally enlarged and atrophied salivary glands of rats. *Am. J. Anat.*, **112**, 65–79.

HARCLERODE, J. E., HOULIHAN, R. T., and ANTHONY, A., 1962. Thyroid function in rats exposed to simulated high altitude. *Am. Zool.*, **2**, 413.

HARDING, C. V., and SRINIVASAN, B. D., 1961. A propagated stimulation of DNA synthesis and cell division. *Exp. Cell Res.*, **25**, 326–340.

HARKNESS, R. D., 1952. Changes in the liver of the rat after partial hepatectomy. *J. Physiol.*, **117**, 267–277.

HARRISON, R. G., 1924. Some unexpected results of the heteroplastic transplantation of limbs. *Proc. Nat. Acad. Sci.*, **10**, 69–74.

HARRISON, R. G., 1929. Correlation in the development and growth of the eye studied by means of heteroplastic transplantation. *Arch. EntwMech. Org.*, **120**, 1–55.

HARRISON, T. R., MASON, M. F., RESNIK, H., and RAINEY, J., 1936. Changes in blood-pressure in relation to experimental renal insufficiency. *Trans. Assn. Am. Phys.*, **51**, 280–284.

HARTMAN, C. G., 1925. Observations on the functional compensatory hypertrophy of the opossum ovary. *Am. J. Anat.*, **35**, 1–24.

HARTMAN, F. W., 1933. Methods and effects of increasing the urinary constituents in the body. *J. Exp. Med.*, **58**, 649–662.

HARTROFT, P. M., 1953. Effects of a depressor and a pressor substance on renal juxtaglomerular cells and blood pressure in rats fed varying amounts of sodium chloride. *Anat. Rec.*, **115**, 319.

HARTROFT, P. M., 1957. Studies on renal juxtaglomerular cells. III. The effects of experimental renal disease and hypertension in the rat. *J. Exp. Med.*, **105**, 501–508.

HARTROFT, P. M., and HARTROFT, W. S., 1952. The effects of dietary factors and administration of desoxycorticosterone acetate (DCA) on juxtaglomerular cells of the rat. *Anat. Rec.*, **112**, 341.

HARTROFT, P. M., and HARTROFT, W. S., 1953. Studies on renal juxtaglomerular cells. I. Variations produced by sodium chloride and desoxycorticosterone acetate. *J. Exp. Med.*, **97**, 415–428.

HASEGAWA, M., 1958. Restitution of the eye after removal of the retina and lens in the newt, *Triturus pyrrhogaster*. *Embryologia*, **4**, 1–32.

HATAI, S., 1915. The growth of organs in the albino rat as affected by gonadectomy. *J. Exp. Zool.*, **18**, 1–67.

HAWKINS, J., and WALKER, J. M., 1952. The effect of colchicine on the enzyme content of regenerating rat liver and on the pressor amine content of the adrenal. *Brit. J. Pharmacol.*, **7**, 152–160.

HAY, E., SEGUIN, P., and LARIVIÉRE, M., 1946. Renotropic effect of the anterior pituitary. *Fed. Proc.*, **5**, 137.

HAY, E. D., 1959. Electron microscopic observations of muscle dedifferentiation in regenerating *Amblystoma* limbs. *Devel. Biol.*, **1**, 555–585.

HAYMAN, J. M., Jr., and STARR, I., 1925. Experiments on the glomerular distribution of blood in the mammalian kidney. *J. Exp. Med.*, **42**, 641–659.

HECHT, L. I., and POTTER, V. R., 1958. Nucleic acid metabolism in regenerating rat liver. *Cancer Res.*, **18**, 186–192.

HEIM, W. G., and KERRIGAN, J. M., 1962. The appearance of slow alpha-two globulin after carbon tetrachloride poisoning and partial hepatectomy. *Am. Zool.*, **2**, 528–529.

HEINBECKER, P., 1948. The pathogenesis of diastolic hypertension. *Surgery*, **23**, 618–638.

HEINBECKER, P., WHITE, H. L., and ROLF, D., 1941. Effects of hypophysectomy on some renal functions. *Proc. Soc. Exp. Biol. Med.*, **46**, 44–47.

HEINEN, J. H., DABBS, G. H., and MASON, H. A., 1949. The experimental production of ectopic cartilage and bone in the muscles of rabbits. *J. Bone Joint Surg.*, **31**-A.

HELLER, C. G., HELLER, E. J., and SEVRINGHAUS, E. L., 1942. Does estrogen substitution materially inhibit pituitary gonadotropic potency? *Endocr.*, **30**, 309–316.

HELLER, C. G., and JUNGCK, E. C., 1947. Regulation of ovarian growth; inhibition by estrogen or stimulation by gonadotrophins? *Proc. Soc. Exp. Biol. Med.*, **65**, 152–154.

HELWIG, E. B., 1940. Hypertrophy and hyperplasia of islands of Langerhans in infants born of diabetic mothers. *Arch. Int. Med.*, **65**, 221–239.

HERLANT, M., 1948. Activité mitotique des cellules rénales au cours de l'hydronéphrose unilaterale. *Bull. Acad. Roy. Med. Belg.*, **13**, 315–330.

HERLANT, M., 1949. Le rôle de la thyroïde dans l'hypertrophie compensatrice du rein. *Ann. d'Endocr.*, **10**, 313–326.

HERRING, P. T., 1917. The action of thyroid upon the growth of the body and organs of the white rat. *Quart. J. Exp. Physiol.*, **11**, 231–253.

HERRMANN, G., DECHERD, G., and ERHARD, P., 1941. Production of cardiac hypertrophy in rats. *Proc. Soc. Exp. Biol. Med.*, **47**, 464–465.

HESS, L., and SAXL, H., 1912. Über den Abbau des Hämoglobins. *Dtsch. Arch. Klin. Med.*, **108**, 180–185.

HIATT, H. H., and BOJARSKI, T. B., 1960. Stimulation of thymidylate kinase activity in rat tissues by thymidine administration. *Biochem. Biophys. Res. Comm.*, **2**, 35–39.

HIGGINS, G. M., and ANDERSON, R. M., 1931. Experimental pathology of the liver. I. Restoration of the liver of the white rat following partial surgical removal. *Arch. Path.*, **12**, 186–202.

HIGGINS, G. M., BERKSON, J., and FLOCK, E., 1932. The diurnal cycle in the liver. I. Periodicity of the cycle, with analysis of chemical constituents involved. *Am. J. Physiol.*, **102**, 673–682.

HIGGINS, G. M., and INGLE, D. J., 1939. Regeneration of the liver in hypophysectomized white rats. *Anat. Rec.*, **73**, 95–104.

HINMAN, F., 1922. Renal counterbalance. An experimental and clinical study with reference to the significance of disuse atrophy. *Trans. Am. Assn. Genito-Urin. Surg.*, **15**, 241–385.

HINMAN, F., and BUTLER, O. W., 1923. Repair in hydronephrosis with reference particularly to early and late changes after relief of brief obstructions when opposite kidney is not disturbed. *J. Am. Med. Assoc.*, **81**, 2021–2023.

HIRAMOTO, R., BERNECKY, J., and JURAND, J., 1962. Immunochemical studies on kidney hypertrophy in the rat. *Proc. Soc. Exp. Biol. Med.*, **III**, 648–651.

HODGSON, G., PERRETA, M., YUDILEVICH, D., and ESKUCHE, I., 1958. Assay of "hemopoietine" in starved animals: properties of urinary hemopoietine. *Proc. Soc. Exp. Biol. Med.*, **99**, 137–142.

HODGSON, G., and TOHÁ, J., 1954. The erythropoietic effect on urine and plasma of repeatedly bled rabbits. *Blood*, **9**, 299–309.

HOERR, N., 1931. The cells of the suprarenal cortex in the guinea-pig: their reaction to injury and their replacement. *Am. J. Anat.*, **48**, 139–197.

HOFFMAN, J., HIMES, M. B., KLEIN, A., POULOS, J., and POST, J., 1956. Responses of the liver to injury. Effects of previous injury upon the healing pattern after acute carbon tetrachloride poisoning. *Arch. Path.*, **62**, 96–102.

HOFFMAN, J., HIMES, M. B., LAPAN, S., RISZKI, R., and POST, J., 1955. Responses of the liver to injury. Effect of acute carbon tetrachloride poisoning. *Arch. Path.*, **59**, 429–438.

HOGEBOOM, G. H., and SCHNEIDER, W. C., 1952. Cytochemical studies. VI. The synthesis of diphosphopyridine nucleotide by liver cell nuclei. *J. Biol. Chem.*, **197**, 611–620.

HOLMES, B. E., and MEE, L. K., 1954. Effect of X-rays and A-methopterin on nucleic acid synthesis in regenerating liver. *Ann. Rep. Brit. Emp. Cancer Campaign*, **32**, 281–283.

HOLSTI, P., 1956. Experimental cirrhosis of the liver in rabbits induced by gastric instillation of desiccated whole bile. *Acta Path. Microbiol. Scand.*, *Suppl.*, **113**, 1–67.

HORN, E. C., and HOUSE, M. E., 1955. A test of specific uptake from organ homogenates by homologous organs in the young mouse. *J. Elisha Mitchell Sci. Soc.*, **71**, 171.

HORN, E. H., and LoMONACO, M. B., 1958. Unilateral adrenalectomy in the cretin rat. *Proc. Soc. Exp. Biol. Med.*, **98**, 817–820.

HORRALL, O. H., and CARLSON, A. J., 1928. The toxic factor in bile. *Am. J. Physiol.*, **85**, 591–606.

HOUSSAY, B. A., BIASOTTI, A., and MAGDALENA, A., 1932. Hypophyse et thyroïde. Hypophyse et hypertrophie compensatrice de la thyroïde. *C. R. Soc. Biol.*, **110**, 142–144.

HUFF, R. L., LAWRENCE, J. H., SIRI, W. E., WASSERMAN, L. R., and HENNESSY, T. G., 1951. Effects of changes in altitude on hemopoietic activity. *Medicine*, **30**, 197–217.

HUGGINS, C. B., 1931. The formation of bone under the influence of epithelium of the urinary tract. *Arch. Surg.*, **22**, 377–408.

HUGHES, P. E., 1960. Humoral factors in liver regeneration. *Austral. Ann. Med.*, **9**, 41–43.

HULTIN, T., and VON DER DECKEN, A., 1958. The activity of cytoplasmic constituents from regenerating rat liver in amino acid incorporating systems. *Exp. Cell Res.*, **15**, 581–594.

HULTQUIST, G. T., 1950. Diabetes and pregnancy. An animal study. *Acta Path. Microbiol. Scand.*, **27**, 695–719.

HUNICUTT, J. A., 1914. The absence of hyperplasia of the remainder of the thyroid in dogs after piecemeal removal of this gland. Auto-transplantation of the thyroid in partially thyroidectomized animals. *Am. J. Med. Sci.*, **148**, 207–214.

HUNT, T. E., 1940. Mitotic activity of the adrenal cortex of rats in different phases of the sexual cycle. *Anat. Rec.*, **78**, 152.

HUNTER, J., 1792. An experiment to determine the effect of extirpating one ovarium upon the number of young produced. In *Observations on Certain Parts of the Animal Oeconomy*, London, 2nd ed., pp. 157–162.

HUROWITZ, R. B., and STUDER, A., 1960. Effect of partial hepatectomy on mitosis rate in CCl_4-induced liver damage of parabiotic rats. *Arch. Path.*, **69**, 511–515.

HURTADO, A., MERINO, C., and DELGADO, E., 1945. Influence of anoxemia on the hemopoietic activity. *Arch. Int. Med.*, **75**, 284–323.

HUXLEY, J. S., 1932. *Problems of Relative Growth*. The Dial Press, New York.

HUXLEY, J. S., and CARR-SAUNDERS, A. M., 1924. Absence of pre-natal effects of lens-antibodies in rabbits. *Brit. J. Exp. Biol.*, **I**, 215–248.

IGLESIAS, R., MARDONES, E., and LIPSCHUTZ, A., 1953. Evolution of lutcoma in intrasplenic ovarian grafts in the guinea pig. *Brit. J. Cancer*, **7**, 214–220.

INGLE, D. J., and FISHER, G. T., 1938. Effect of adrenalectomy during gestation on the size of the adrenal glands of new-born rats. *Proc. Soc. Exp. Biol. Med.*, **39**, 149–150.

INGLE, D. J., and HIGGINS, G. M., 1938. Autotransplantation and regeneration of the adrenal gland. *Endocr.*, **22**, 458–464.

INGLE, D. J., and KENDALL, E. C., 1937. Atrophy of the adrenal cortex of the rat produced by the administration of large amounts of cortin. *Science*, **86**, 245.

INGRAM, D. L., and KROHN, P. L., 1956. Factors influencing the survival of ovarian homografts in rats. *J. Endocr.*, **14**, 110–120.

ISLAMI, A. H., PACK, G. T., and HUBBARD, J. C., 1959. The humoral factor in regeneration of the liver in parabiotic rats. *Surg. Gynec. Obstet.*, **108**, 549–554.

ITAMI, S., 1910. Weitere Studien über Blutregeneration. *Arch. Exp. Path.*, **62**, 104–117.

IVY, A. C., GROSSMAN, M. I., and BACHRACH, W. H., 1950. *Peptic Ulcer*, The Blakiston Co., Philadelphia.

JACKSON, B., 1959. Time-associated variations of mitotic activity in livers of young rats. *Anat. Rec.*, **134**, 365–377.

JACKSON, B., and BOHNEL, B., 1962. Effect of serum injections on body weight and liver regeneration of partially hepatectomized rats. *Fed. Proc.*, **21**, 301.

JACKSON, C. M., and LEVINE, N. M., 1929. Rate and character of the compensatory renal hypertrophy after unilateral nephrectomy in young albino rats. *Anat. Rec.*, **41**, 323–333.

JACKSON, C. M., and SHIELS, M., 1927. Compensatory hypertrophy of the kidney during various periods after unilateral nephrectomy in very young albino rats. *Anat. Rec.*, **36**, 221–238.

JACOBJ, W., 1925. Über das rhythmische Wachstum der Zellen Verdopplung ihres Volumens. *Arch. EntwMech. Org.*, **106**, 124–192.

JACOBSON, L. O., GOLDWASSER, E., PLZAK, L., and FRIED, W., 1957a. Studies on erythropoiesis. IV. Reticulocyte response of hypophysectomized and polycythemic rodents to erythropoietin. *Proc. Soc. Exp. Biol. Med.*, **94**, 243–249.

JACOBSON, L. O., GOLDWASSER, E., FRIED, W., and PLZAK, L., 1957b. Role of the kidney in erythropoiesis. *Nature*, **179**, 633–634.

JACOBY, F., 1953. Mitotic activity in the gall bladder epithelium of the guinea pig after ligation of the common bile duct. *J. Physiol.*, **119**, 21P–22P.

JACOBY, F., 1959. In *Mitogenesis* (Ducoff, H. S., and Ehret, C. F., eds.), U. of Chicago Press, pp. 55–62.

JAFFE, H. L., and BODANSKY, A., 1930. Experimental fibrous osteodystrophy (ostitis fibrosa) in hyperparathyroid dogs. *J. Exp. Med.*, **52**, 669–694.

JAFFE, J. J., 1954. Diurnal mitotic periodicity in regenerating rat liver. *Anat. Rec.*, **120**, 935–954.

JARDETZKY, C. D., BARNUM, C. P., and VERMUND, H., 1956. Deoxyribonucleic acid and phospholipide metabolism in regenerating liver and the effect of X-radiation. *J. Biol. Chem.*, **222**, 421–433.

JÄRVI, O., and TEIR, H., 1951. Experimental alterations of cell size and mitotic activity in the outer orbital gland of the white rat. III. The influence of experimental scar tissue inside and around the gland. *Acta Path. Microbiol. Scand.*, **29**, 401–415.

JOHNSON, F. P., 1919. The development of the lobule of the pig's liver. *Am. J. Anat.*, **25**, 299–331.

JOHNSON, F. R., and McMINN, R. M. H., 1956. Transitional epithelium in osteogenesis. *J. Anat.*, **90**, 106–116.

JOHNSON, F. R., and McMINN, R. M. H., 1960. The cytology of wound healing of body surfaces in mammals. *Biol. Rev.*, **35**, 364–412.

JOHNSON, H. A., 1963. Redundancy and biological aging. *Science*, **141**, 910–912.

JOHNSON, R. M., and ALBERT, S., 1952. The uptake of radioactive phosphorus by rat livers following partial hepatectomy. *Arch. Biochem. Biophys.*, **35**, 340–345.

JONES, M., LLOYD, C., and WYATT, T., 1953. A study of the interrelationships of maternal and fetal adrenal glands of rats. *Endocr.*, **53**, 182–191.

JOST, A., 1948. Influence de la décapitation sur le développement du tractus génital et des surrénales de l'embryon de lapin. *C. R. Soc. Biol.*, **142**, 273–275.

JUNQUEIRA, L. C. U., and RABINOVITCH, M., 1954. Reversibility of the phenomena induced by excretory duct ligature in the rat submaxillary gland. *Texas Rep. Biol. Med.*, **12**, 94–97.

KALLAS, H., 1929. Sur le passage de substances hypophysaires pendant la parabiose. *C. R. Soc. Biol.*, **102**, 280–282.

KARASAKI, W., 1963. An electron microscope study of lens regeneration in the adult newt. *Amer. Soc.Cell Biol.,Third Annual Meeting,Abstract No.208:*86A.

KARSNER, H. T., BUNKER, H. A., Jr., and GRABFIELD, G. P., 1915. A note on the immediate effects of reduction of kidney substance. *J. Exp. Med.*, **22**, 544–550.

KARSNER, H. T., SAPHIR, O., and TODD, T. W., 1925. The state of the cardiac muscle in hypertrophy and atrophy. *Am. J. Path.*, **1**, 351–371.

KARSNER, H. T., STRAUS, R., MOORE, R. A., and HANZAL, R. F., 1932. Urea tolerance after unilateral nephrectomy in rabbits. *J. Exp. Med.*, **55**, 27–30.

KELLEHER, P. C., KENYON, C. D., and VILLEE, C. A., 1963. Serum protein synthesis by the fetal rat. *Science*, **139**, 839–840.

KELLY, L. S., and JONES, H. B., 1953. Influence of homologous tissue factors on DNA turnover and radiation protection. *Am. J. Physiol.*, *172*, 575–578.

KENNEDY, G. C., 1958. Age and renal disease. In *Ciba Foundation Colloquia on Ageing*, J. and A. Churchill, Ltd., London, **4**, 250–263.

KENNEDY, G. C., PEARCE, W. M., and PARROT, D. M. V., 1958. Liver growth in the lactating rat. *J. Endocr.*, **17**, 158–160.

KHAN, M. Y., 1962. Effect of chlorpromazine upon ovarian hypertrophy. *Anat., Rec.*, **142**, 248.

KHANOLKAR, V. R., 1922. Partial activity of the kidney and the "all or nothing" principle. *J. Path. Bact.*, **25**, 414–424.

KITCHELL, R. L., 1950. Effects of steroid hormones upon the adrenal of fetal rats. *Anat. Rec.*, **108**, 598–599.

KITCHELL, R. L., 1954. Compensatory hypertrophy of the intact adrenal of fetal rats subjected to unilateral adrenalectomy. *Proc. Soc. Exp. Biol. Med.*, **75**, 824–827.

KITCHELL, R. L., and WELLS, L. J., 1952. Reciprocal relation between the hypophysis and adrenals in fetal rats; affect of unilateral adrenalectomy and of implanted cortisone, DOCA and sex hormones. *Endocr.*, **50**, 83–93.

KITTELSON, J. A., 1917. The postnatal growth of the kidney of the albino rat, with observations on an adult human kidney. *Anat., Rec.*, **13**, 385–408.

KLEIN, M., 1952. Ovarian tumorigenesis following intrasplenic transplantation of ovaries from weanling, young adult and senile mice. *J. Nat. Cancer Inst.*, **12**, 877–881.

KNIGGE, K. M., 1961. Normal thyroid function and response to hemithyroidectomy in the cat. *Anat. Rec.* **141**, 151–158.

KNOBIL, E., and BRIGGS, F. N., 1955. Fetal-maternal interrelationships: The hypophysis-adrenal system. *Endocr.*, **57**, 147–152.

KNOWLTON, A. I., STOERK, H., SEEGAL, B. C., and LOEB, E. N., 1946. Influence of adrenal cortical steroids upon the blood-pressure and the rate of progression of experimental nephritic rats. *Endocr.*, **38**, 315–324.

KOCHAKIAN, C. D., and STETTNER, C. E., 1948. Effect of testosterone propionate and growth hormone on the weight and composition of the body and organs of the mouse. *Am. J. Physiol.*, **155**, 255–261.

KOHN, R., 1958. Effect of administration of rat serum on rat liver regeneration. *Exp. Cell Res.*, **14**, 228–230.

KOLLROS, J. J., 1953. The development of the optic lobes in the frog. I. The effects of unilateral enucleation in embryonic stages. *J. Exp. Zool.*, **123**, 153–188.

KORENCHEVSKY, V., 1961. *Physiological and Pathological Ageing*, Hafner Pub. Co., Inc., New York.

KORENCHEVSKY, V., DENNISON, M., and KOHN-SPEYER, A., 1933. Changes produced by testicular hormone in normal and in castrated rats. *Biochem. J.*, **27**, 557–579.

KORNFELD, W., 1958. Endocrine influences upon the growth of the rudimentary gonad of fowl. *Anat. Rec.*, **130**, 619–638.

KORNFELD, W., and NALBANDOV, A. V., 1954. Endocrine influences on the development of the rudimentary gonad of fowl. *Endocr.*, **55**, 751–761.

KULANGARA, A. C., and SCHJEIDE, O. A., 1962. Fetal synthesis and transplacental passage of homologous serum proteins in the rabbit. *Nature*, **105**, 811–812.

KURNICK, N. B., 1951. Cytochemical studies on the kidney. I. Role of cell multiplication in normal growth. *J. Exp. Med.*, **94**, 373–376.

KURNICK, N. B., 1955. Cytochemical changes during normal growth and compensatory hypertrophy of the rat kidney. *J. Histochem. Cytochem.*, **3**, 290–294.

KURU, M., KOSAKI, G., AOKI, Y., MORISHITA, S., UTSONOMIYA, T., and WATANABE, H., 1960. Isolation of the mitosis promoting substance from regenerating rat liver and chick embryo. *Gann (Suppl.)*, **51**, 233–234.

KUUSI, T., and TEIR, H., 1953. Studies on the nucleic acids of the outer orbital gland of the white rat. *Ann. Med. Exp. Biol. Fenn.*, **31**, 391–397.

KYRLE, J., 1909. Über die Regenerationsvorgänge im tierischen Pancreas. *Arch. Mikr. Anat.*, **72**, 141–160.

KYRLE, J., 1911. Über die Regenerationsvorgänge im tierischen und menschlichen Hoden. *S.-B. Akad. Wiss. Wien.*, **120**, 3–24.

LACASSAGNE, A., and CAUSSÉ, R., 1941. Modifications des glandes salivaires de la souris consécutivement à la section de la corde du tympan. *C. R. Soc. Biol.*, **135**, 241–244.

LACQUET, A. M., 1932. Experimental pathology of the liver. VIII. Effects of carbon tetrachloride on the normal and on the restored liver after partial hepatectomy. *Arch. Path.*, **14**, 164–176.

LACROIX, P., 1951. *The Organization of Bones*. The Blakiston Co., Philadelphia.

LAHTIHARJU, A., 1961. Influence of autolytic and necrotic liver tissue on liver regeneration in rat. *Acta Path. Microbiol. Scand.*, *Suppl.*, **150**, 1–99.

LAMIRANDE, G., and CANTERO, A., 1952. Electrophoretic analysis of plasma protein constituents in rats bearing regenerating and preneoplastic livers. *Cancer Res.*, **12**, 330–333.

LANDAUER, W., 1937. Loss of body heat and disease. *Am. J. Med. Sci.*, **194**, 667–674.

LANE, C. E., and MARKEE, J. E., 1941. Responses of ovarian intraocular transplants to gonadotropins. *Growth*, **5**, 61–67.

LANGMAN, J., 1959. The first appearance of specific antigens during induction of the lens. *J. Emb. Exp. Morph.*, **7**, 193–202.

LANGMAN, J., 1960a. The effect of lens antibodies on lens formation *in vitro* and *in vivo*. *Anat. Rec.*, **136**, 228.

LANGMAN, J., 1960b. Morphological development of the lens in relation to antigenic properties. *Anat. Rec.*, **136**, 228.

LANGMAN, J., MAISEL, H., and SQUIRES, J., 1962. The influence of lens antibodies on the development of lens antigen-containing tissues in the chick embryo. *J. Emb. Exp. Morph.*, **10**, 178–190.

LANGMAN, J., and PRESCOTT, B. D., Jr., 1959. An immunological approach to the problem of lens regeneration. *J. Emb. Exp. Morph.*, **7**, 549–555.

LAQUERRIÈRE, R., and LAUMONIER, R., 1960. Variations du taux d'acide désoxyribonucléique dans le foie du rat albinos après injection de sérum de rat hépatectomisé. *C. R. Soc. Biol.*, **154**, 286–289.

LARSELL, O., 1931. The effect of experimental excision of one eye on the development of the optic lobe and opticus layer in larvae of the tree-frog (*Hyla regilla*). *J. Exp. Zool.*, **58**, 1–20.

LATTA, J. S., and HARVEY, H. T., 1942. Changes in the islets of Langerhans of the albino rat induced by insulin administration. *Anat. Rec.*, **82**, 281–296.

LEATHEM, J. H., 1945. The plasma protein concentrations and organ weights of rats on a high protein diet. *Endocr.*, **37**, 157–164.

LEBLOND, C. P., VULPE, M., and BERTALANFFY, F. D., 1955. Mitotic activity of epithelium of urinary bladder in albino rat. *J. Urol.*, **73**, 311–313.

LEDUC, E. H., 1949. Mitotic activity in the liver of the mouse during inanition followed by refeeding with different levels of protein. *Am. J. Anat.*, **84**, 397–430.

LEDUC, E. H., COONS, A. H., and CONNOLLY, J. M., 1955. Studies on antibody production. II. The primary and secondary responses in the popliteal lymph node of the rabbit. *J. Exp. Med.*, **102**, 61–72.

LEDUC, E. H., and WILSON, J. W., 1958. Injury to liver cells in carbon tetrachloride poisoning. *Arch. Path.*, **65**, 147–157.

LEEVY, C. M., HOLLISTER, R. M., SCHMID, R., MacDONALD, R. A., and DAVIDSON, C. S., 1959. Liver regeneration in experimental carbon tetrachloride intoxication. *Proc. Soc. Exp. Biol. Med.*, **102**, 672–675.

LENIQUE, P., 1959. Studies on homologous inhibition in the chick embryo. *Acta Zool.*, **41**, 141–202.

LEONG, G. F., GRISHAM, J. W., and HOLE, B., 1963. Effect of rapid "total" exchange transfusion on hepatic DNA synthesis in partially hepatectomized rats. *Fed. Proc.*, **22**, 192.

LEVANDER, G., 1938. A study of bone regeneration. *Surg. Gynec. Obst.*, **67**, 705–714.

LEVENSON, G., CROWLEY, L. V., OATES, J. F., and GLINOS, A. D., 1959. Effect of severe burn on liver regeneration. *Surg. Forum*, **9**, 493.

LEVI-MONTALCINI, R., and ANGELETTI, P. U., 1961. Growth control of the sympathetic system by a specific protein factor. *Quart. Rev. Biol.*, **36**, 99–108.

LEVINE, L., 1944. Some effects of increased food consumption on the composition of carcass and liver of hypophysectomized rats. *Am. J. Physiol.*, **141**, 143–150.

LI, M. H., and GARDNER, W. U., 1952. Influence of the age of the host and ovaries on tumorigenesis in intrasplenic and intrapancreatic ovarian grafts. *Cancer Res.*, **10**, 162–165.

LI, R. C., and P'AN, S. Y., 1940. The adrenal weight in rats living parabiotically with adrenalectomized partners. *Chinese J. Physiol.*, **15**, 327–334.

LIANG, D. S., and GOSS, R. J., 1963. Regeneration of the bladder after subtotal cystectomy in rats. *J. Urol.*, **89**, 427–430.

LINMAN, J. W., and BETHELL, F. H., 1956. The plasma erythropoietic stimulating factor. Observations on circulating erythrocytes and bone marrow of rats receiving protein-free extracts of rabbit plasma. *Blood*, **11**, 310–323.

LINMAN, J. W., and BETHELL, F. H., 1957. The plasma erythropoietic stimulating factor in man. Observations on patients with polycythemia vera and secondary polycythemia. *J. Lab. Clin. Med.*, **49**, 113–127.

LINZELL, J. L., 1963. Some effects of denervating and transplanting mammary glands. *Quart. J. Exp. Physiol.*, **48**, 34–60.

LIOSNER, L. D., KHARLOVA, G. V., and LEVITINA, B. M., 1961. Spleen regeneration in mammals following injury. In *Regeneration and Cell Division in Animals* (Liosner, L. D., and Dobrokhotov, V. N., eds.), Trans. Moscow Soc. of Naturalists, Biological Series, **2**, 17–32.

LIPSCHÜTZ, A., 1922. Compensatory hypertrophy of the testicle after unilateral castration. *J. Physiol.*, **56**, 451–458.

LIPSCHÜTZ, A., 1928. New developments in ovarian dynamics and the law of follicular constancy. *Brit. J. Exp. Biol.*, **5**, 283–291.

LIPSCHÜTZ, A., and ADAMBERG, L., 1925. Nouvelles expériences sur la loi de la contance folliculaire. *C. R. Soc. Biol.*, **93**, 1464–1466.

LIPSCHÜTZ, A., OTTOW, B., WAGNER, C., and BORMANN, F., 1922a. On the hypertrophy of the interstitial cells in the testicle of the guinea pig under different experimental conditions. *Proc. Roy. Soc. B.*, **93**, 132–142.

LIPSCHÜTZ, A., and VOSS, H. E., 1925. Further developments on the dynamics of ovarian hypertrophy. *Brit. J. Exp. Biol.*, **3**, 35–41.

LIPSCHÜTZ, A., WAGNER, C., TAMM, R., and BORMANN, F., 1922b. Further experimental investigations on the hypertrophy of the sexual glands. *Proc. Roy. Soc. B.*, **94**, 83–92.

LISK, R. D., 1960. Estrogen-sensitive centers in the hypothalamus of the rat. *J. Exp. Zool.*, **145**, 197–207.

LOEB, L., 1919. Studies on compensatory hypertrophy of the thyroid gland. I. A quantitative analysis of compensatory hypertrophy of the thyroid gland. *J. Med. Res.*, **40**, 199–228.

LOEB, L., 1920. Studies on compensatory hypertrophy of the thyroid gland. IV. The influence of iodine on hypertrophy of the thyroid gland. *J. Med. Res.*, **41**, 481–494.

LOEB, L., 1926. Studies on compensatory hypertrophy of the thyroid gland. VII. Further investigation of the influence of iodine on hypertrophy of the thyroid gland with an interpretation of the differences in the effects of iodine on the thyroid gland under various pathologic conditions. *Am. J. Path.*, **2**, 19–32.

LOEB, L., 1928a. Studies on compensatory hypertrophy of the thyroid gland. VIII. A comparison between the effect of administration of thyroxin, thyroid, and anterior pituitary on the compensatory hypertrophy of the thyroid gland in the guinea pig. *Am. J. Path.*, **5**, 71–78.

LOEB, L., 1928b. Studies on compensatory hypertrophy of the thyroid gland. IX. The influence of variations in size of the remaining part of the gland, in mode of administration and in quantity of potassium iodide on the hypertrophy of the thyroid in the guinea pig. *Am. J. Path.*, **5**, 79–86.

LOEB, L., BASSETT, R. B., and FRIEDMAN, H., 1930. Further investigations concerning the stimulating effect of anterior pituitary gland preparation on the thyroid gland. *Proc. Soc. Exp. Biol. Med.*, **28**, 209–213.

LOEB, L., and KAPLAN, E. E., 1924. Studies on compensatory hypertrophy of the thyroid gland. VI. The effect of feeding anterior lobe of the pituitary gland on the hypertrophy of the thyroid gland in the guinea pig. *J. Med. Res.*, **44**, 557–578.

LOGOTHETOPOULOS, J. H., and DONIACH, I., 1955. Compensatory hypertrophy of the rat thyroid after partial thyroidectomy. *Brit. J. Exp. Path.*, **36**, 617–627.

LOMBARDO, A. V., 1964. Adrenal relationships in the maternal-fetal system. *Thesis, Brown University.*

LORIN-EPSTEIN, M. J., 1927. Über einige allgemeine Faktoren der Wiederherstellungsprozesse und ihre Bedeutung für die chirurgische Pathologie. *Arch. Klin. Chir.*, **144**, 632–666.

LOWENSTEIN, L. M., and STERN, A., 1963. Serum factor in renal compensatory hyperplasia. *Science* **142**, 1479–1480.

LOWRANCE, P., and CHANUTIN, A., 1942. The effect of partial hepatectomy on blood volume in the white rat. *Am. J. Physiol.*, **135**, 606–608.

LUCE, E. M., 1923. The size of the parathyroids of rats and the effect of a diet deficiency of calcium. *J. Path. Bact.*, **26**, 200–206.

LUDEWIG, S., MINOR, G. R., and HORTENSTINE, J .C., 1939. Lipid distribution in rat liver after partial hepatectomy. *Proc. Soc. Exp. Biol. Med.*, **42**, 158–161.

MACDONALD, R. A., and PECHET, G., 1961. Liver cell regeneration due to biliary obstruction. *Arch. Path.*, **72**, 133–141.

MACDONALD, R. A., and ROGERS, A. E., 1961. Control of regeneration of the liver. Lack of effect of plasma from partially hepatectomized, cirrhotic, and normal rats upon deoxyribonucleic acid synthesis and mitosis in rat liver. *Gastroenterology*, **41**, 33–38.

MACDONALD, R. A., ROGERS, A. E., and PECHET, G., 1962. Regeneration of the liver. Relation of regenerative responses to size of partial hepatectomy. *Lab. Invest.*, **11**, 544–548.

MACKAY, E. M., and MACKAY, L. L., 1931. Factors which determine renal weight. X. The effect of feeding desiccated thyroid. *J. Nutrition*, **4**, 33–37.

MACKAY, E. M., and MACKAY, L. L., 1938. Influence of adrenal cortex extract upon compensatory hypertrophy of the adrenal cortex. *Endocr.*, **23**, 237–240.

MacKay, E. M., MacKay, L. L., and Addis, T., 1928. Factors which determine renal weight. V. The protein intake. *Am. J. Physiol.*, **86**, 459–465.

MacKay, L. L., Addis, T., and MacKay, E. M., 1938. The degree of compensatory renal hypertrophy following unilateral nephrectomy. I. The influence of the protein intake. *J. Exp. Med.*, **67**, 515–519.

MacKay, L. L., and MacKay, E. M., 1927. Factors which determine renal weight. II. Age. *Am. J. Physiol.*, **83**, 191–195.

MacKay, L. L., MacKay, E. M., and Addis, T., 1927. Influence of age on degree of renal hypertrophy produced by high protein diets. *Proc. Soc. Exp. Biol. Med.*, **24**, 335–336.

MacKay, L. L., MacKay, E. M., and Addis, T., 1931. Factors which determine renal weight. XII. The nitrogen intake as varied by the addition of urea to the diet. *J. Nutrition*, **4**, 379–383.

MacKay, L. L., MacKay, E. M., and Addis, T., 1932. The degree of compensatory renal hypertrophy following unilateral nephrectomy. I. Influence of age. *J. Exp. Med.*, **56**, 255–265.

Madden, S. C., and Zeldis, L. J., 1958. Plasma protein control by the liver. In *Liver Function* (Brauer, R. W., ed.), *Am. Inst. Biol. Sci. Pub. No.* 4, pp. 325–333.

Magdalena, A., 1935. Hypertrophie compensatrice de la thyroïde des crapauds hypophysoprives. *C. R. Soc. Biol.*, **118**, 489–490.

Maisel, H., and Harmison, C., 1963. An immunoembryological study of the chick iris. *J. Emb. Exp. Morph.*, **11**, 483–491.

Maisel, H., and Langman, J., 1961. Lens proteins in various tissues of the chick eye and in the lens of animals throughout the vertebrate series. *Anat. Rec.*, **140**, 183–193.

Maley, F., and Maley, G. F., 1960. Nucleotide interconversions. II. Elevation of deoxycytidylate deaminase and thymidylate synthetase in regenerating rat liver. *J. Biol. Chem.*, **235**, 2968–2970.

Mall, F. P., 1906. A study of the structural unit of the liver. *Am. J. Anat.*, **5**, 227–308.

Malmgren, R. A., 1956. Observations on a liver mitotic stimulant present in tumor tissue. *Cancer Res.*, **16**, 232–236.

Mandel, P., Mandel, L., and Jacob, M., 1950. Étude biochemique de l'hypertrophie rénale compensatrice au cours du jeûne protéique. *C. R. Soc. Biol.*, **144**, 1548–1551.

Mangalik, V. S., Mehrotra, R. M. L., and Agarwal, K. C., 1954. Role of thyroid gland in liver regeneration. *Indian J. Med. Sci.*, **8**, 477–483.

Mann, F. C., and Magath, T. B., 1922. The production of chronic liver insufficiency. *Am. J. Physiol.*, **59**, 485.

Marine, D., 1908. Review of some recent work on the thyroid gland. *Cleveland Med. J.*, **7**, 105–108.

Marine, D., 1914. Parathyroid hypertrophy and hyperplasia in fowls. *Proc. Soc. Exp. Biol. Med.*, **11**, 117–118.

Marine, D., 1926. Control of compensatory hyperplasia of the thyroid of guinea pigs by the administration of iodine. *Arch. Path.*, **2**, 829–839.

MARSHAK, A., and BYRON, R. L., Jr., 1945. The use of regenerating liver as a method of assay. *Proc. Soc. Exp. Biol. Med.*, **59**, 200–202.

MARSHAK, A., and WALKER, A. C., 1945. Effect of liver fractions on mitosis in regenerating liver. *Am. J. Physiol.*, **143**, 226–234.

MATOTH, Y., and BEN-PORATH (ARKIN), E., 1959. Effect of erythropoietin on the mitotic rate of erythroblasts in bone marrow cultures. *J. Lab. Clin. Med.*, **54**, 722–727.

MAYR, E., 1961. Cause and effect in biology. *Science*, **134**, 1501–1506.

MCARDLE, A. H., and CREASER, E. H., 1963. Nucleoproteins in regenerating rat liver. I. Incorporation of $^{32}P_i$ into the ribonucleic acid of liver during early stages of regeneration. *Biochem. Biophys. Acta*, **68**, 561–568.

MCCANCE, R. A., and MORRISON, A. B., 1956. The effects of equal and limited rations of water, and of 1, 2, and 3 per cent solutions of sodium chloride on partially nephrectomized and normal rats. *Quart. J. Exp. Physiol.*, **41**, 365–386.

MCCREIGHT, C. E., and SULKIN, N. M., 1959. Cellular proliferation in the kidneys of young and senile rats following unilateral nephrectomy. *J. Gerontol.*, **14**, 440–443.

MCCREIGHT, C. E., and SULKIN, N. M., 1962a. Compensatory renal hyperplasia following experimental surgical deletions of the kidney complement. *Am. J. Anat.*, **110**, 199–292.

MCCREIGHT, C. E., and SULKIN, N. M., 1962b. Effects of unilateral nephrectomy in hypophysectomized rats. *Anat. Rec.*, **142**, 256.

MCFARLANE, A. S., 1957. Use of labelled plasma proteins in the study of nutritional problems. *Progr. Biophys. Biophys. Chem.*, **7**, 115–163.

MCJUNKIN, F. A., and BREUHAUS, H. C., 1931. Homologous liver as a stimulus to hepatic regeneration. *Arch. Path.*, **12**, 900–908.

MCJUNKIN, F. A., and MATSUI, T., 1931. Effect of homologous macerated skin on the regeneration of epidermis. *Arch. Path.*, **12**, 794–801.

MCJUNKIN, F. A., and ROBERTS, B. D., 1932. Effect of excessive insulin on the pancreatic islets of young rats. *Proc. Soc. Exp. Biol. Med.*, **29**, 893.

MCJUNKIN, F. A., TWEEDY, W. R., and BREUHAUS, H. C., 1932. The parathyroid hormone. Its regulatory action on the parathyroid glands and toxic effect on the tissues of the rat. *Arch. Path. Lab. Med.*, **14**, 649–659.

MCKEEHAN, M. S., 1961. The capacity for lens regeneration in the chick embryo. *Anat. Rec.*, **141**, 227–230.

MCKELLAR, M., 1949. The postnatal growth and mitotic activity of the liver of the albino rat. *Am. J. Anat.*, **85**, 263–295.

MCMINN, R. M. H., and JOHNSON, F. R,. 1955. The repair of artificial ulcers in the urinary bladder of the cat. *Brit. J. Surg.*, **43**, 99–103.

MCMINN, R. M. H., and JOHNSON, F. R., 1957. Wound healing in the gallbladder of the cat. *Brit. J. Surg.*, **45**, 76–80.

MCQUEEN-WILLIAMS, M., and THOMPSON, K. W., 1939. The effect of ablation of the hypophysis upon the weight of the kidney of the rat. *Yale J. Biol. Med.*, **12**, 531–542.

MEGIBOW, R. S., KATZ, L. N., and RODBARD, S., 1942. The mechanism of arterial hypertension in experimental hydronephrosis. *Am. J. Med. Sci.*, **204**, 340–350.

MESSIER, B., and LEBLOND, C. P., 1960. Cell proliferation and migration as revealed by radioautography after injection of thymidine-H^3 into male rats and mice. *Am. J. Anat.*, **106**, 247–285.

MESSIER, B., LEBLOND, C. P., and SMART, I., 1958. Presence of DNA synthesis and mitosis in the brain of young adult mice. *Exp. Cell Res.*, **14**, 224–226.

METCALF, D., 1963. Spleen graft growth in splenectomized mice. *Austral. J. Exp. Biol.*, **41**, 52–60.

MIKAMI, Y., 1941. Experimental analysis of the Wolffian lens regeneration in adult newt, *Triturus pyrrhogaster*. *Japan. J. Zool.*, **9**, 269–302.

MILLER, L. L., and BALE, W. F., 1954. Synthesis of all plasma protein fractions except gamma globulins by the liver. *J. Exp. Med.*, **99**, 125–132.

MILSTEIN, B. B., 1950. Regeneration in the submaxillary gland of the rat. *Brit. J. Exp. Path.*, **31**, 664–669.

MITCHELL, R. M., 1948. Histological changes and mitotic activity in the rat adrenal during postnatal development. *Anat. Rec.*, **101**, 161–185.

MIYADA, D. S., and KURNICK, N. B., 1960. Further studies on rat kidney growth: compensatory renal growth following unilateral nephrectomy in the rat. *Fed. Proc.*, **19**, 325.

MOLL, J., 1955. Quantitative microscopic-anatomical observations on compensatory renal hypertrophy. *Anat. Rec.*, **121**, 343.

MOORE, R. A., 1929. Number of glomeruli in kidney of adult white rat unilaterally nephrectomized in early life. *J. Exp. Med.*, **50**, 709–712.

MOORE, R. A., and HELLMANN, L. M., 1930. The effect of unilateral nephrectomy on the senile atrophy of the kidney of the white rat. *J. Exp. Med.*, **51**, 51–57.

MOORE, R. A., and LUKIANOFF, G. F., 1929. The effect of unilateral nephrectomy on the total number of open glomeruli in the rabbit. *J. Exp. Med.*, **50**, 227–232.

MORGAN, T. H., 1901. *Regeneration*. The Macmillan Co., New York.

MORRISON, A. B., 1962. Experimentally induced chronic renal insufficiency in the rat. *Lab. Invest.*, **11**, 321–332.

MORTON, R. K., 1958. Enzymic synthesis of coenzyme I in relation to chemical control of cell growth. *Nature*, **181**, 540–542.

MOYA, F. J., 1963. Inhibition of growth by post-hepatectomy blood serum. Effect on regenerating liver and on tissue culture. *Exp. Cell Res.*, **31**, 457–469.

MUGGIA, A., 1927. Modificazioni istologiche delle isole di Langerhans nella iperglicemia e nella ipoglicemia sperimentale. *Arch. Sci. Med.*, **50**, 185–190.

MUN, A. M., KOSIN, I. L., and SATO, I., 1959a. The effects of spleens from different animals on the growth of the chick embryo spleen. *Anat. Rec.*, **134**, 613–614.

MUN, A. M., KOSIN, I. L., and SATO, I., 1959b. Enhancement of growth of chick host spleens following chorio-allantoic membrane grafts of homologous tissues. *J. Emb. Exp. Morph.*, **7**, 512–525.

MUN, A. M., TARDENT, P., ERRICO, J., EBERT, J. D., DeLANNEY, L. E., and ARGYRIS, T. S., 1962. An analysis of the initial reaction in the sequence resulting in homologous splenomegaly in the chick embryo. *Biol. Bull.*, **123**, 366–387.

MURPHY, J. B., 1916. The effect of adult chicken organ grafts on the chick embryo. *J. Exp. Med.*, **24**, 1–6.

MYREN, J., 1956. Injury of liver tissue in mice after single injections of carbon tetrachloride. *Acta Path. Microbiol. Scand.*, *Suppl.*, **116**, 1–64.

MYREN, J., and OYE, I., 1960. Serum proteins in rabbit after single injections of carbon tetrachloride (CCl_4). *Acta Path. Microbiol. Scand.*, **48**, 201–204.

NAETS, J. P., 1958a. Erythropoiesis in nephrectomized dogs. *Nature*, **181**, 1134–1135.

NAETS, J. P., 1958b. The kidney and erythropoiesis. *Nature*, **182**, 1516–1517.

NAETS, J. P., 1958c. Erythropoiesis in nephrectomized dog. *Experientia*, **14**, 74.

NASWITIS, K., 1922. Ueber Auslösung von Zellvermehrungen durch Wundhormone bei hoheren Saugetieren und den Menschen. *Dtsch. Med. Wschr.* **48**, 187–188.

NETTLESHIP, A., 1943. The effects of homologous tissue extracts on rate of epithelization. *Am. J. Clin. Path.*, **13**, 349–351.

NEWBURGH, L. II., 1919. The production of Bright's disease by feeding high protein diets. *Arch. Int. Med.*, **24**, 359–377.

NEWMARK, L. N., HARTROFT, P. M., and EDELMEN, R., 1959. Effects of dietary sodium deficiency and adrenalectomy on renal juxtaglomerular cells and adrenal cortex of the cat. *Anat. Rec.*, **133**, 316.

NORRIS, J. L., BLANCHARD, J., and POVOLNY, C., 1942. Regeneration of rat liver at different ages. *Arch. Path.*, **34**, 208–217.

NOTHNAGEL, H., 1903. Über Anpassung und Ausgleichungen bei pathologischen Zuständen. *Z. Klin. Med.*, **11**, 217–231.

NOVIKOFF, A. B., and POTTER, V. R., 1948. Biochemical studies on regenerating liver. *J. Biol. Chem.*, **173**, 223–232.

NYGAARD, O., and RUSCH, H. P., 1955. Incorporation of radioactive phosphate into nucleic acids of regenerating rat liver. *Cancer Res.*, **15**, 240–245.

OGAWA, K., and NOWINSKI, W. W., 1958. Mitosis stimulating factor in serum of unilaterally nephrectomized rats. *Proc. Soc. Exp. Biol. Med.*, **99**, 350–354.

OGAWA, K., and SINCLAIR, J. G., 1958. Study of mitosis in the compensatory hypertrophic kidney following unilateral nephrectomy in the rat. *Texas Rep. Biol. Med.*, **16**, 215–218.

OGAWA, T., 1962a. Studies on the lens-regeneration in the larval newt lacking pigment of the eye. *Embryologia*, **7**, 95–108.

OGAWA, T., 1962b. Cross reaction of antisera against the chick and newt lens on lenses of other vertebrates. *Embryologia*, **7**, 201–207.

OGAWA, T., 1963. Appearance and localization of lens antigens during the lens regeneration in the adult newt. *Embryologia*, **7**, 279–284.

OGAWA, T., 1964. The influence of lens antibody on the lens regeneration in the larval newt. *Embryologia*, **8**, 146–157.

OKA, A., 1932. Influence of the cell constituents of erythrocytes and various organs on recovery from experimental anemia. I. Experiment of parenteral administration of erythrocytes and bone marrow cell constituents. *Jap. J. Exp. Med.*, **10**, 203–222.

Y

OLIVER, J., 1924. The regulation of renal activity. X. The morphologic study. *Arch. Int. Med.*, **34**, 258–265.

OLIVER, J., 1942. Urinary system. In *Problems of Ageing* (Cowdry, E. V., ed.), Williams and Wilkins Co., Baltimore, Chap. 11, pp. 302–321.

OLIVER, J., BLOOM, F., and MACDOWELL, M., 1941. Structural and functional transformations in the tubular epithelium of the dog's kidney in chronic Bright's disease and their relation to mechanisms of renal compensation and failure. *J. Exp. Med.*, **73**, 141–160.

ONO, M., 1926. An experimental study of the erythropoietic function of the bone marrow. *Sci. Rep. Gov. Inst. Infect. Dis.*, **5**, 471–533.

OPITZ, E., 1951. Increased vascularization of the tissue due to acclimatization to higher altitudes and its significance for oxygen transport. *Exp. Med. Surg.*, **9**, 389–403.

OPPENHEIMER, M. J., and FLOCK, E.V., 1947. Alkaline phosphatase levels in plasma and liver following partial hepatectomy. *Am. J. Physiol.*, **149**, 418–421.

OSBORNE, T. B., MENDEL, L. B., PARK, E. A., and WINTERNITZ, M. C., 1927. Physiological effects of diets unusually rich in protein or inorganic salts. *J. Biol. Chem.*, **71**, 317–350.

O'STEEN, W. K., 1958. Regeneration of the intestine in adult urodeles. *J. Morph.*, **103**, 435–477.

O'STEEN, W. K., 1959. Regeneration and repair of the intestine in *Rana clamitans* larvae. *J. Exp. Zool.*, **141**, 449–476.

O'STEEN, W. K., and WALKER, B. E., 1960. Radioautographic studies of regeneration in the common newt. I. Physiological regeneration. *Anat. Rec.*, **137**, 501–509.

PAPACONSTANTINOU, J., 1959, 1960. Characterization of the lens proteins. In *Annual Report of the Director of the Department of Embryology*, Carnegie Inst. of Wash. Year Books, **58**, 379–385, **59**, 378–380.

PASCHKIS, K. E., 1958. Growth-promoting factors in tissues: A Review. *Cancer Res.*, **18**, 981–991.

PASCHKIS, K. E., and CANTAROW, A., 1958. Pregnancy, tumor growth and liver regeneration. *Cancer Res.*, **18**, 1060–1066.

PASCHKIS, K. E., CANTAROW, A., and GODDARD, J. W., 1957. Growth stimulating actions of liver preparations. *Fed. Proc.*, **16**, 98.

PATT, H. M., and LUCKHARDT, A. B., 1942. Relationship of a low blood calcium to parathyroid secretion. *Endocr.*, **31**, 384–392.

PEARCE, R. M., 1908. The influence of the reduction of kidney substance upon nitrogenous metabolism. *J. Exp. Med.*, **10**, 632–644.

PECKHAM, B. M., and GREEN, R. R., 1952. Experimentally produced granulosa cell tumors in rabbits. *Cancer Res.*, **12**, 654–656.

PENCHARZ, R. I., 1929. Experiments concerning ovarian regeneration in the white rat and white mouse. *J. Exp. Zool.*, **54**, 319–341.

PETERS, R., 1962. Die Mitosehäufigkeit in der Rattenleber in Abhängigkeit von der Tageszeit, dem Gewicht der Tiere und der Ernährung. *Z. Naturf.*, **17B**, 164–169.

PETERSON, D. L., EDGREN, R. A., and JONES, R. C., 1962. The pituitary-blocking effect of various steroids in the hemi-castrate rat. *Am. Zool.*, **2**, 547.

PICKERING, G. W., and PRINZMETAL, M., 1938. Experimental hypertension of renal origin in the rabbit. *Clin. Sci.*, **3**, 357–368.

PIERRE, M., DE BOISSEZON, P., and LOMBARD, C., 1939. Variations pondérales des parathyroïdes externes du lapin et du chien sous l'influence d'injections parentérales répétées de phosphate de sodium et du gluconate de calcium. *C. R. Soc. Biol.*, **130**, 341–342.

PILIERO, S. J., MEDICI, P. T., PANSKY, B., LUHBY, A. L., and GORDON, A. S., 1956. Erythropoietic stimulating effects of plasma extracts from anemic human subjects. *Proc. Soc. Exp. Biol. Med.*, **93**, 302–305.

PISI, E., and CAVALLI, G., 1955. Teneur en acid désoxyribonucléique et activité mitotique dans le rein du rat blanc dans diverses conditions expérimentales. *Arch. Biol.*, **66**, 439–482.

PITCOCK, J. A., and HARTROFT, P. M., 1958. The juxtaglomerular cells in man and their relationship to the level of plasma sodium and to the zona glomerulosa of the adrenal cortex. *Am. J. Path.*, **34**, 863–883.

PLATT, H., 1950. Mitotic activity in the parathyroid glands of the rat following bilateral nephrectomy. *J. Path. Bact.*, **62**, 383–387.

POLITZER, G., 1952. Röntgenstrahlen and Regeneration. *Radiol. Austriaca.*, **5**, 147–158.

POMERAT, G. R., 1940. Mitotic activity in the pituitary of the white rat, with particular reference to its role in the changes which take place in cell populations following castration. *Thesis, Harvard University.*

PONFICK, E., 1890. Experimentelle Beiträge zur Pathologie der Leber. *Virchow's Arch. Path. Anat.*, **119**, 193–240.

POTTER, E. L., SECKEL, H. P. G., and STRYKER, W. A., 1941. Hypertrophy and hyperplasia of the islets of Langerhans of the fetus and of the newborn infant. *Arch. Path.*, **31**, 467–482.

POTTER, V. R., and AUERBACH, V. H., 1959. Adaptive enzymes and feedback mechanisms. *Lab. Invest.*, **8**, 495–509.

PRADO, J. L., and VALLE, J. R., 1952. Grafting of kidneys from rats with desoxycorticosterone hypertension into normotensive receptors. *Acta Physiol. Latino-americana*, **2**, 56–64.

PRICE, J. M., and LAIRD, A. K., 1950. A comparison of the intracellular composition of regenerating liver and induced liver tumors. *Cancer Res.*, **10**, 650–658.

QUASTLER, H., and SHERMAN, F. G., 1959. Cell population kinetics in the intestinal epithelium of the mouse. *Exp. Cell Res.*, **17**, 420–438.

RABINOVITCH, M., ROTHSCHILD, A. A., and JUNQUEIRA, L. C. U., 1952. Nucleic acid phosphorus in submaxillary glands of mice after duct ligation. *J. Biol. Chem.*, **194**, 835–838.

RAMBACH, W. A., ALT, H. L., and COOPER, J. A. D., 1957. The mode of action and nature of a heat-stable plasma erythropoietic factor. *Blood*, **12**, 1101–1113.

RAMBACH, W. A., COOPER, J. A. D., and ALT, H. L., 1958a. Purification of erythropoietin by ion-exchange chromatography. *Proc. Soc. Exp. Biol. Med.*, **98**, 602–604.

RAMBACH, W. A., SHAW, R. A., COOPER, J. A. D., and ALT, H. L., 1958b. Acid hydrolysis of erythropoietin. *Proc. Soc. Exp. Biol. Med.*, **99**, 482–483.

RAYNAUD, A., and FRILLEY, M., 1947. Destruction du cerveau des embryons de souris au treizième jour de la gestation, par irradiation au moyen des rayons X. *C. R. Soc. Biol.*, **141**, 658–662.

REICHLIN, S., 1957. The effect of hypothalamic lesions upon the thyroid response to partial thyroidectomy. *Endocr.*, **60**, 567–569.

REISSMANN, K. R., 1950. Studies on the mechanism of erythropoietic stimulation in parabiotic rats during hypoxia. *Blood*, **5**, 372–380.

REITER, R. J., and McCREIGHT, C. E., 1963. Autoradiographic study of experimental renal hyperplasia with tritiated thymidine. *Anat. Rec.*, **145**, 274.

RENSCH, B., 1948. Histological changes correlated with evolutionary changes in body size. *Evolution*, **2**, 218–230.

RENSCH, B., 1959. *Evolution Above the Species Level*. Methuen, London.

REYER, R. W., 1950. An experimental study of lens regeneration in *Triturus viridescens viridescens*. I. Regeneration of a lens after lens extirpation in embryos and larvae of different ages. *J. Exp. Zool.*, **107**, 217–268.

REYER, R. W., 1954. Regeneration of the lens in the amphibian eye. *Quart. Rev. Biol.*, **29**, 1–46.

REYER, R. W., 1956. Lens regeneration from homoplastic and heteroplastic implants of dorsal iris into the eye chamber of *Triturus viridescens* and *Amblystoma punctatum*. *J. Exp. Zool.*, **133**, 145–190.

REYER, R. W., 1962. Regeneration in the amphibian eye. In *Regeneration* (Rudnick, D., ed.), The Ronald Press Co., New York, Ch. 8, pp. 211–265.

REYNOLDS, S. R. M., 1949. *Physiology of the Uterus*. Paul B. Hoeber, New York.

RIBBERT, H., 1895. Beiträge zur kompensatorischen Hypertrophie und zur Regeneration. *Atch. EntwMech. Org.*, **1**, 69–90.

RICHARDS, A. N., and SCHMIDT, C. F., 1924. A description of the glomerular circulation in the frog's kidney and observations concerning the action of adrenalin and various other substances upon it. *Am. J. Physiol.*, **71**, 178–208.

ROBERTS, J. R., and WEARN, J. T., 1941. Quantitative changes in the capillary-muscle relationship in human hearts during normal growth and hypertrophy. *Am. Heart. J.*, **21**, 617–633.

ROBERTS, S., and WHITE, A., 1949. Studies on the origin of the serum proteins. *J. Biol. Chem.*, **180**, 505–516.

ROBERTSON, O. H., 1917. The effects of experimental plethora on blood production. *J. Exp. Med.*, **26**, 221–237.

ROESSLE, R., and ROULET, F., 1932. *Mass und Zahl in der Pathologie*. J. Springer, Berlin.

ROGERS, A. E., SHAKA, J. A., PECHET, G., and MacDONALD, R. A., 1961. Regeneration of the liver: Absence of a "humoral factor" affecting hepatic regeneration in parabiotic rats. *Am. J. Path.*, **39**, 561–578.

ROGOFF, J. N., and STEWART, G. N., 1927. Studies on adrenal insufficiency. III. The influence of pregnancy upon the survival period in adrenalectomized dogs. *Am. J. Physiol.*, **79**, 508–535.

ROLLASON, H. D., 1949. Compensatory hypertrophy of the kidney of the young rat with special emphasis on the role of cellular hyperplasia. *Anat. Rec.*, **104**, 263–286.

ROLLASON, H. D., 1961. Growth and differentiation of the fetal kidney following bilateral nephrectomy of the pregnant rat at $18\frac{1}{2}$ days of gestation. *Anat. Rec.*, **141**, 183–193.

ROSE, S. M., 1952. A hierarchy of self-limiting reactions as the basis of cellular differentiation and growth control. *Am. Nat.*, **86**, 337–354.

ROSE, S. M., 1957. Cellular interaction during differentiation. *Biol. Rev.*, **32**, 351–382.

ROSEN, V. J., Jr., and COLE, L. J., 1960. Radiosensitivity of mouse kidney undergoing compensatory hypertrophy. *Nature*, **187**, 612–614.

ROSENTHAL, O., ROGERS, C. S., VARS, H. M., and FERGUSON, C. C., 1951. Argenase, adenosine pyrophosphatase and rhodanase in regenerating rat liver. *J. Biol. Chem.*, **189**, 831–843.

ROSSE, W. F., and GURNEY, C. W., 1959. Studies on erythropoiesis. X. The use of bone marrow tissue culture in demonstrating erythropoietin. *J. Lab. Clin. Med.*, **53**, 446–456.

ROSSI, V., and CAMPAGNARI, E., 1959. Il comportamento del DNA nucleare nelle cellule glomerulari del rene in ipertrofia compensatoria. *Riv. Istach. Norm. Pathol.*, **5**, 131–142.

ROUS, P., and LARIMORE, L. D., 1920. Relation of the portal blood to liver maintenance. A demonstration of liver atrophy conditional on compensation. *J. Exp. Med.*, **31**, 609–632.

ROWLANDS, I. W., 1934. The effect of unilateral castration on the remaining testis of the mouse. *J. Exp. Biol.*, **11**, 402–407.

ROYCE, P. C., 1963. Inhibition of renal growth following unilateral nephrectomy in the rat. *Proc. Soc. Exp. Biol. Med.*, **113**, 1046–1049.

RUPP, J. J., 1952. Action of liver on thyroid hormone following intrasplenic implantation of the thyroid. *Endocr.*, **51**, 306–310.

SACERDOTTI, C., 1896. Ueber die compensatorische Hypertrophie der Nieren. *Virchow's Arch. Path. Anat.*, **146**, 267–297.

SAETREN, H., 1956. A principle of auto-regulation of growth. Production of organ specific mitose-inhibitors in kidney and liver. *Exp. Cell Res.*, **11**, 229–232.

SALGADO, E., 1954. Effect of thyroidectomy on hypertension, nephrosclerosis and cardiac lesions produced by desoxycorticosterone acetate (DCA) treatment in the rat. *Endocr.*, **55**, 377–386.

SANDERS, A. G., and FLOREY, H. W., 1940. The effects of the removal of lymphoid tissue. *Brit. J. Exp. Path.*, **21**, 275–287.

SANDERS, F. K., and YOUNG, J. Z., 1946. The influence of peripheral connection on the diameter of regenerating nerve fibres. *J. Exp. Biol.*, **22**, 203–212.

SANTLER, J. E., 1957. Growth in the cell populations of the thyroid gland of rats treated with thiouracil. *J. Endocr.*, **15**, 151–161.

SAPHIR, O., 1927. The state of the glomerulus in experimental hypertrophy of the kidneys of rabbits. *Am. J. Path.*, **3**, 329–342.

SATO, A., 1963. Some observations on induced polyovulation and superpregnancy in mature mice. *Embryologia*, **7**, 285–294.

SCHAFFENBURG, C. A., MASSON, G. M. C., and CORCORAN, A. C., 1954. Renin inhibition of compensatory renal hypertrophy. *Proc. Soc. Exp. Biol. Med.*, **87**, 469–473.

SCHALM, L., BAX, H. R., and MANSENS, B. J., 1956. Atrophy of the liver after occlusion of the bile ducts or portal vein and compensatory hypertrophy of the unoccluded portion and its clinical importance. *Gastroenterology*, **31**, 131–155.

SCHILLER, H., 1923. Regeneration of resected urinary bladders in rabbits. *Surg. Gynec. Obstet.*, **36**, 24–26.

SCHILLING, T., 1905. Prüfung der Nierenfunktion nach Nephrektomie. *Arch. Exp. Path. Pharmakol.*, **52**, 140–172.

SCHOELLER, W., and GEHRKE, M., 1933. Über Hemmungsfaktoren und den Mechanismus der Wirkung gegengeschlechtlicher Sexualhormon auf die Entwicklung der Keimdrüsen. *Biochem. Z.*, **264**, 352–356.

SCHMIDT, J. G., and HOFFMAN, R. G., 1954. Effects of ACTH on pregnant monkeys and their offspring. *Anat. Rec.*, **118**, 351–352.

SCHMIEDT, E., 1951. Zellkerngrösse und sogenannte kompensatorische Hypertrophie der Mäuseniere. *Z. Mikr. Anat. Forsch.*, **57**, 249–275.

SCHULTZE, B., and OEHLERT, W., 1960. Autoradiographic investigation of incorporation of H^3-thymidine into cells of the rat and mouse. *Science*, **131**, 737–738.

SELYE, H., 1940. Compensatory atrophy of the adrenals. *J. Am. Med. Assoc.*, **115**, 2246–2252.

SEYLE, H., 1941. Effect of hypophysectomy on morphological appearance of kidney and on renotrophic action of steriod hormones. *J. Urol.*, **46**, 110–131.

SELYE, H., 1946. Transformation of kidney into an exclusively endocrine organ. *Nature*, **158**, 131.

SELYE, H., BROWNE, T. S., and COLLIP, J. B., 1936. Effect of large doses of progesterone in the female rat. *Proc. Soc. Exp. Biol. Med.*, **34**, 472–474.

SELYE, H., and McKEOWN, T., 1934. On the regenerative power of the uterus. *J. Angt.*, **69**, 79–81.

SELYE, H., and STONE, H., 1946. Pathogenesis of the cardiovascular and renal changes which usually accompany malignant hypertension. *J. Urol.*, **56**, 399–419.

SELYE, H., STONE, H., NIELSEN, K., and LEBLOND, C. P., 1945. Studies concerning the effects of various hormones upon renal structure. *Canad. Med. Assn. J.*, **52**, 571–682.

SELYE, H., VEILLEUX, R., and CANTIN, M., 1961. Excessive stimulation of salivary gland growth by isoproterenol. *Science*, **133**, 44–45.

SEMENOVA, N. F., 1961. Cellular activation following injury of the kidneys. *Bull. Exp. Biol. Med. (English translation)*, **51**, 122–126.

SHIH, H. E., 1934. Absence of compensatory hypertrophy of Cowper's glands in the albino rat. *Proc. Soc. Exp. Biol. Med.*, **31**, 423–424.

SHOCK, N., 1962. The physiology of aging. *Sci. Amer.*, **206**, 100–110.

SIMMLER, G. M., 1947. The effects of wing bud extirpation on the brachial sympathetic ganglia of the chick embryo. *J. Exp. Zool.*, **110**, 247–257.

SIMONSEN, M., 1950. The endocrine kidney. *Acta Path. Microbiol. Scand.*, **27**, 520–536.

SIMONSEN, M., 1957. The impact on the developing embryo and the newborn animal of adult homologous cells. *Acta Path. Microbiol. Scand.*, **40**, 480–500.

SIMPSON, D. P., 1960. An investigation of the nature and stimulus of "compensatory hypertrophy" of the kidney. *Fed. Proc.*, **19**, 361.

SIMPSON, G. E. C., and FINCKH, E. S., 1963. The pattern of regeneration of rat liver after repeated partial hepatectomies. *J. Path. Bact.*, **86**, 361–370.

SIMPSON, M. E., LI, C. H., and EVANS, H. M., 1946. Absence of renotrophic action of pure adrenocorticotrophic hormone (ACTH). *Endocr.*, **39**, 78.

SINGER, M., 1960. Nervous mechanisms in the regeneration of body parts in vertebrates. In *Developing Cell Systems and their Control* (Rudnick, D., ed.), Ronald Press, New York, Ch. 6, pp. 115–133.

SKELTON, F. R., 1953. The production of hypertension, nephrosclerosis and cardiac lesions by methylandrostenediol treatment in the rat. *Endocr.*, **53**, 492–505.

SKÖLD, O., 1960. Enzymes of uracil metabolism in tissues with different growth characteristics. *Biochem. Biophys. Acta*, **44**, 1–12.

SLAUNWHITE, W. R., Jr., MIRAND, E. A., and PRENTICE, T. C., 1957. Probable polypeptidic nature of erythropoietin. *Proc. Soc. Exp. Biol. Med.*, **96**, 616–619.

SMITH, A. H., and MOISE, T. S., 1927. Diet and tissue growth. IV. The rate of compensatory renal enlargement in the white rat. *J. Exp. Med.*, **45**, 263–276.

SMITH, C. H., SCHULMAN, I., ANDO, R. E., and STERN, G., 1955. Studies in Mediterranean (Cooley's) anemia. II. The suppression of hematopoiesis by transfusions. *Blood*, **10**, 707–717.

SMITH, P. E., 1930. Hypophysectomy and a replacement therapy in the rat. *Am. J. Anat.*, **45**, 205–273.

SMITH, P. E., 1955. The endocrine glands in hypophysectomized pregnant rhesus monkeys (Macaca mulatta) with special reference to the adrenal glands. *Endocr.*, **56**, 271–284.

SMITHCORS, J. F., 1945. Effects of thiouracil on the mammary gland. *Proc. Soc. Exp. Biol. Med.*, **59**, 197–200.

SMYTHE, R. L., and MOORE, R. O., 1958. A study of possible humoral factors in liver regeneration in the rat. *Surgery*, **44**, 561–569.

SOLOMON, J. B., 1961. The onset and maturation of the graft-versus-host reaction in chickens. *J. Emb. Exp. Morph.*, **9**, 355–369.

SOLOPAEV, B. P., 1957. Bile secretion after partial resection of the liver of dogs with an exteriorized common bile duct. *Bull. Exp. Biol. Med. (English translation)*, **43**, 628–631.

SPERBER, I., 1944. Studies on the mammalian kidney. *Zoologiska Bidrag Fran Uppsala*, **22**, 249–432.

STANDISH, S. M., and SHAFER, W. G., 1957. Serial histologic effects of rat submaxillary and sublingual salivary gland duct and blood vessel ligation. *J. Dent. Res.*, **36**, 866–879.

STEEN, T. P., and Thornton, C. S., 1963. Tissue interaction in amputated aneurogenic limbs of Ambystoma larvae. *J. Exp. Zool.*, **154**, 207–221.

STEPHENSON, G. W., 1932. Experimental pathology of the liver. IX. Restoration of the liver after partial hepatectomy and partial ligation of the portal vein. *Arch. Path.*, **14**, 484–490.

STEPHENSON, K. L., 1952. The production of ectopic cartilage. *Plast. Reconstr. Surg.*, **9**, 302–320.

STEUART, C. D., 1958. A humoral factor regulating organ regeneration. In *Annual Report of the Director of the Department of Embryology*, Carnegie Inst. of Wash. Year Book 57, pp. 347–349.

STEVENS, C. E. R., DAOUST, R., and LEBLOND, C. P., 1953. Rate of synthesis of desoxyribonucleic acid and mitotic rate in liver and intestine. *J. Biol. Chem.*, **202**, 177–186.

STEVENS, L. C., 1955. Survival of ovarian grafts in castrate and unilaterally ovariectomized female mice. *Transpl. Bull.*, **2**, 45–46.

STICH, H. F., 1960. Regulation of mitotic rate in mammalian organisms. *Ann. N. Y. Acad. Sci.*, **90**, 603–609.

STICH, H. F., and FLORIAN, M. L., 1958. The presence of a mitosis inhibitor in the serum and liver of adult rats. *Canad. J. Biochem. Physiol.*, **36**, 855–859.

STICKNEY, J. C., and VAN LIERE, E. J., 1953. Acclimatization to low oxygen tension. *Physiol. Rev.*, **33**, 13–34.

STOHLMAN, F., Jr., 1961. Humoral regulation of erythropoiesis. VI. Mechanisms of action of erythropoietine in the irradiated animal. *Proc. Soc. Exp. Biol. Med.*, **107**, 751–754.

STOHLMAN, F., Jr., and BRECHER, G., 1956. Stimulation of erythropoiesis in sublethally irradiated rats by a plasma factor. *Proc. Soc. Exp. Biol. Med.*, **91**, 1–4.

STONE, L. S., 1945. Heteroplastic lens grafts related to factors inhibiting lens regeneration in *Triturus*. *Proc. Soc. Exp. Biol. Med.*, **60**, 10.

STONE, L. S., 1950a. Neural retina degeneration followed by regeneration from surviving retinal pigment cells in grafted adult salamander eyes. *Anat. Rec.*, **106**, 89–110.

STONE, L. S., 1950b. The role of retinal pigment cells in regenerating neural retinae of adult salamander eyes. *J. Exp. Zool.*, **113**, 9–32.

STONE, L. S., 1952. An experimental study of the inhibition and release of lens regeneration in adult eyes of *Triturus v. viridescens*. *J. Exp. Zool.*, **121**, 181–224.

STONE, L. S., 1953. An experimental analysis of lens regeneration. *Amer. J. Ophthal.*, **36**, 31–39.

STONE, L. S., 1954a. Further experiments on lens regeneration in eyes of the adult newt, *Triturus v. viridescens*. *Anat. Rec.*, **120**, 599–624.

STONE, L. S., 1954b. Lens regeneration in secondary pupils experimentally produced in eyes of the adult newt, *Triturus v. viridescens*. *J. Exp. Zool.*, **127**, 463–492.

STONE, L. S., 1955. Regeneration of the iris and lens from retina pigment cells in adult newt eyes. *J. Exp. Zool.*, **129**, 505–534.

STONE, L. S., 1957. Further experiments on lens regeneration from retina pigment cells in adult newt eyes. *J. Exp. Zool.*, **136**, 75–88.

STONE, L. S., 1958a. Inhibition of lens regeneration in newt eyes by isolating the dorsal iris from the neural retina. *Anat. Rec.*, **131**, 151–172.

STONE, L. S., 1958b. Lens regeneration in adult newt eyes related to retina pigment cells and the neural retina factor. *J. Exp. Zool.*, **139**, 69–84.

STONE, L. S., 1959a. Experiments testing the capacity of iris to regenerate neural retina in eyes of adult newts. *J. Exp. Zool.*, **142**, 285–308.

STONE, L. S., 1959b. Regeneration of the retina, iris, and lens. In *Regeneration in Vertebrates* (Thornton, C. S., ed.), Univ. of Chicago Press, Chicago, pp. 3–14.

STONE, L.S., 1963. Experiments dealing with the role played by the aqueous humor and retina in lens regeneration of adult newts. *J. Exp. Zool.*, **153**, 197–207.

STONE, L. S., and GALLAGHER, S. B., 1958. Lens regeneration restored to iris membranes when grafted to neural retina environment after cultivation *in vitro. J. Exp. Zool.*, **139**, 247–262.

STONE, L. S., and GRIFFITH, B. H., 1954. Regeneration of the iris and lens in eyes of adult *Triturus v. viridescens. J. Exp. Zool.*, **127**, 153–180.

STONE, L. S., and STEINITZ, H., 1953. The regeneration of lenses in eyes with intact and regenerating retina in adult *Triturus v. viridescens. J. Exp. Zool.*, **124**, 435–468.

STONE, L. S., and STEINITZ, H., 1957. Regeneration of neural retina and lens from retina pigment cell grafts in adult newts. *J. Exp. Zool.*, **135**,301–318.

STONE, L. S., and VULTEE, J. H., 1949. Inhibition and release of lens regeneration in the dorsal iris of *Triturus v. viridescens. Anat. Rec.*, **103**, 560–561.

STOTSENBURG, J. M., 1913. The effect of spaying and semi-spaying young albino rats (*Mus norvegicus albinus*) on the growth in body weight and body length. *Anat. Rec.*, **7**, 183–194.

STOWELL, R. E., 1948. Nucleic acid and cytologic changes in regenerating rat liver. *Arch. Path.*, **46**, 164–178.

STRAUBE, R. L., and PATT, H. M., 1961. Effect of local X-irradiation on growth capacity of mouse kidney. *Proc. Soc. Exp. Biol. Med.*, **108**, 808–810.

SULKIN, N. M., 1949. Cytologic studies of the remaining kidney following unilateral nephrectomy in the rat. *Anat. Rec.*, **105**, 95–112.

SULKIN, N. M., 1950. Histochemical analysis of ribonucleic acid in the normal and hyperplastic kidney of the rat. *Anat. Rec.*, **106**, 290.

SUNDELL, B., 1957. Hormonal influence on testis grafts in the spleen of rats. *Acta Endocr.*, **25**, 419–426.

SURVIS, J., KENNEDY, R., and HASS, G. M., 1962. Humoral factors in liver regeneration. *Fed. Proc.*, **21**, 301.

SWANN, M. M., 1958. The control of cell division: A review. II. Special mechanisms. *Cancer Res.*, **18**, 1118–1160.

SWICK, R. W., KOCH, A. L., and HANDA, D. T., 1956. The measurement of nucleic acid turnover in rat liver. *Arch. Biochem. Biophys.*, **63**, 226–242.

SWIFT, H., 1953. Nucleoproteins in the mitotic cycle. *Texas Rep. Biol. Med.*, **11**, 755–774.

SWINYARD, C. A., and BRUNER, H. D., 1940. Compensatory hypertrophy of the dog adrenal gland following unilateral adrenalectomy. *Endocr.*, **26**, 886–890.

TABER, E., CLAYTOR, M., KNIGHT, J., FLOWERS, J., GAMBRELL, D., and AYERS, C., 1958a. Some effects of sex hormones and homologous gonadotrophins on the early development of the rudimentary gonad in fowl. *Endocr.*, **63**, 435–448.

z

TABER, E., CLAYTOR, M., KNIGHT, J., GAMBRELL, D., FLOWERS, J., and
AYERS, C., 1958b. Ovarian stimulation in the immature fowl by desiccated
avian pituitaries. *Endocr.*, **62**, 84–89.

TABER, E., KNIGHT, J., FLOWERS, J., GAMBRELL, D., and CLAYTOR, M., 1955.
Hormonal inhibition of medullary development of the right gonad in
sinistrally ovariectomized brown leghorn fowl. *Anat. Rec.*, **122**, 451–452.

TABER, E., and SALLEY, K. W., 1954. The effects of sex hormones on the
development of the right gonad in female fowl. *Endocr.*, **54**, 415–424.

TABER, E., SALLEY, K. W., and KNIGHT, J. S., 1956. The effects of hypo-
adrenalism and chronic inanition on the development of the rudimentary
gland in sinistrally ovariectomized fowl. *Anat. Rec.*, **126**, 177–193.

TAGAKI, Y., HECHT, L. I., and POTTER, B. R., 1956. Nucleic acid metabolism
in regenerating rat liver. II. Studies on growing rats. *Cancer Res.*, **16**,
994–998.

TAKANO, K., 1958. On the lens-effect in the Wolffian lens regeneration in
Triturus pyrrhogaster. Mie Med. J., **8**, 385–403.

TAKANO, K., YOSHIDA, Y., OHASHI, T., OGASAWARA, T., TAKEUCHI, A.,
MASAKI, H., MIYAZAKI, A., and MIKAMI, Y., 1957. Experimental analysis
of the effect of lens upon the Wolffian lens regeneration in adults of the
newt, *Triturus phyrrhogaster. Mie Med. J.*, **7**, 257–271.

TAKATA, C., ALBRIGHT, J. F., and YAMADA, T., 1963. Lens antigens in transformation of adult newt iris into the lens. *Amer. Soc. Cell Biol., Third
Annual Meeting, Abstract No. 167:* 69A–70A.

TAKATA, K., 1952. Ribonucleic acid and lens-regeneration. *Experientia*, **8**,
217–222.

TEIR, H., 1949. On the sizes of the nuclei in the glandula infraorbitalis of
the white rat. *Acta Path.*, **26**, 620–635.

TEIR, H., 1950. Remarkable mitotic activity after parenteral application of
tissue extract. *Acta Path.*, **27**, 645–646.

TEIR, H., 1951. Experimental alterations of cell size and mitotic activity in
the outer orbital gland of the white rat. I. Patho-physiological investigations. *Soc. Sci. Fenn. Comm. Biol.*, **13**, 17–32.

TEIR, H., 1952a. Experimental alterations of cell size and mitotic activity in
the outer orbital gland of the white rat. IV. Influence of parenterally
applied extracts of outer orbital gland. *Acta Path. Microbiol. Scand.*, **30**,
158–183.

TEIR, H., 1952b. Experimental alterations of cell size and mitotic activity in
the outer orbital gland of the white rat. V. Observations on the chemical
and biological properties of the mitosis stimulating agent in homologous
tissue extracts. *Growth*, **16**, 85–108.

TEIR, H., and ISOTALO, A., 1954. Influence of cortisone on mitosis. III. Effect
of simultaneously applied cortisone and cell suspensions. *Ann. Med. Exp.
Biol. Fenn.*, **32**, 1–4.

TEIR, H., LARMO, A., ALHO, A., and BLOMQVIST, K., 1957. Influence of
intraperitoneally injected homogenates of the outer orbital gland and the
liver on RNA and DNA in these organs in rats. *Exp. Cell Res.*, **13**, 147–157.

TEIR, H., and NYSTROM, B., 1962. Organ homogenates to stimulate wound
healing in rats. Parenteral application. *Arch. Path.*, **74**, 499–508.

TEIR, H., and RAVANTI, K., 1953. Mitotic activity and growth factors in the liver of the white rat. *Exp. Cell Res.*, **5**, 500–507.

TEIR, H., and SUNDELL, B., 1953. Experimental alterations of cell size and mitotic activity in the outer orbital gland of the white rat. VIII. Influence of extirpation and of intra-abdominal implantation of outer orbital gland tissue. *Acta Path. Microbiol. Scand.*, **32**, 492–499.

TELKKÄ, A., and TEIR, H., 1955. Influence of thymus suspension on mitotic rate in the thymus, liver, and outer orbital gland of rat. *Acta Path. Microbiol. Scand.*, **36**, 323–326.

TERASAKI, P. I., 1959. Identification of the type of blood-cell responsible for the graft-versus-host reaction in chicks. *J. Emb. Exp. Morph.*, **7**, 394–408.

THOMAS, E. D., 1955. *In vitro* studies of erythropoiesis. Effect of normal serum on heme synthesis and oxygen consumption by bone marrow. *Blood*, **10**, 600–611.

THOMAS, O. L., 1945. The vascular bed in normal and thiourea activated thyroid glands of the rat. *Anat. Rec.*, **93**, 23–45.

THOMPSON, D. W., 1917. *On Growth and Form.* The Univeristy Press, Cambridge.

THOMPSON, J. F., and MOSS, E. M., 1955. Effect of adrenalectomy on tryptophan peroxidase, adenosine deaminase, and arginase content of regenerating rat liver. *Proc. Soc. Exp. Biol. Med.*, **89**, 230–233.

THORNTON, C. S., 1954. The relation of epidermal innervation to limb regeneration in Amblystoma larvae. *J. Exp. Zool.*, **127**, 577–602.

TITOVA, I. I., 1957. A study of the antigenic properties of the crystalline lens in Wolffian regeneration. *Bull. Exp. Biol. Med. URSS*, **43**, 70–74.

TOBIAN, L., 1960. Interrelationship of electrolytes, juxtaglomerular cells and hypertension. *Physiol. Rev.*, **40**, 280–312.

TOBIAN, L., THOMPSON, J., TWEDT, R., and JANECEK, J., 1958. The granulation of juxtaglomerular cells in renal hypertension, desoxycorticosterone and post-desoxycorticosterone hypertension, adrenal regeneration hypertension, and adrenal insufficiency. *J. Clin. Invest.*, **37**, 660–671.

TOBIAN, L., TOMBOULIAN, A., and JANECEK, J., 1959. The effect of high perfusion pressures on the granulation of juxtaglomerular cells in an isolated kidney. *J. Clin. Invest.*, **38**, 605–610.

TOBIN, C. E., 1939. The influence of adrenal destruction in the pre-natal development of the albino rat. *Am. J. Anat.*, **65**, 151–177.

TOHÁ, J., ESKUCHE, I., ABARCA, F., SALVATORE, F., and HODGSON, G., 1955. Chemical properties of a plasma factor accelerating hemoglobin recovery in bled rabbits. *Nature*, **175**, 167–168.

TROTTER, N. L., 1961. The effect of partial hepatectomy on subcutaneously transplanted hepatomas in mice. *Cancer Res.*, **21**, 778–782.

TSUBOI, K. K., STOWELL, R. E., and LEE, C. S., 1951. Chemical alterations induced in mouse liver following a single feeding of carbon tetrachloride. *Cancer Res.*, **11**, 87–93.

TSUBOI, K. K., YOKOYAMA, H. O. STOWELL, R. E., and WILSON, M. E., 1954. The chemical composition of regenerating mouse liver. *Arch. Biochem. Biophys.*, **48**, 275–292

TUCKER, H. A., and REECE, R. P., 1963. Nucleic acid content of rat mammary gland after teat ligation. *Proc. Soc. Exp. Biol. Med.*, **113**, 717–720.

TUMANISHVILI, G. D., DZHANDIERI, K. M., and SVANIDZE, I. K., 1956. Specific stimulation of the growth of the organs of the chicken by tissue extracts. *Doklady Adak. Nauk SSSR*, **106**, 1107–1109.

TURNER, M. L., and HALL, V. E., 1943. The effect of removal of a large part of the lymphoid system on the weight of the portion remaining *in situ*. *Anat. Rec.*, **85**, 401–412.

TWITTY, V. C., 1940. Size-controlling factors. *Growth, Suppl., Second Symposium on Development and Growth*, pp. 109–120.

TWOMBLY, G. H., MEISEL, D., and STOUT, H. P., 1949. Leydig cell tumours induced experimentally in the rat. *Cancer*, **2**, 884–892.

UHR, J, W., and BAUMANN, J. B., 1961. I. The suppression of antibody formation by passively administered antibody. *J. Exp. Med.*, **113**, 935–957.

VAN ALTEN, P. J., and FENNELL, R. A., 1959. The effects of chorioallantoic grafts on the developing chick embryo. I. Studies on weight and histology of homologous and heterologous tissues. *J. Emb. Exp. Morph.*, **7**, 459–475.

VAN DETH, J. H. M. G., 1940. Induction et régénération du cristallin chez l'embryon de la poule. *Acta Neerlandica Morph.*, **3**, 219–236.

VAN DYKE, D. C., CONTOPOULOS, A. N., WILLIAMS, B. S., SIMPSON, M. E., LAWRENCE, J. H., and EVANS, H. M., 1954. Hormonal factors influencing erythropoiesis. *Acta Haemat.*, **11**, 203–222.

VAN DYKE, D. C., GARCIA, J. F., and LAWRENCE, J. H., 1957a. Concentration of highly potent erythropoietic activity from urine of anaemic patients. *Proc. Soc. Exp. Biol. Med.*, **96**, 541–544.

VAN DYKE, D. C., HUFF, R. L., and EVANS, H. M., 1948. The efficiency of the vascular union in parabiosis. *Stanford Med. Bull.*, **6**, 271–275.

VAN DYKE, D. C., SIMPSON, M. E., CONTOPOULOS, A. N., and EVANS, H. M., 1957b. The separate existence of the pituitary erythropoietic hormone. *Blood*, **12**, 539–548.

VAN LANCKER, J. L., and BORISON, H. L., 1961. Incorporation of tritium-labelled thymidine into rat liver deoxyribonucleic acid after exchange transfusion with blood from partially hepatectomized rats. *Biochem. Biophys. Acta*, **51**, 171–172.

VAN LANCKER, J. L., and SEMPOUX, D. G., 1959. Incorporation of orotic acid-C^{14} in rat liver DNA after partial hepatectomy of one partner of a parabiotic pair. *Arch. Biochem. Biophys.*, **80**, 337–345.

VAN WAGENEN, G., and GARDNER, W. V., 1950. Functional intrasplenic ovarian transplants in monkeys. *Endocr.*, **46**, 265–272.

VERZÁR, F., 1954. Compensatory hypertrophy of kidney and adrenal in the life-span of rats. In *Old Age in the Modern World*. E. S. Livingston, Ltd., Edinburgh.

VERZÁR, F., and HÜGIN, F., 1957. Einfluss des Alters auf die Entwicklung der Arbeitshypertrophie von Organen. Kompensatorische Hypertrophie der Niere und der Nebenniere. *Acta Anat.*, **30**, 918–927.

VON DER DECKEN, A., and HULTIN, T., 1958. The activity of microsomes from regenerating rat liver in amino acid incorporating systems. *Exp. Cell Res.*, **14**, 88–96.

VOUTILAINEN, A., HOPSU, V. K., and TEIR, H., 1959. Effects of intraperitoneal injections of normal and X-ray irradiated outer orbital gland tissue
on the mitotic activity in this organ in young rats. *Acta Path. Microbiol.
Scand.*, **45**, 49–52.

VYAZOV, O. E., and SAZHINA, M. V., 1961. Immuno-biological study of the
process of lens regeneration in *Triton taeniatus. Zh. Obsch. Biol.*, **22**, 305–
310.

VYASOV, O. E., VOLKOVA, L. S., TITOVA, I. I., and MURASHOVA, A. I., 1962.
Humoral relationship between mother and fetus in clinic and experiment.
Ves. Akad. Med. Nauk, SSSR, **17**, 23. (English translation: *Fed Proc.*,
22, T964–T968).

WALKER, B. E., 1959. Radioautographic observations on regeneration of
transitional epithelium. *Texas Rep. Biol. Med.*, **17**, 375–384.

WALAAS, E., and WALAAS, O., 1944. Studies on the compensatory hypertrophy of the fetal adrenal glands in the albino rat, produced by adrenalectomy during pregnancy. *Acta Path. Microbiol. Scand.*, **21**, 640–672.

WALTER, F., and ADDIS, T., 1939. Organ work and organ weight. *J. Exp.
Med.*, **69**, 467–484.

WALTER, H., ALLMAN, D. W., and MAHLER, H. R., 1956. Influence of adult
tissue homogenates on formation of similar embryonic proteins. *Science*,
124, 1251–1252.

WARBURTON, F. E., 1955. Feedback in development and its evolutionary
significance. *Am. Nat.*, **89**, 129–140.

WEARN, J. T., 1941. Alterations in the heart accompanying growth and
hypertrophy. *Bull. Johns Hopkins Hosp.*, **68**, 363–374.

WEINBREN, K., 1953. The effect of bile duct obstruction in regeneration of
the rat's liver. *Brit. J. Exp. Path.*, **34**, 280–289.

WEINBREN, K., 1959. Regeneration of the liver. *Gastroenterology*, **37**, 657–668.

WEINBREN, K., and BILLING, B. H., 1956. Hepatic clearance of bilirubin as
an index of cellular function in the regenerating rat liver. *Brit. J. Exp.
Path.*, **37**, 195–204.

WEINBREN, K., and FITSCHEN, W., 1959. The influence of sodium fluoro-
acetate on regeneration of the rat's liver. *Brit. J. Exp. Path.*, **40**, 107.

WEISS, P., 1952. Self-regulation of organ growth by its own products.
Science, **115**, 487–488.

WEISS, P., 1955. Specificity in growth control. In *Biological Specificity and
Growth* (Butler, E. G., ed.), pp. 195–206.

WEISS, P., 1959. In *Mitogenesis* (Ducoff, H. S., and Ehret, C. F., eds.), U. of
Chicago Press, pp. 86–87.

WEISS, P., and JAMES, R., 1955. Skin metaplasia *in vitro* induced by brief
exposure to vitamin A. *Exp. Cell Res. Suppl.*, **3**, 381–394.

WEISS, P., and KAVANAU, J. L., 1957. A model of growth and growth control
in mathematical terms. *J. Gen. Physiol.*, **41**, 1–47.

WEISS, P., and MATOLTSY, A. G., 1959. Wound healing in chick embryos *in
vivo* and *in vitro. Devel. Biol.*, **1**, 302–326.

WEISS, P., and WANG, H., 1941. Growth response of the liver of embryonic
chick hosts to the incorporation in the area vasculosa of liver and other
organ fragments. *Anat. Rec.*, **79**, 62–63

WELLS, H., 1960. Inhibition by surgical procedures and drugs of the accelerated growth of salivary glands of rats. *Am. J. Physiol.*, **199**, 1037–1040.

WELLS, H., 1962. Submandibular salivary gland weight increase by administration of isoproterenol to rats. *Am. J. Physiol.*, **202**, 425–428.

WELLS, H., and MUNSON, P. L., 1960. Experimental enlargement of the submandibular salivary glands of rats. *Am. J. Physiol.*, **199**, 63–66.

WELLS, H., ZACKIN, S. J., GOLDHABER, P., and MUNSON, P. L., 1959. Increase in weight of the submandibular salivary glands of rats following periodic amputation of the erupted portion of the incisor teeth. *Am. J. Physiol.*, **196**, 827–830.

WELLS, H., HANDELMAN, C., and MILGRAM, E., 1961. Regulation by the sympathetic nervous system of the accelerated growth of salivary glands of rats. *Am. J. Physiol.*, **201**, 707–710.

WELLS, L. J., 1946a. Effects of injections of equine gonadotrophin upon the gonads and adrenals of fetal rats. *Proc. Soc. Exp. Biol. Med.*, **62**, 250–254.

WELLS, L. J., 1946b. Experimental acceleration of secretion of urine in fetal rats. *Proc. Soc. Exp. Biol. Med.*, **62**, 287–289.

WELLS, L. J., 1946c. Effects of androgen upon reproductive organs of normal and castrated fetuses with note on adrenalectomy. *Proc. Soc. Exp. Biol. Med.*, **63**, 417–419.

WELLS, L. J., 1946d. Observations on secretion of urine in fetal rats. *Anat. Rec.*, **94**, 504.

WELLS, L. J., 1947. Progress of studies designed to determine whether the fetal hypophysis produces hormones that influence development. *Anat. Rec.*, **97**, 409.

WELLS, L. J., 1948. Some experimental evidence of production of adrenotrophin by the fetal hypophysis. *Proc. Soc. Exp. Biol. Med.*, **68**, 487–488.

WELLS, L. J., 1949. Microscopical studies of the adrenals of fetuses deprived of the hypophysis and given adrenocorticotrophin. *Anat. Rec.*, **103**, 563–564.

WENNEKER, A. S., and SUSSMAN, N., 1951. Regeneration of liver tissue following partial hepatectomy in parabiotic rats. *Proc. Soc. Exp. Biol. Med.*, **76**, 683–686.

WHITE, E. L., 1948. An experimental study of the relationship between the size of the eye and the size of the optic tectum in the brain of the developing teleost, *Fundulus heteroclitus*. *J. Exp. Zool.*, **108**, 439–469.

WHITE, H. L., HEINBECKER, P., and ROLF, D., 1947. Some endocrine influences on renal function and cardiac output. *Am. J. Physiol.*, **157**, 47–51.

WHITNEY, C., 1928. Hyperplasia of lymphoid tissue and lymphocytes. *Medicine*, **7**, 1–29.

WIEDMAN, M. L., DUNIHUE, F. W., and ROBERTSON, W. VAN B., 1958. Effect of sodium chloride intake and mineralocorticoid level on the granularity of juxtaglomerular cells. *J. Endocr.*, **17**, 261–264.

WIGGLESWORTH, V. B., 1937. Wound healing in an insect (*Rhodnius prolixus* Hemiptera). *J. Exp. Biol.*, **14**, 364–381.

WILBUR, K. M., and CHAMBERS, R., 1942. Cell movements in the healing of micro-wounds *in vitro*. *J. Exp. Zool.*, **91**, 287–302.

WILLIAMS, G. E. G., 1961. Some aspects of compensatory hyperplasia of the kidney. *Brit. J. Exp. Path.*, **42**, 386–396.

WILLIAMS, G. E. G., 1962a. Effect of starvation and of adrenalectomy on compensatory hyperplasia of the kidney. *Nature*, **196**, 1221–1222.

WILLIAMS, G. E. G., 1962b. Studies on the control of compensatory hyperplasia of the kidney in the rat. *Lab. Invest.*, **11**, 1295–1302.

WILLIER, B. H., 1924. The endocrine glands and the development of the chick. I. The effects of thyroid grafts. *Am. J. Anat.*, **33**, 67–103.

WILSON, C., and BYROM, F. B., 1939. Renal changes in malignant hypertension. *Lancet*, **1**, 136–139.

WILSON, C., and BYROM, F. B., 1941. The vicious cycle in chronic Bright's disease. Experimental evidence from the hypertensive rat. *Quart. J. Med.*, **10**, 65–94.

WILSON, J. W., 1948. Diurnal rhythm of mitotic activity in the liver of the mouse. *Anat. Rec.*, **101**, 672–673.

WILSON, J. W., 1955. Desiccated ox gall and cholic acid as mitotic stimulants and poisons in mouse liver. *Am. J. Physiol.*, **183**, 673–674.

WILSON, J. W., and LEDUC, E. H., 1947. Mitotic rate in mouse liver following intra-peritoneal injection of liver, kidney and egg yolk. *Anat. Rec.*, **97**, 471–493.

WILSON, J. W., and LEDUC, E. H., 1948. The occurrence and formation of binucleate and multinucleate cells and polyploid nuclei in the mouse liver. *Am. J. Anat.*, **82**, 353–392.

WILSON, J. W., and LEDUC, E. H., 1949. The effect of biotin on mitotic activity in the liver of the mouse. *Growth*, **13**, 309–318.

WILSON, J. W., and LEDUC, E. H., 1950. The effect of coramine on mitotic activity and growth in the liver of the mouse. *Growth*, **14**, 13–48.

WILSON, M. E., STOWELL, R. E., YOKOYAMA, O., and TSUBOI, K. K., 1953. Cytological changes in regenerating mouse liver. *Cancer Res.*, **13**, 86–92.

WINKERT, J., GORDON, A. S., MEDICI, P. T., PILIERO, S. J., LUHBY, A. L., and TANNENBAUM, M., 1958. Erythropoietic stimulating activity of urine from anemic human subjects. *Proc. Soc. Exp. Biol. Med.*, **97**, 191–193.

WISLOCKI, G. B., and SINGER, M., 1946. The occurrence and function of nerves in the growing antlers of deer. *J. Comp. Neurol.*, **85**, 1–19.

WOERNER, C. A., 1938. Studies of the islands of Langerhans after continuous intravenous injection of dextrose. *Anat. Rec.*, **71**, 33–58.

WRBA, H., RABES, H., RIPOLL-GÓMEZ, M., and RANZ, H., 1962. Serum teilhepatektomierter Tiere auf Leberkulturen. *Exp. Cell Res.*, **26**, 70–77.

WRBA, H., RANZ, H., and RIPOLL-GÓMEZ, M., 1960. Zur Spezifität des "Regenerationsfaktors" im Blutserum nach Hepatektomie. *Naturwiss.*, **47**, 306.

WRETE, M., 1946. The influence of unilateral nephrectomy on the weight of the endocrine organs in mice. *Acta Anat.*, **2**, 81–97.

WRIGHT, G. P., 1958. *An Introduction to Pathology.* (3rd ed.) Longmans, Green & Co., London.

YAKAITIS, A. A., and WELLS, L. J., 1956. Hypophysis-adrenal system in the fetal rat. Adrenals in fetuses subjected to cortisone, DCA, hypophyseoprivia and growth hormone. *Am. J. Anat.*, **98**, 205–229.

YAMADA, T., 1962. The inductive phenomenon as a tool for understanding the basic mechanism of differentiation. *J. Cell. Comp. Physiol.*, *Suppl.*, **60**, 49–64.

352 ADAPTIVE GROWTH

YNTEMA, C. L., 1959. Regeneration in sparsely innervated and aneurogenic forelimbs of Amblystoma larvae. *J. Exp. Zool.*, **140**, 101–123.
YOKOYAMA, H. O., WILSON, M. E., TSUBOI, K. K., and STOWELL, R. E., 1953. Regeneration of mouse liver after partial hepatectomy. *Cancer Res.*, **13**, 80–85.
YOUNG, J. S., FISHER, J. A., and YOUNG, M., 1941. Some observations on the healing of experimental wounds in the skin of the rabbit. *J. Path. Bact.*, **52**, 225–246.
ZAKI, F. G., 1954. Maximum mitosis and water content in regenerating liver. *Z. Naturf.*, **96**, 239–241.
ZALOKAR, M., 1944. Contribution à l'étude de la régénération du crystallin chez le *Triton*. *Rev. Suisse Zool.*, **51**, 443–521.
ZECKWER, I. T., 1940. Histologic changes in the pituitaries of parabiotic rats. *Arch. Path.*, **30**, 461–464.
ZECKWER, I. T., 1946. Compensatory growth of the kidney after unilateral nephrectomy in thyroidectomized rats. *Am. J. Physiol.*, **145**, 681–684.
ZIMMERMAN, M., and CELOZZI, E., 1960. Stimulation of cell division in normal rat liver by a factor in serum from hepatectomized rats. *Fed. Proc.*, **19**, 139.
ZWEIFACH, B. W., ROSENFELD, S., BAEZ, S., and SHORR, E., 1947. The relation of the adrenal glands to the renal vasoexciter mechanism during experimental hypertension. In *Factors Regulating Blood-Pressure* (Zweifach, B. W., and Shorr, E., eds.), Trans. of the First Conference on Factors Regulating Blood-Pressure, J. Macy, Jr. Foundation Publication, pp. 72–79.

Index